Step-By-Step Repair Manual

It doesn't necessarily take a highly trained service technician to make most repairs on an appliance. This book shows you just how easy it can be to repair your own dishwasher. Whether you're an avid do-it-yourselfer or just a beginner, the step-by-step photo instructions and detailed explanations will help you perform the majority of dishwasher repairs you're likely to encounter.

By learning to do as many of your own repairs as possible, you save time and money.

Safety Information: Dishwashers are complex electromechanical devices. Any attempt to repair your dishwasher may, if improperly performed, result in personal injury and property damage. GE cannot be responsible for the interpretation of this manual, nor can it assume any liability in connection with its use. For more detailed safety information see page 2 of this manual.

If your appliance is still under warranty: Before you attempt any repairs, check to see if your appliance is covered under warranty. If you or any unauthorized service technician tries to repair an appliance under warranty, the warranty may be voided.

Step-By-Step Repair Manual for GE/Hotpoint Dishwashers
General Electric Company

Contents

How to use this manual 1
Safety information 2
Parts information 3
How your dishwasher operates 5
Models covered 6
Problem diagnostic charts 7-17
Repair procedures 18-90
Inspecting circuit breakers and fuses 19-20
Inspecting power connections 21-22
Removing service panels 23-26
Repairing wiring and connections 27-28
Loading dishwasher 29-30
Checking water and detergent 31-32
Inspecting air gap and drain lines 33-34
Inspecting and replacing door latch mechanism 35-36
Inspecting and replacing timer 37-40
Inspecting and replacing pushbutton switches 41-42
Inspecting and replacing cycle extender switch 43-44
Inspecting and replacing water inlet valve 45-46
Inspecting and replacing float switch 47-48
Inspecting and replacing drain valve solenoid 49-50
Inspecting and replacing motor/pump assembly 51-54
Inspecting and replacing water system parts 55-60
Inspecting and replacing single or dual cup detergent dispenser 61-62
Inspecting and replacing molded-cup type detergent dispenser 63-64
Inspecting and replacing electrical rinse agent dispenser 65-66
Inspecting and replacing mechanical rinse agent dispenser 67-68
Inspecting and replacing Calrod® heating unit 69-70
Inspecting and replacing thermostats 71-74
Inspecting and replacing racks 75-78
Inspecting and replacing gaskets 79-82
Cosmetic repairs 83-84
Inspecting and replacing anti-tip mechanism and door springs 85-86
Inspecting and replacing unicouple 87-90
Technical assistance/service record 91
Preventive maintenance 92
Tools and testing equipment 93-98
Dishwasher accessories 99
Glossary of terms 100-102
Index 103-107

Note: Pages 1 through 7 contain important information. Be sure to carefully read these pages before you begin any repair procedures.

How to use this manual

GE has recognized the growing need for the homeowner to perform as many of the service operations as possible around the house. Consequently, we have prepared this manual to provide the typical homeowner with the information necessary to perform the majority of dishwasher repairs. This manual is written in an easy to follow, step-by-step, photo guide format to instruct you how to do your own repairs.

Before you begin your repair

It is important that before you begin any repair or diagnosis on your dishwasher you take the time to read the general information on pages 2 through 7. By acquiring a basic understanding of dishwasher repair and important safety information, you'll be a step ahead on diagnosing and remedying the problem.

Problem Diagnostic Charts

When a problem does occur, refer to the Problem Diagnostic Chart section of the manual (pages 7-17). These charts will help you to pinpoint your trouble by listing possible causes from the most likely to the least common cause. The charts will refer you to the repair procedures (pages 18-90) that use photography and illustrations to show you step-by-step how to remedy the problem. Be sure to read the entire repair procedure carefully before attempting any work.

Glossary of Terms

If you find a term you don't understand, you may find it listed in the Glossary of Terms listed at the end of this manual (pages 100-102). Also, don't forget to use the index as reference when searching for various information.

Read your *Use and Care Book*

After you have read the introductory sections in this manual, you may want to re-read the ***Use and Care Book*** that accompanies your dishwasher. The ***Use and Care Book*** can tell you how to remedy many problems that aren't due to equipment faults, such as incorrect loading and too low water heater temperature. You may just discover that your dishwasher has useful features you've forgotten.

Preventive Maintenance

When you have completed your repair, the Preventive Maintenance section (page 92) can help you obtain the best results from your GE or Hotpoint dishwasher. Preventive maintenance is a vital key to long life for your dishwasher. The few minutes you invest in caring for your dishwasher properly can save you a great deal of time and trouble.

What repairs are covered?

Although GE has introduced hundreds of dishwasher models through the years, similarities in basic components allow this manual to cover most common repairs. Some procedures may not apply to your dishwasher; they may be applicable only for a particular brand (GE or Hotpoint), or model type (built-in or convertible). For instance, built-in dishwashers will not have a unicouple because it is a component used only on convertible models. The component being repaired may also vary somewhat with different dishwasher models, such as the motor/pump assembly which is mounted horizontally or vertically depending on model. Major differences between models will be noted in the repair procedure.

Safety information

Dishwashers are complex electromechanical appliances. Any attempt to repair your dishwasher may, if improperly performed, result in personal injury and property damage. GE cannot be responsible for the interpretation of this manual, nor can it assume any liability in connection with its use.

Safety Precautions
To minimize the risk of personal injury or property damage it is important that the following safe service practices be observed:

1. **Be sure you are operating your dishwasher properly. Read carefully the *Use and Care Book* that comes with your dishwasher.**

2. **Know the location of your dishwasher's circuit breaker or fuse. Clearly mark all switches and fuses for quick reference. If you are unfamiliar with circuit breakers and fuses, please refer to Procedure #1 on page 19.**

3. **Before servicing your dishwasher, turn all dishwasher controls OFF. Disconnect the power supply at the distribution panel by removing the fuse or switching off the circuit breaker. For convertible models, also unplug power cord from receptacle before inspecting, testing, or removing any access panel. None of the repairs or tests in this manual require voltage to be applied to the dishwasher for testing.**

4. **To prevent burns from hot water, turn off water at house shut-off valve before disconnecting any water hoses on built-in models. Be careful when removing hoses that residual hot water in the hose does not leak onto you.**

5. **When working with Calrod® heating unit, be certain unit has cooled before handling.**

6. **Be careful when handling access panels, dishwasher parts or any components which may have sharp edges. Avoid placing your hand into any area which you cannot first visually inspect for sharp edges.**

7. **Always use the correct tool for a job and be sure tools are in good condition. Worn, faulty, and misused tools can cause accidents.**

8. **Never interfere with or bypass the operation of any switch, component or feature of your dishwasher.**

9. **Use only replacement parts of the same size and capacity as the original part. If you have any questions, contact your authorized local appliance parts dealer.**

10. **When replacing any dishwasher component, be sure any green ground wires are reconnected securely in their original positions to avoid danger of shock or short circuit.**

11. **Before reconnecting the power supply, make sure no uninsulated wires or terminals are touching the cabinet. Electrical wiring and grounds must be correctly reconnected and secured away from sharp edges, high temperature components, and moving parts. All panels and covers should be reinstalled before the power supply is reconnected.**

12. **Carefully read through the entire repair procedure for a specific repair before attempting the job. If you don't fully understand the repair procedure or doubt your ability to complete it, call a qualified service technician.**

13. **Throughout this manual, additional safety precautions dealing with specific repair procedures will be presented. This information should be carefully read.**

14. **Hydrogen gas can be produced and can build up in a water heater if you have not used hot water for a period of two weeks or more. HYDROGEN GAS CAN BE EXPLOSIVE UNDER THESE CIRCUMSTANCES. To prevent possible damage or injury, run hot water from the kitchen faucet for several minutes before using your dishwasher or any other appliance connected to a hot water system that has not been in use. This will allow any hydrogen to escape. If the gas is present, you may hear a slight hissing or sputtering noise from the faucet as the water begins to flow. Do not smoke or allow any open flame near the faucet at this time.**

Parts information

Obtaining replacement parts

If you're going to the time and trouble of repairing your appliance, it is important that you get the correct replacement part. First, be sure you have the complete model number for your appliance when ordering replacement parts. Even if you take in the original part, a salesperson may not be able to supply the correct replacement part without your complete model number. Second, to assure proper fit and performance, use Genuine GE Renewal Parts.

GE specification plate is mounted on the left side of the dishwasher tub, inside the door.

Hotpoint specification plate is mounted on the right side of the dishwasher tub, inside the door.

GE dishwasher specification plate.

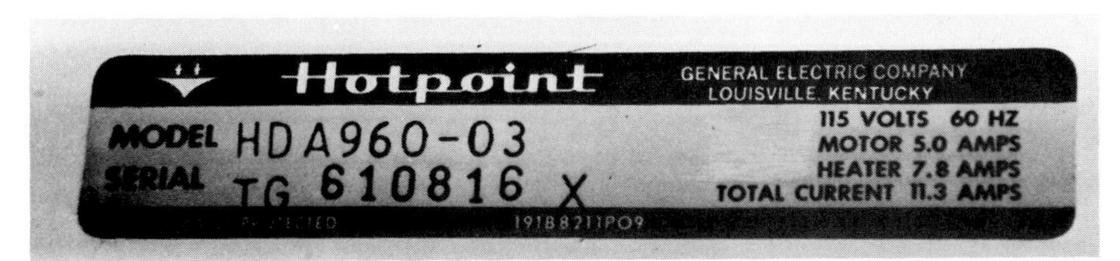

Hotpoint dishwasher specification plate.

Finding your model number

The model and serial numbers of your dishwasher are stamped on a metal model specification plate. On GE dishwashers, you'll find the model specification plate on the left side of the dishwasher tub, just inside the door. On some Hotpoint models, the plate is located on the right side of the dishwasher tub, inside the door. A few Hotpoint models may have the specification plate mounted on the side of the dishwasher door.

The complete model number must be used when ordering exact replacement parts. Be sure to copy this number correctly and record it on page 91 of this manual for future reference.

Genuine GE Renewal Parts

All parts are not created equal when it comes to your GE or Hotpoint dishwasher. Some non-GE parts may require extra brackets and adaptors to make them fit. Others may not be designed for the exact electrical specifications of your dishwasher and, as a result, may cause substandard performance. With Genuine GE Renewal Parts you are assured a proper fit and performance match for the original part--an assurance that's backed in writing with a one-year limited warranty.

For your convenience in obtaining parts, GE has company-owned parts stores and authorized parts dealers throughout the country. To find the outlet nearest you, look in the Yellow Pages under major headings,"Appliances--Household--Major" or "Dishwashers", then subheads, "Service & Repair" or "Supplies & Parts". If you are unable to find where GE parts are sold in your area, call the GE Answer Center® consumer information service toll free 800-626-2000 for assistance.

Genuine GE Renewal Parts are backed by a one-year limited warranty to assure you proper fit and performance.

Some dealers feature the Quick Fix® system of common GE replacement parts and parts kits. Designed specifically for do-it-yourselfers, Quick-Fix® parts come in clearly marked packages complete with hardware and step-by-step replacement instructions.

Whether it's the Quick-Fix® system or the regular GE line of parts, you should insist on the performance and quality of Genuine GE Renewal Parts. After all, if you're investing time and money to care for your appliance, it's better to do it right the first time and not chance problems later from using an unsuitable part.

How your dishwasher operates

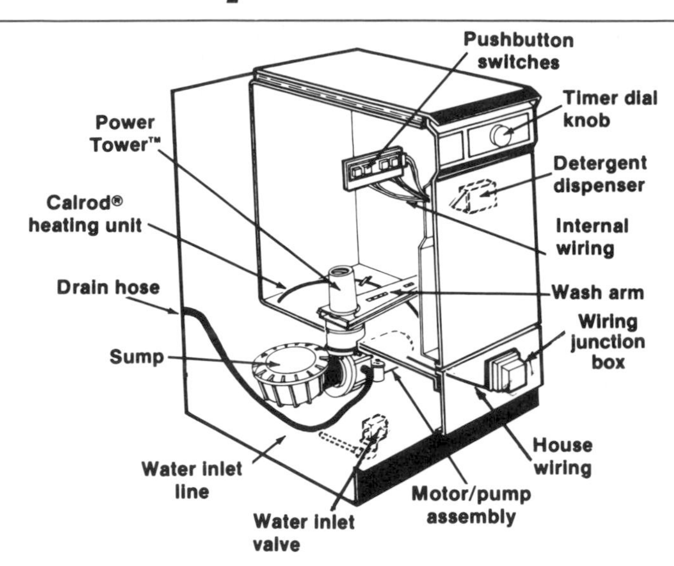

The purpose of this section is to give you some background information on how a dishwasher operates. The more you know about the operation of your dishwasher, the easier it will be for you to understand the causes and solutions to a problem. For example, in order to wash a load of dishes, you simply turn the dishwasher controls to the desired setting. But what causes the water to circulate and drain and how do the dishwasher controls regulate the functions? Answers to these questions could make it easier for you to repair your dishwasher. So let's take a look at how your dishwasher operates.

It all starts with the electrical power and water. Built-in dishwashers are directly wired to a 15-amp circuit and also have a permanent attachment to hot water and drain lines. Convertible dishwashers use a power cord that plugs into a standard 120-volt wall receptacle, and they receive their water through an attachment to the kitchen sink faucet. From the power supply, electricity is conducted to dishwasher components through the door latch switch and the dishwasher controls. Through a network of internal wiring and parts, the electricity is distributed from the dishwasher's timer control system. The timer's switches turn power on and off to various components of the dishwasher, allowing completely automatic washing and drying of your dishes.

During the fill, a water valve in the incoming hot water line opens for the required length of time, which is determined by the timer. A float switch in the tub bottom prevents over-filling in the event of an electrical malfunction. During washing, the dishwasher motor drives a pump to recirculate water mixed with detergent.

The water is forced under pressure through the revolving spray arm, Power Tower™ sprayer and on some models, a Power Shower® spray arm. When the timed prewash period has elapsed, a solenoid coil is energized by the timer to open the drain line and allow the water to pump out. The timer then closes the drain valve and opens the water inlet valve to admit water for the next portion of the cycle. During the second washing, the machine fills as before, and the timer opens the closed section of the detergent dispenser to add fresh detergent to the water. As the water recirculates through the pump, it passes through a soft food disposer which chops up soft food particles and allows them to be flushed away down the drain.

After completing all wash, rinse, and drain periods, the timer switches on the Calrod® heating unit to dry the dishes. An energy-efficient convection drying system allows air to circulate without the use of a fan in many models; cool air enters the tub at the bottom and rises naturally as it warms, venting near the top of the dishwasher. Some models also use a blower to speed drying; on the other models, the Energy Saver Dry option allows selection of a no-heat drying cycle. When Energy Saver Dry is chosen, the Calrod® unit is not energized. Dishes dry naturally by convection air currents over a longer period of time, such as overnight.

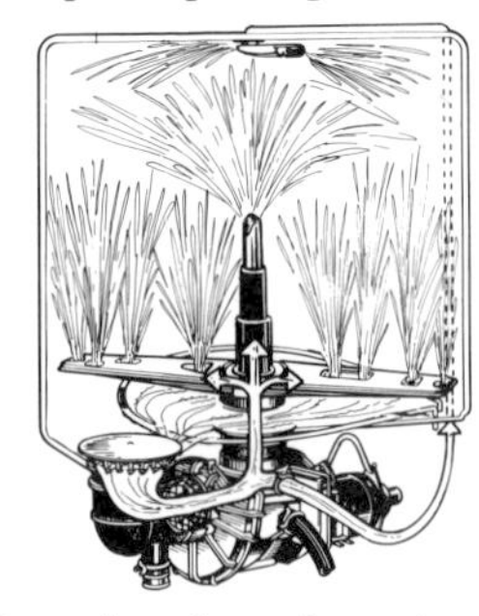

Three-level wash system

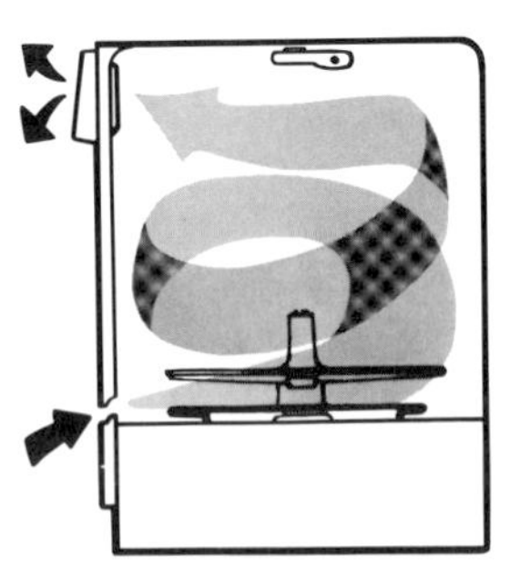

Convection drying system

Models covered

Over the years, GE and Hotpoint have produced hundreds of various dishwasher models. Repairs on most models are similar, so most problems that may arise with your dishwasher are likely to be covered in this manual.

Exception: This manual does not cover repairs for electronic touch control mechanisms, but will apply for some standard component repairs on the "touch control" dishwashers.

Built-in dishwasher is designed to install permanently under kitchen counter, giving a custom appearance. On most models, water and electrical connections are up-front for easier installation and service.

Convertible dishwasher rolls out for easy use. The dishwasher plugs into standard 120-volt wall receptacle, attaches to hot water faucet, and drains into kitchen sink. Used initially as a portable, it can be later installed as a built-in.

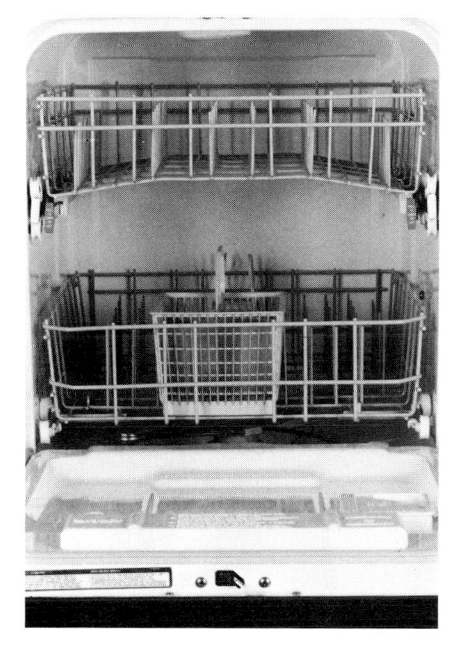

Dishwasher interiors also vary somewhat. The PermaTuf® interior, found on many GE built-in dishwashers, is a smooth seamless white polypropylene. Other GE models, both built-in and convertible, feature the Tuff-Tub® interior of lightly textured pastel vinyl over steel. Gleaming white porcelain enamel forms a durable interior for some Hotpoint dishwashers, as well as some GE convertible models.

Problem diagnostic charts

How to use the problem diagnostic charts

The problem diagnostic charts help you with one of the most difficult tasks in do-it-yourself repairs...locating the possible causes and solutions to your problem. Before using the charts, make note of the problem you are experiencing with your dishwasher. Keen observation can often lead you to the area where the problem lies. Watch for anything that deviates from normal operation. Note everything that is or is not working. Once you have identified a problem, then you can begin to solve it by referring to the Problem Diagnostic Charts.

Each page of the Problem Diagnostic Charts has four columns of information: (1) **Problem**; (2) **Possible Cause**; (3) **Repair Procedure**; and (4) **Skill Level**. The first column, **Problem**, lists examples of problems you may encounter with your dishwasher. In the second column, there is a list of **Possible Causes** that may be the reason for the problem. The possible causes for each problem are listed in the order in which they might be expected to occur from the most likely to the least likely. A **Repair Procedure** for each possible cause is listed in column three. Repair procedure information refers you to a course of action to remedy the possible cause of your dishwasher problem.

The final column, **Skill Level**, indicates a skill level rating for each repair task. This rating will help you decide which repairs you feel confident of completing.

●	Easy	No previous experience needed
●●	Average	Requires removal of service panels. Mechanical ability is helpful.
●●●	Difficult	May require the use of an ohmmeter and/or splicing of electrical wires. Repair or replacement of component parts is more difficult.
●●●●	Very Difficult	May require the use of an ohmmeter and the ability to read a circuit diagram. Repair or replacement of component parts is complex.

No matter what skill level assigned to a task, study the repair procedure and safety instructions carefully before proceeding.

NOTE:
The problems listed below are numbered exactly as they appear in the PROBLEM column of the Problem Diagnostic Charts.

I. All dishwasher models

1. Motor and timer do not run (no water fill)
2. Motor does not run or hum (initial water fill OK and timer advances)
3. Motor hums, but does not run
4. Too little or no water fill
5. Water does not shut off
6. Timer does not shut dishwasher off
7. Timer does not advance
8. Water does not pump out
9. Dishwasher leaks
10. Detergent remains in detergent cup
11. Rinse agent dispenser does not release agent (electrical dispenser)
12. Rinse agent dispenser does not release agent (mechanical dispenser)
13. Rinse agent dispenser leaks (electrical dispenser)
14. Rinse agent dispenser leaks (mechanical dispenser)
15. Poor dishwashing results
16. Poor drying
17. Condensation on dishwasher door
18. Dishwasher door is difficult to open or close
19. Dishwasher door falls open
20. Racks binding or out of place
21. Rack finish defects
22. Tub and inner door liner finish defects
23. Cabinet exterior defects
24. Noise during operation

II. Convertible dishwasher models

25. Top defective
26. Anti-tip mechanism noisy or inoperative
27. Unicouple leaks
28. Unicouple hoses won't store
29. Power cord won't store

Problem diagnostic charts

I. ALL DISHWASHER MODELS

Problem	Possible Cause	Repair Procedure	Skill Level
1. Motor and timer do not run (no water fill)	No power to dishwasher (house fuse or circuit breaker blown)	Check Power Supply (See p.19 & Procedure #1)	•
	Poor power supply connection at dishwasher	Check Power Connection (See p.21 & Procedure #2)	•••
	Power cord defective (convertible models and some built-ins)	Check Power Cord (See p.21 & Procedure #2)	•••
	Open wire to timer, latch switch or pushbutton switch	Check Wiring and Connections (See p.27 & Procedure #4)	•••
	Open door latch switch	Check Switch (See p.35 & Procedure #8) Check Wiring and Connections (See p.27 & Procedure #4)	••• •••
	Open pushbutton switch	Check Switch (See p.41 & Procedure #10) Check Wiring and Connections (See p.27 & Procedure #4)	•••• •••
	Timer defective	Check Timer (See p.37 & Procedure #9) Check Wiring and Connections (See p.27 & Procedure #4)	•••• •••
2. Motor does not run or hum (initial water fill OK and timer advances)	Open wire between timer and motor	Check Wiring and Connections (See p.27 & Procedure #4)	•••
	Motor defective	Check Motor/Pump Assembly (See p.51 & Procedure #15) Check Wiring and Connections (See p.27 & Procedure #4)	•••• •••
	Open timer contacts	Check Timer (See p.37 & Procedure #9) Check Wiring and Connections (See p.27 & Procedure #4)	•••• •••
3. Motor hums, but does not run	Grader/cutter bound	Check Cutter (See p.51 & Procedure #15)	••••
	Motor seal stuck	Check Motor Seal (See p.51 & Procedure #15)	••••

Skill Level Index: • Easy •• Average ••• Difficult •••• Very Difficult

Problem diagnostic charts (continued)

Problem	Possible Cause	Repair Procedure	Skill Level
4. Too little or no water fill	Timer knob turned past beginning of fill	Select Cycles Correctly (See *Use & Care Book*)	
	Closed house water valve or faucet	Open Valve or Faucet (See p.92 Preventive Maintenance)	•
	Low house water pressure, kinked or clogged pipes	Repair Plumbing (See p.33 & Procedure #7)	••
	Clogged water inlet valve screen	Check Water Inlet Valve (See p.45 & Procedure #12)	•••
	Open wire to water inlet valve	Check Water Inlet Valve (See p.45 & Procedure #12)	•••
		Check Wiring and Connections (See p.27 & Procedure #4)	•••
	Open or improperly adjusted float switch	Check Float Switch (See p.47 & Procedure #13)	•••
		Check Wiring and Connections (See p.27 & Procedure #4)	•••
	Open water inlet valve solenoid coil	Check Water Inlet Valve (See p.45 & Procedure #12)	•••
		Check Wiring and Connections (See p.27 & Procedure #4)	•••
	Open timer contacts	Check Timer (See p.37 & Procedure #9)	••••
		Check Wiring and Connections (See p.27 & Procedure #4)	•••
	Kinked fill hose (convertible models only)	Straighten Hose (See p.87 & Procedure#27)	••
5. Water does not shut off	Float obstructed or binding	Check Float (See p.47 & Procedure #13)	•
	Water inlet valve stuck open	Check Water Inlet Valve (See p.45 & Procedure #12)	•••
6. Timer does not shut dishwasher off	Open cycle extender switch (POTSCRUBBER models)	Check Switch (See p.43 & Procedure #11)	•••
		Check Wiring and Connections (See p.27 & Procedure #4)	•••
	Timer defective	Check Timer (See p.37 & Procedure #9)	••••
		Check Wiring and Connections (See p.27 & Procedure #4)	•••

Skill Level Index: • Easy •• Average ••• Difficult •••• Very Difficult

Problem	Possible Cause	Repair Procedure	Skill Level
7. Timer does not advance	Poor connection of terminal in timer connector block	Check Timer (See p.37 & Procedure #9) Check Wiring and Connections (See p.27 & Procedure #4)	•••• •••
	Open cycle extender switch (POTSCRUBBER models)	Check Switch (See p.43 & Procedure #11) Check Wiring and Connections (See p.27 & Procedure #4)	••• •••
	Timer defective	Check Timer (See p.37 & Procedure #9) Check Wiring and Connections (See p.27 & Procedure #4)	•••• •••
8. Water does not pump out	Some water should remain in sump	(See *Use and Care Book*)	
	Clogged air gap, kinked or clogged drain hose	Check Air Gap & Drain Lines (See p.33 & Procedure #7)	••
	Disposer hopper not empty	Check Disposer (See p.33 & Procedure #7)	••
	Plug left in disposer drain line connection	Check Drain Line Connection (See p.92 Preventive Maintenance)	•
	Foreign object in pump	Check Motor/Pump Assembly (See p.51 & Procedure #15)	••••
	Drain valve solenoid binding or damaged	Check Drain Valve Solenoid (See p.49 & Procedure #14)	•••
	Poor connections at drain valve solenoid	Check Drain Valve Solenoid (See p.49 & Procedure #14) Check Wiring and Connections (See p.27 & Procedure #4)	••• •••
	Open drain valve solenoid	Check Drain Valve Solenoid (See p.49 & Procedure #14)	•••
	Open timer contacts	Check Timer (See p.37 & Procedure #9) Check Wiring and Connections (See p.27 & Procedure #4)	•••• •••

Skill Level Index: • Easy •• Average ••• Difficult •••• Very Difficult

Problem diagnostic charts (continued)

Problem	Possible Cause	Repair Procedure	Skill Level
9. Dishwasher leaks	Dishwasher not level	Adjust Leveling Legs (See p.92 Preventive Maintenance)	•
	Door not closing tightly	Adjust Latch Strike (See p.35 & Procedure #8)	•
	Gasket damaged	Check Gaskets (See p.79 & Procedure #24)	••
	Split hose--built-in models	Replace Hose (See p.52 & Procedure #15)	••••
	Split hose--convertible models	Replace Hose (See p.87 & Procedure #27)	••
	Loose connection at water inlet valve	Check Water Inlet Valve (See p.45 & Procedure #12)	•••
	Loose connection at pump housing	Adjust Clamps (See p.51 & Procedure #15)	••••
	Damaged pump housing	Check Motor/Pump Assembly (See p.51 & Procedure #15)	••••
	Motor seal defective	Replace Motor Seal (See p.51 & Procedure #15)	••••
	Crack in water inlet valve	Check Water Inlet Valve (See p.45 & Procedure #12)	•••
	Excess suds produced in wash cycle	Use correct amount of dishwashing detergent (See *Use and Care Book*) Wipe up any rinse agent spilled when filling dispenser Scrape plates and rinse glasses before loading (See p. 29 & Procedure #5)	•
10. Detergent remains in detergent cup	Detergent is old and caked	Clean Detergent Cup (See *Use and Care Book*) Use Fresh Detergent (See p.31 & Procedure #6)	•
	Dishes block water from detergent cup	Load Dishwasher Properly (See p.29 & Procedure #5)	•
	Not enough water pressure to get water to cup	Check Water Inlet Valve (See p.45 & Procedure #12)	•••
	Detergent cup cover is binding--single or dual cup	Replace Detergent Cup (See p.61 & Procedure #17)	••
	Detergent cup cover is binding--molded-cup type	Replace Detergent Cup Cover (See p.63 & Procedure #18)	••

Skill Level Index: • Easy •• Average ••• Difficult •••• Very Difficult

Problem	Possible Cause	Repair Procedure	Skill Level
10. Detergent remains in detergent cup (continued)	Detergent dispenser mechanism inoperative--single or dual cup type	Check Detergent Dispenser (See p.61 & Procedure #17)	••
	Detergent dispenser mechanism inoperative--molded-cup type	Check Detergent Dispenser (See p.63 & Procedure #18)	••
11. Rinse agent dispenser does not release rinse agent (electrical dispenser)	No rinse agent in dispenser	Check Rinse Agent level (See *Use and Care Book*)	
	Bimetal inoperative	Check Rinse Agent Dispenser (See p.65 & Procedure #19)	•••
		Check Wiring and Connections (See p.27 & Procedure #4)	•••
	Open timer contacts	Check Timer (See p.37 & Procedure #9)	••••
		Check Wiring and Connections (See p.27 & Procedure #4)	•••
12. Rinse agent dispenser does not release rinse agent (mechanical dispenser)	No rinse agent in dispenser	Check Rinse Agent Level (See *Use and Care Book*)	
	Trip arm bent or broken	Check Rinse Agent Dispenser (See p.67 & Procedure #20)	••
	Timer trip lever bushing missing or damaged	Check Rinse Agent Dispenser (See p.67 & Procedure #20)	••
13. Rinse agent dispenser leaks (electrical dispenser)	Fill cap not tight	Check Fill Cap Fit (See p.65 & Procedure #19)	•
	Valve pin not seating	Check Rinse Agent Dispenser (See p.65 & Procedure #19)	•••
	Dispenser tank cracked	Replace Tank (See p.65 & Procedure #19)	••
	Bimetal improperly adjusted	Adjust Bimetal (See p.65 & Procedure #19)	•••
14. Rinse agent dispenser leaks (mechanical dispenser)	Fill cap not tight	Check Fill Cap Fit (See p.67 & Procedure #20)	•
	Dispenser tank cracked	Replace Tank (See p.67 & Procedure #20)	••

Skill Level Index: • Easy •• Average ••• Difficult •••• Very Difficult

Problem diagnostic charts (continued)

Problem	Possible Cause	Repair Procedure	Skill Level
15. Poor dishwashing results	Water not hot enough	Adjust Water Heater (See p.31 & Procedure #6)	•
		Check Control Thermostat (some models) (See p.71 & Procedure #22)	•••
	Improper loading	Load Dishwasher Correctly (See p.29 & Procedure #5)	•
	Detergent old, or incorrect type or amount	Use Fresh Detergent, Correct Type and Amount (See p.31 & Procedure #6)	•
	Detergent cup caked	Clean Detergent Cup (See *Use and Care Book*)	
	Improper cycle selection	Choose Proper Cycle (See *Use and Care Book*)	
	Pushbutton not fully seated	(See *Use and Care Book*)	
	Suds in dishwasher tub	Clean Rinse Agent Spills Immediately (See p.92 Preventive Maintenance)	•
		Use Proper Dishwasher Detergent (See p.31 & Procedure #6)	•
	Clogged house drain or air gap	Clean Drain or Air Gap (See p.33 & Procedure #7)	•
	Kinked or clogged drain hose	Check Drain Hose (See p.33 & Procedure #7)	••
	Foreign object in pump	Check Motor/Pump Assembly (See p.51 & Procedure #15)	••••
	Foreign object in wash system	Check Wash System (See p.55 & Procedure #16)	•••
	Spray arm hub broken or inoperative	Check Wash System (See p.55 & Procedure #16)	•••
		Check Motor/Pump Assembly (See p.51 & Procedure #15)	••••
	Power Tower™ sprayer incorrectly threaded on hub	Check Wash System (See p.55 & Procedure #16)	•••
	Pump gate valve not seating	Check Drain Valve Solenoid (See p.49 & Procedure #14)	•••
		Check Motor/Pump Assembly (See p.51 & Procedure #15)	••••
	Water inlet valve solenoid opens when hot (intermittent)	Check Water Inlet Valve (See p.45 & Procedure #12)	•••
	Detergent dispenser inoperative--single or dual cups	Check Detergent Dispenser (See p.61 & Procedure #17)	••

Skill Level Index: • Easy •• Average ••• Difficult •••• Very Difficult

Problem	Possible Cause	Repair Procedure	Skill Level
15. Poor dishwashing results (continued)	Detergent dispenser inoperative--molded-cup type	Check Detergent Dispenser (See p.63 & Procedure #18)	••
	Wash system gasket defective	Check Wash System (See p.55 & Procedure #16)	•••
	Rinse agent leaks into tub during wash or dry period--electrical dispenser	Check Rinse Agent Dispenser (See p.65 & Procedure #19)	•••
	Rinse agent leaks into tub during wash or dry period--mechanical dispenser	Check Rinse Agent Dispenser (See p.67 & Procedure #20)	••
	Drain valve return spring broken or missing	Check Drain Valve Solenoid (See p.49 & Procedure #14)	•••
16. Poor drying	Water not hot enough	Adjust Water Heater (See p.31 & Procedure #6)	•
	Energy Saver Dry option selected (some models)	(See *Use and Care Book*)	
	Rinse agent not used	Use Rinse Agent (See p.31 & Procedure #6)	•
	Rinse agent does not dispense properly--electrical dispenser	Check Rinse Agent Dispenser (See p.65 & Procedure #19) Check Wiring & Connections (See p.27 & Procedure #4)	••• •••
	Rinse agent does not dispense properly--mechanical dispenser	Check Rinse Agent Dispenser (See p.67 & Procedure #20)	••
	Poor connections at Calrod® heating unit	Check Calrod® Heating Unit (See p.69 & Procedure #21) Check Wiring & Connections (See p.27 & Procedure #4)	••• •••
	Defective Calrod® heating unit	Check Calrod® Heating Unit (See p.69 & Procedure #21)	•••
	Calrod® heating unit fuse blown (some models)	Check Calrod® Heating Unit (See p.69 & Procedure #21)	•••
	Open timer contacts	Check Timer (See p.37 & Procedure #9) Check Wiring & Connections (see p.27 & Procedure #4)	•••• •••

Skill Level Index: • Easy •• Average ••• Difficult •••• Very Difficult

Problem diagnostic charts (continued)

Problem	Possible Cause	Repair Procedure	Skill Level
16. Poor drying (continued)	Open safety thermostat (some models)	Check Safety Thermostat (See p.71 & Procedure #22)	•••
17. Condensation on dishwasher door	Some is normal--caused by steam from vent	(See *Use and Care Book*)	
18. Dishwasher door is difficult to open or close	Door latch strike bent or out of position	Adjust Door Latch Strike (See p.35 & Procedure #8)	•
	Cabinet opening out of square (built-in models)	Install Correctly (See p.92 Preventive Maintenance)	•
	Door drags on cabinet (built-in models)	Install Correctly (See p.92 Preventive Maintenance)	•
	Door hits countertop mounting screws (built-in models)	Adjust Mounting Screws (See p.92 Preventive Maintenance)	•
19. Dishwasher door falls open	Door spring(s) worn or broken	Replace Door Springs (See p.85 & Procedure #26)	••
20. Racks binding or out of place	Roller missing	Replace Roller (See p.75 & Procedure #23)	••
	Lower rack roller axles bent	Adjust Roller Axles (See p.75 & Procedure #23)	••
	Rollers binding	Adjust Rollers and Axles (See p.75 & Procedure #23)	••
	Upper rack slide bent	Adjust Slide (See p.75 & Procedure #23)	••
21. Rack finish defects	Cuts, scratches or blisters	Repair with Epoxy Kit (See p.83 & Procedure #25)	•
22. Tub and inner door liner finish defects	Tuff Tub® interior cuts, scratches or blisters	Repair with Epoxy Kit (See p.83 & Procedure #25)	•
	PermaTuf® inner door cuts	Replace Inner Door (See p.23 & Procedure #3)	••

Skill Level Index: • Easy •• Average ••• Difficult •••• Very Difficult

Problem	Possible Cause	Repair Procedure	Skill Level
23. Cabinet exterior defects	Minor scratches	Repair with Touch-Up Kit or Spray Paint (See p.83 & Procedure #25)	•
	Damaged panel	Replace Panel (See p.23 & Procedure #3)	••
24. Noise during operation	Dishes rattling	Load Dishwasher Correctly (See p.29 & Procedure #5)	•
	Panels vibrating	Tighten Panels or Add Pads (see p.23 & Procedure #3)	••
	Detergent cup opening	Some Noise is Normal (See *Use and Care Book*)	
	Drain valve solenoid vibrates	Some Noise is Normal (See *Use and Care Book*) Tighten Mounting (See p.49 & Procedure #14)	•••
	Foreign object in pump or grader/cutter	Check Motor/Pump Assembly (See p.51 & Procedure #15)	••••
	Motor fan loose	Replace Motor/Pump Assembly (See p.51 & Procedure #15)	••••
	Power Tower™ sprayer bounces	Check Wash System (See p.55 & Procedure #16)	•••
	Timer buzzes or hums	Tighten Timer Mounting (See p.37 & Procedure #9)	••
	Water inlet line hammers	Check Float Switch (See p.47 & Procedure #13)	•••

Skill Level Index: • Easy •• Average ••• Difficult •••• Very Difficult

Problem diagnostic charts (continued)

II. CONVERTIBLE DISHWASHER MODELS

Problem	Possible Cause	Repair Procedure	Skill Level
25. Top defective	Stains	Refinish Top (See p.92 Preventive Maintenance)	•
	Wood warped or split	Replace Top (See p.23 & Procedure #3)	••
26. Anti-tip mechanism noisy or inoperative	Roller bent or out of place	Check Anti-Tip Mechanism (See p.85 & Procedure #26)	••
	Spring detached or missing	Check Anti-Tip Mechanism (See p.85 & Procedure #26)	••
	Mechanism binding	Check Anti-Tip Mechanism (See p.85 & Procedure #26)	••
	Cable detached	Check Anti-Tip Mechanism (See p.85 & Procedure #26)	••
27. Unicouple leaks	"O" Rings worn or missing	Replace "O" Rings (See p.87 & Procedure #27)	•••
	Drain hose washer defective	Replace Washer (See p.87 & Procedure #27)	•••
	Pressure relief slide binding (some models)	Check Unicouple (See p.87 & Procedure #27)	•••
28. Unicouple hoses won't store	Hose jammed or twisted	Remove Top and Adjust Hoses (See p.87 & Procedure #27)	•••
29. Power cord won't store	Cord jammed or twisted	Pull Cord Out and Straighten (See p.21 & Procedure #2)	•

Skill Level Index: • Easy •• Average ••• Difficult •••• Very Difficult

Repair procedures

How to use the repair procedures

The following dishwasher repair procedures take you step-by-step through repairs for most of the dishwasher problems you are likely to encounter. The Problem Diagnostic Charts on pages 7-17 will help you to pinpoint the likely causes of your problem. Beginning with the most likely cause, you can then refer to the appropriate repair procedure section. Like the Problem Diagnostic Charts, the Repair Procedures are divided into two categories – repairs that apply to all model dishwashers and repairs that only apply to convertible models.

Each repair procedure is a complete inspection and repair process for a single dishwasher component, containing the information you need to test a component that may be faulty and to replace it, if necessary. This format breaks down even some of the most complex repair problems into separate, easy-to-handle units. Following the instructions given, you can test each component separately, isolating the cause of the problem and replacing any faulty parts. If one procedure fails to locate the failed component, you simply refer back to the Problem Diagnostic Charts for the next most likely cause of the problem.

Featuring a close-up photograph of the component you will be testing, the repair procedure begins with a description of what the component does and how it works. In the case of a component which varies with different dishwasher models, you will be shown how to determine which type is found on your dishwasher.

Instructions showing how to test and replace the component begin with steps that must be followed to assure your safety. Other initial steps indicate the skills and equipment that will be needed for the task. If you are uncertain about a process that will be used, such as reading a circuit diagram, using an ohmmeter, or removing access panels, you are referred to the pages in this manual where that process is discussed in detail. No matter what your skill level, careful attention must be paid to these instructions and safety precautions before you begin any procedure.

Clear photographs of typical dishwasher models illustrate each step of every repair procedure, proceeding from visual inspection and testing to replacement of the component. Because of the diversity of dishwasher models available, your dishwasher may differ somewhat from the illustrated model. However, each procedure has been carefully designed to be representative of the entire GE/Hotpoint lines, and as much information as possible has been included to help you make repairs on most GE/Hotpoint dishwashers.

NOTE:
The repair procedures are listed below in the order in which they appear in this section. Refer to the Problem Diagnostic Charts on pages 7-17 for the procedure most likely to remedy your problem, then use this list to locate the desired procedure.

All dishwasher models

1. Circuit Breakers and Fuses
2. Power Connections
3. Service Panels
4. Wiring and Connections
5. Loading
6. Water and Detergents
7. Air Gap and Drain Lines
8. Door Latch Mechanism
9. Timer
10. Pushbutton Switches
11. Cycle Extender Switch
12. Water Inlet Valve
13. Float Switch
14. Drain Valve Solenoid
15. Motor/Pump Assembly
16. Wash System Parts
17. Single or Dual Cup Detergent Dispenser
18. Molded-Cup Type Detergent Dispenser
19. Electrical Rinse Agent Dispenser
20. Mechanical Rinse Agent Dispenser
21. Calrod® Heating Unit
22. Thermostats
23. Racks
24. Gaskets
25. Dishwasher Body Cosmetics
26. Door Springs

Convertible dishwasher models

26. Anti-tip Mechanism
27. Unicouple

Procedure 1

Inspecting circuit breakers and fuses

Skill Level Rating: | **Easy** | Average | Difficult | Very Difficult |

Electricity produced by the power company is delivered to your house through a series of connecting power lines. A power supply distribution panel is located at the point where the main line from the power company enters your home. One of two types of distribution panels services your household: either a circuit breaker panel or a fuse panel. From the distribution panel the power line is divided into a number of smaller circuits which are distributed to various household appliances, receptacles, and lights. Each of these circuits is protected from becoming overloaded by either a circuit breaker or a fuse. It's important to know which breakers or fuses protect each circuit in your home. It's also wise to label them when everything is operating correctly, so you'll know which breaker or fuse to look for if the need arises.

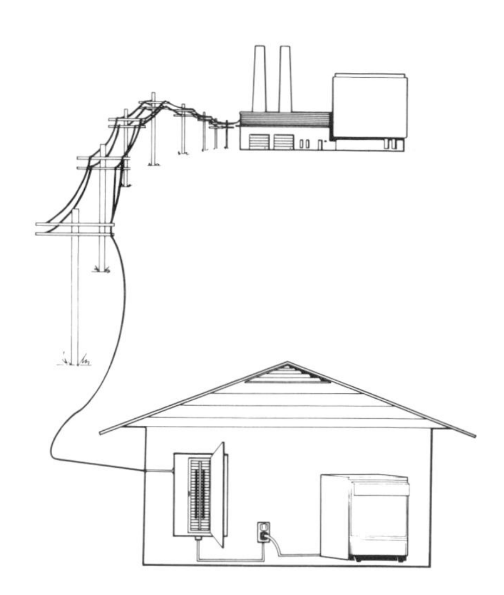

The distribution panel is the place to turn off all power to the dishwasher circuit before servicing. And it's the first place to look if problems occur. A tripped circuit breaker or blown fuse is a minor problem, but it can stop the entire dishwasher from working.

CAUTION: If your dishwasher is a built-in model, directly connected to the household wiring, take extra precautions to be sure the dishwasher's fuse or circuit breaker has been disconnected.

Circuit breaker type panel

Fuse type panel

Circuit breakers and fuses (continued)

Step 1: Be sure all dishwasher controls are turned **OFF.** Avoid touching any grounded objects such as water pipes when working around power supply. Stand on an insulated surface such as dry board.

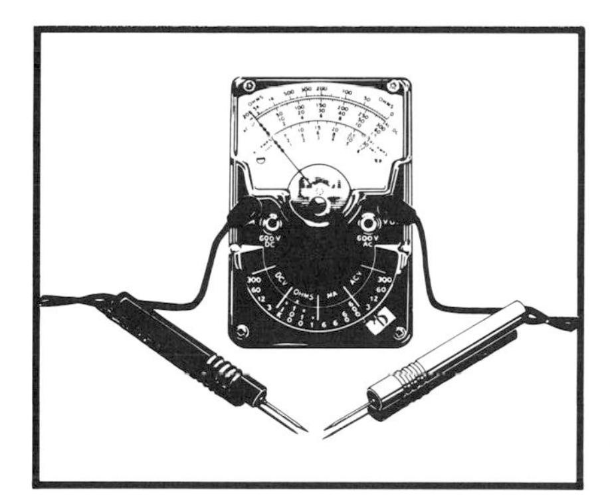

Step 2: This procedure may require the use of an ohmmeter. For instructions on how to use an ohmmeter, please refer to Tools and Testing Equipment, page 95.

Step 3: Other than opening the door to the distribution panel, never remove any cover or expose any electrical terminals.

Step 4: Circuit breakers. Circuit breaker distribution panels contain rows of switches. When a breaker "trips", power is shut off and the breaker switch moves to an intermediate position between the "ON" and "OFF" points.

Step 5: To restore power, turn the breaker switch to "OFF" position, then back to "ON". If the breaker trips again, the circuit is still overloaded. Further exploration of the problem is necessary before power supply can be restored.

Step 6: Fuses. A second type of distribution panel is protected by fuses. To restore power when a fuse "blows", it is necessary to replace the old fuse with a new one of the same amperage. Your dishwasher should be on a separate 15-amp circuit.

Step 7: Faulty or blown fuses cannot always be discovered simply by looking. Some will be obviously blown while others may have only invisible changes within that can interrupt the flow of current.

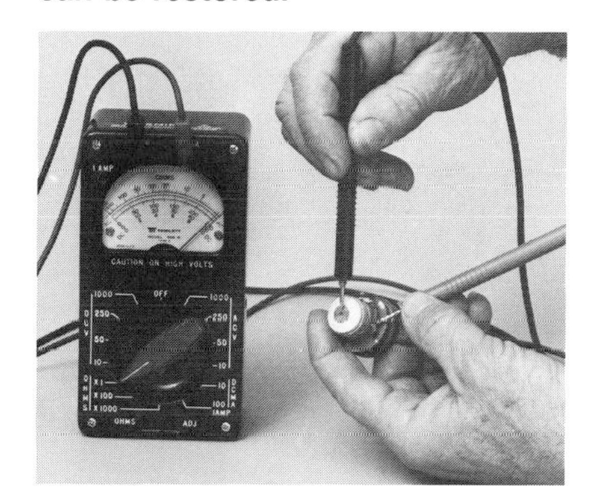

Step 8: Fuses can be checked with ohmmeter. Set ohmmeter to R x 1. Touch one test probe to brass tip and other probe to shell at base of fuse. If test shows no continuity, replace fuse.

Procedure 2

Inspecting power connections

Skill Level Rating: | Easy | Average | **Difficult** | Very Difficult |

For built-in dishwashers, power cords are generally not needed, since the dishwasher is usually connected directly to the house wiring. Convertible dishwashers plug into standard 120-volt wall receptacles with a three-pronged (grounding) plug.

If the dishwasher fails to operate properly, the power cord or direct connection may be preventing power from reaching the dishwasher. Most problems of the power cord or connection are caused by damage and loose connections, and will likely be visible.

If your dishwasher is built in and directly wired, take extra precaution to be sure the dishwasher's circuit breaker or fuse has been disconnected before performing any inspections or repairs. Refer to Procedure #1: Inspecting and replacing circuit breakers and fuses, for additional information.

CAUTION: To minimize the possibility of electric shock, be certain that the wall receptacle and circuit are properly grounded before using the dishwasher. Use of an adapter plug to plug the dishwasher into a two-pronged receptacle is not recommended. Under no circumstances should you attempt to cut off the third (grounding) prong from the plug.

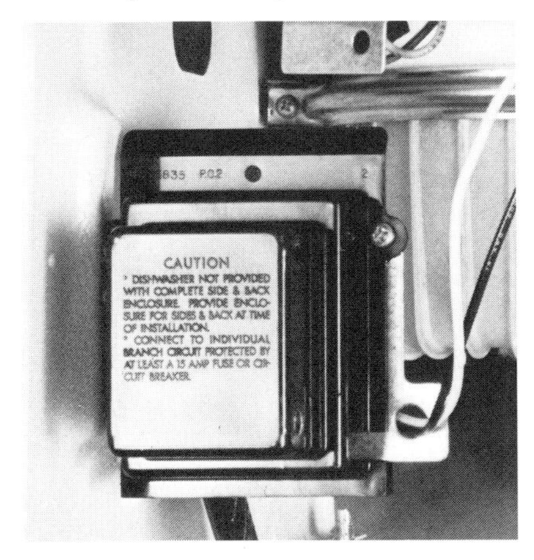

Built-in dishwasher junction box

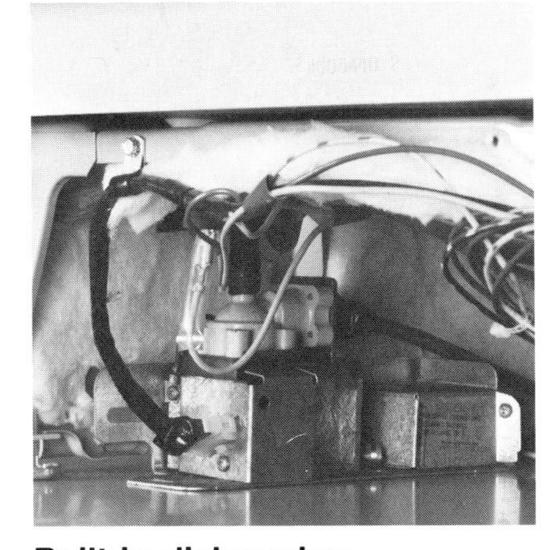

Built-in dishwasher installation module

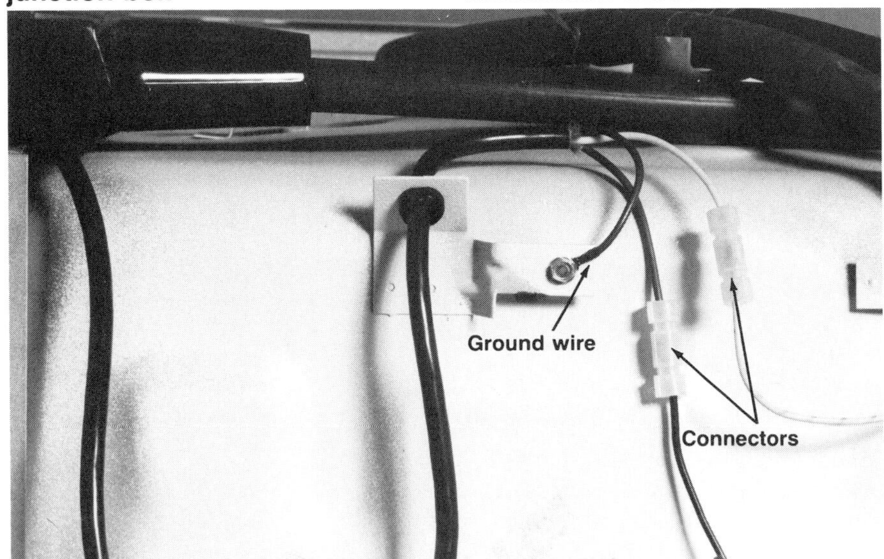

Convertible dishwasher power cord connections

Power connections (continued)

Step 1: Be sure all dishwasher controls are turned **OFF.** Disconnect power supply at the distribution panel.

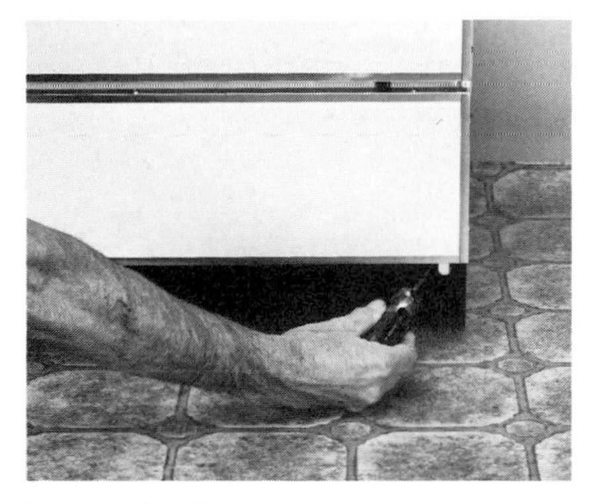

Step 2: This procedure may require removal of service panels from your dishwasher. If you are unfamiliar with this process, please refer to Procedure #3: Removing Service Panels.

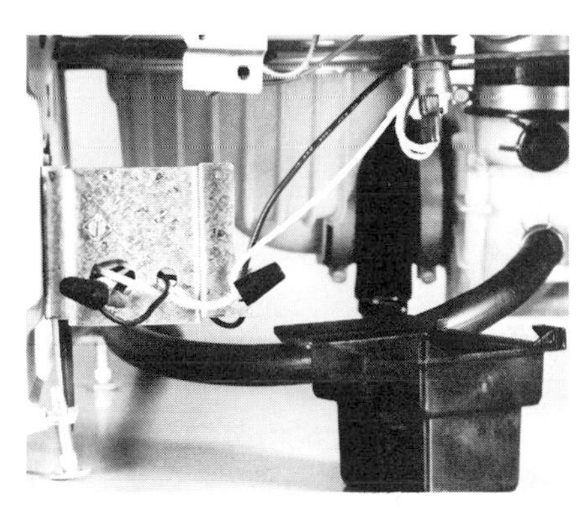

Step 3: For most built-in dishwashers, remove lower access panel. Remove cover from junction box and inspect power connections. Connections must be tight, with no broken or damaged wires.

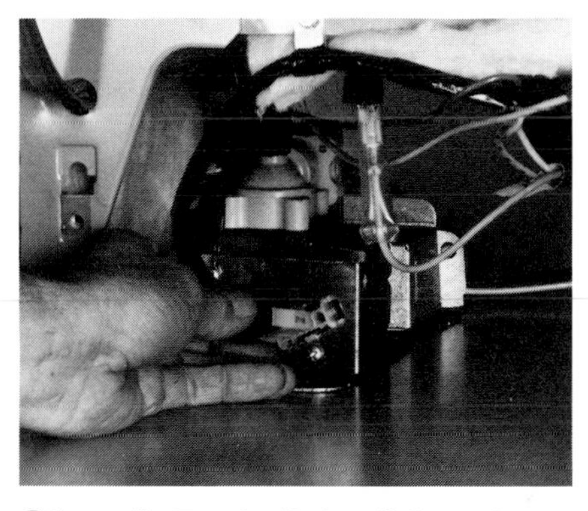

Step 4: For built-in dishwashers with installation module, inspect terminal block connection at the module. Connection must be tight, with no signs of damaged or broken wires.

Step 5: For convertible dishwashers with power cord, inspect power cord at connection to receptacle. Improper connection could be the sole cause of trouble.

Step 6: Pull plug from receptacle with a firm, quick tug. Always grasp by plug and never by cord. Be careful not to contact blades of plug.

Step 7: Inspect plug carefully for damaged, corroded or loose terminals. Look for signs of overheating around molded portion. If plug is damaged, replace cord. For access, remove side panel.

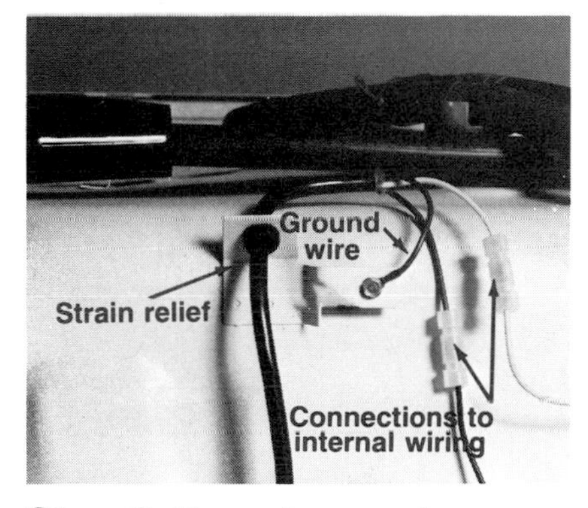

Step 8: To replace cord, disconnect where attached to internal wiring. (For installation reference, make note of how wires are connected.) Thread new cord through back of unit and strain relief, and connect same as original installation.

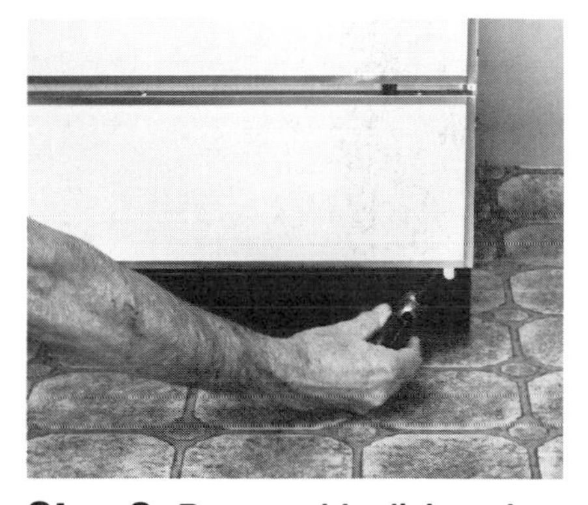

Step 9: Reassemble dishwasher and reconnect power supply.

Procedure 3

Removing service panels

Skill Level Rating: | Easy | **Average** | Difficult | Very Difficult |
|---|---|---|---|

For reasons of safety and appearance, most electrical and mechanical components of a dishwasher are enclosed. Many repairs require the removal of service panels in order to reach the parts.

Most wiring and electrical connections are found behind the control panel. Mechanical components such as the detergent and rinse agent dispensers are located between the door panels. A lower access panel conceals the dishwasher motor/pump assembly, water and electrical connections, water inlet valve and hoses. The top and side panels of convertible dishwashers are also removable.

Important Note: On certain models, you may find it difficult to work on certain components inside the lower access panel without pulling the dishwasher out and tilting it back. Should you have to move the dishwasher, take extra precaution to protect floor and cabinets from damage. Also be aware that some water will likely leak out from the hoses. Cover floor with old towels.

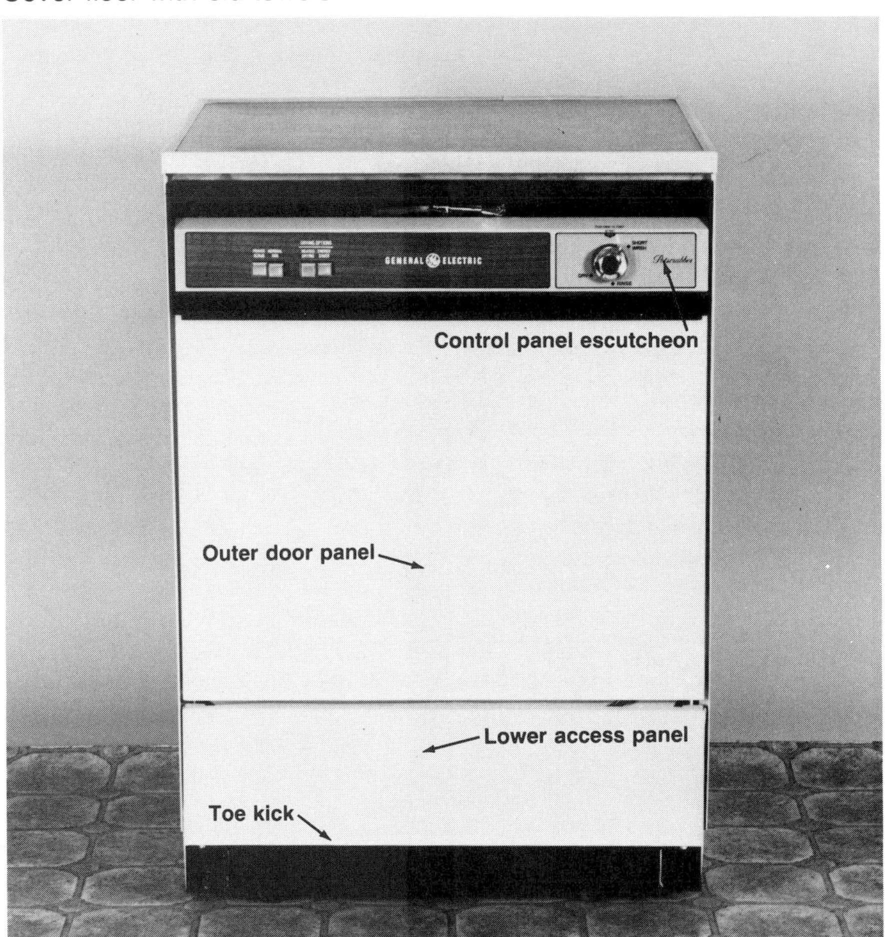

Service panels

Service panels (continued)

Step 1: Be sure all dishwasher controls are turned **OFF**. Disconnect power supply at distribution panel. For convertible models, also unplug power cord from receptacle. Watch for sharp edges.

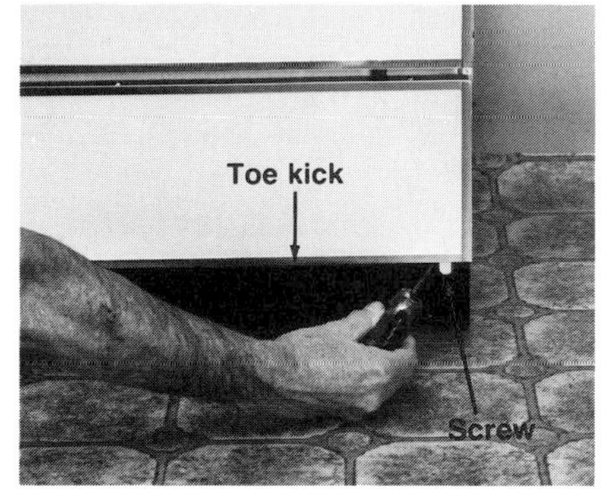

Step 2: Lower access panel. Remove screws on each side of toe kick which fasten the lower panel. Raise panel, which hooks at top, and remove panel and toe kick from dishwasher.

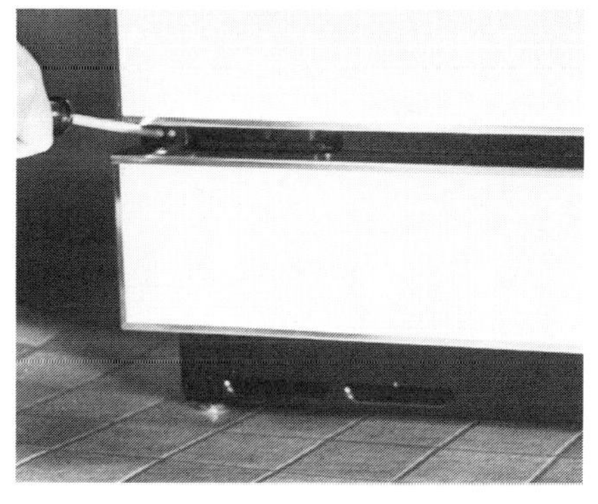

Step 3: Some models do not have hooks at top of panel, but two additional screws that are removed with a Phillips screwdriver or nutdriver.

Step 4: Other models have additional holding screws located on top of the access panel at each side. Remove the screws which secure the toe kick, then open the dishwasher door for access to these screws.

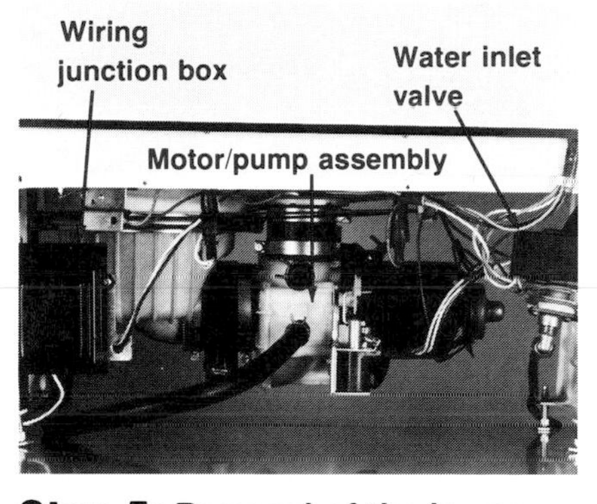

Step 5: Removal of the lower access panel allows you to reach the dishwasher motor/pump assembly, water and electrical connections, and water inlet valve and hoses.

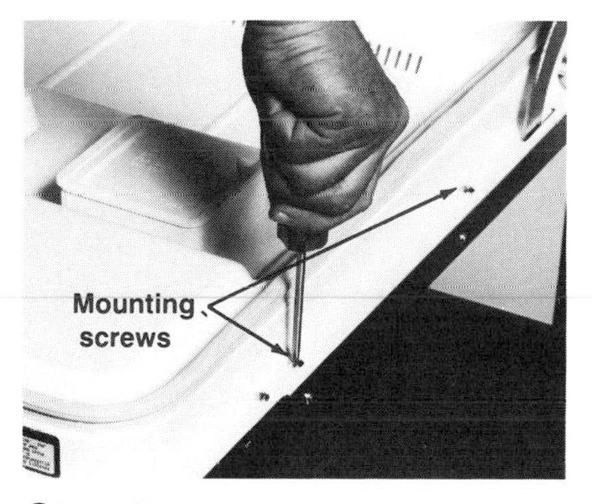

Step 6: Type A door panel. On some models, certain electrical and mechanical components are located on the outside of the inner door panel. To separate outer door panel, open door and remove mounting screws from inside.

Step 7: Remove screw from latch knob as shown and detach knob. Separate door panels.

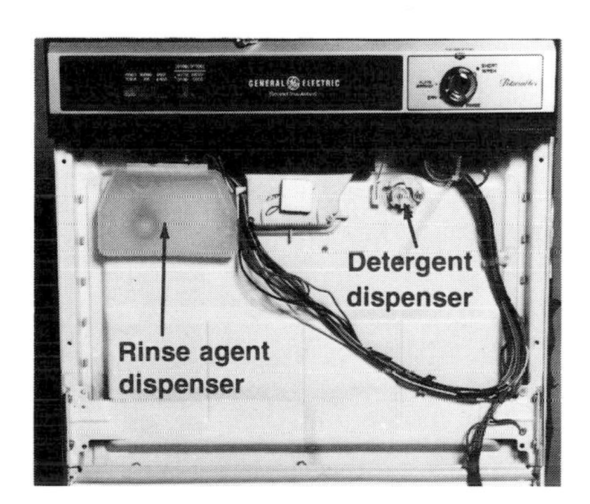

Step 8: With outer door panel removed, mechanical components such as the detergent and rinse agent dispensers are visible on outside of inner door.

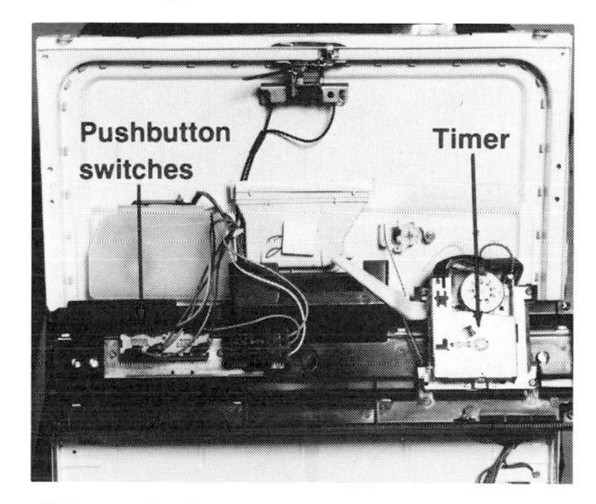

Step 9: On these models, the electrical controls are located in a control escutcheon on the outside of inner door. With outer door panel removed, pull control panel escutcheon up and forward, lowering it gently. Be sure to support panel to avoid damaging wiring.

Service panels (continued)

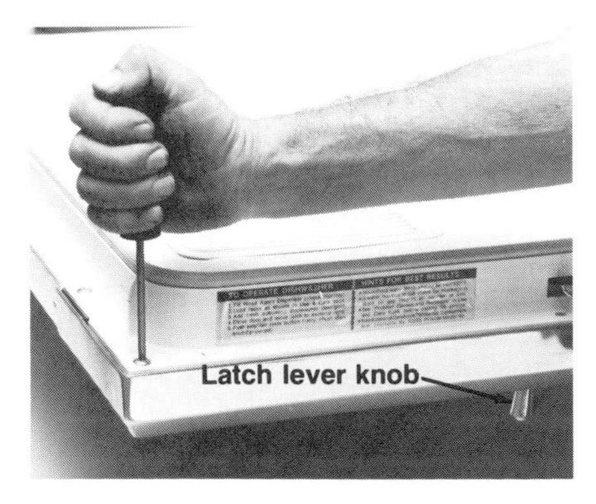

Step 10: Type B Door panel. On some models with PermaTuf® interiors, inner door removes for access to components. Open door and remove all retaining screws around edge.

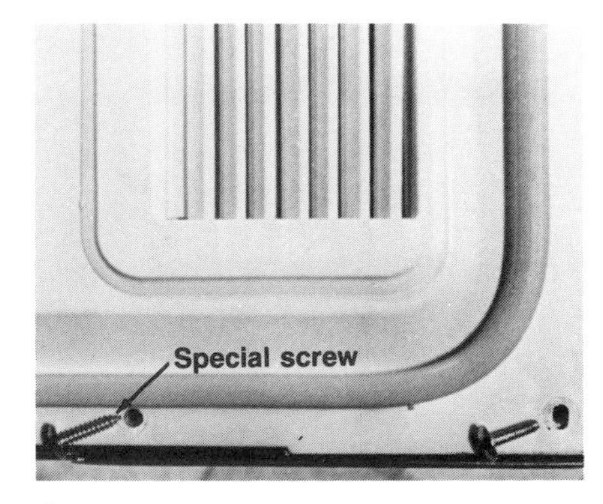

Step 11: Some models use a different retaining screw in first hole down side from corner. (When replacing screws be sure to place these special screws in right hole). Remove latch screw (see Step 7) and separate panels.

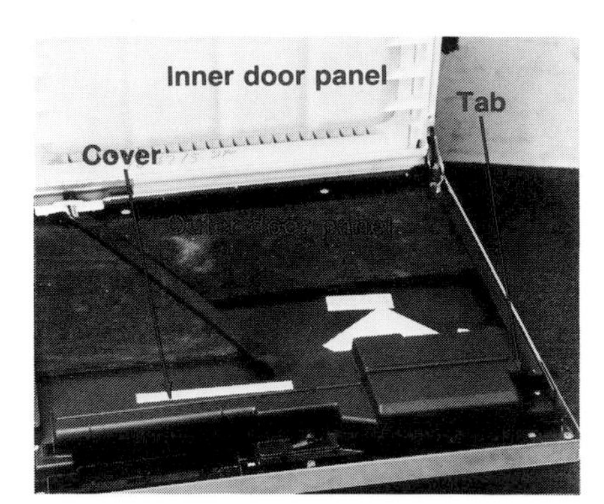

Step 12: Electrical controls are housed inside a plastic cover on the inside of the outer door. Squeeze tabs at each end and lift up to release cover. To replace, fit tabs back into slots and press.

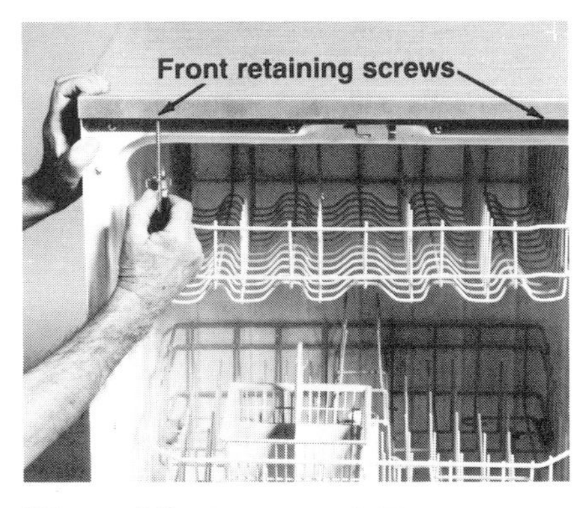

Step 13: Top panel. To remove top of convertible models, remove front retaining screws. On some models, top hooks at rear can be pulled forward and off. On other models, remove additional screws at back before pulling top off.

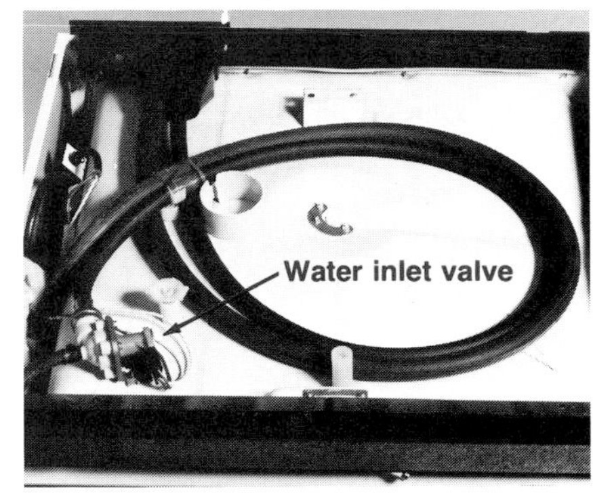

Step 14: Removing top gives access to the water hoses and power cord. On most GE models, water inlet valve is also reached through the top. On other GE and Hotpoint models, water inlet valve is behind lower access panel.

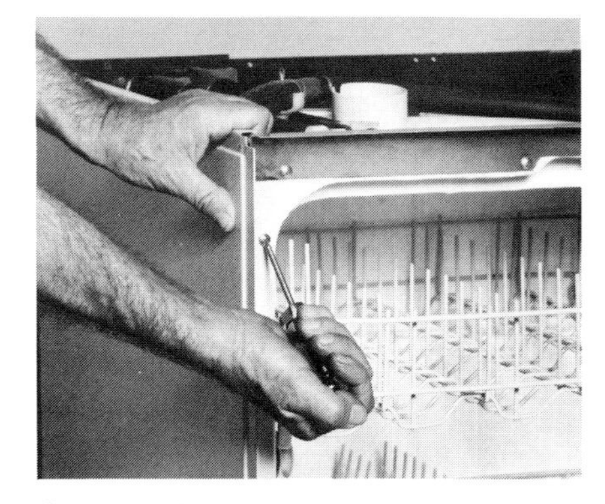

Step 15: Side panels. To remove side panels of convertible model, remove top. Open door and remove front holding screws. Remove lower access panel if necessary to reach bottom screw. Remove screws from back of unit and pull panel off.

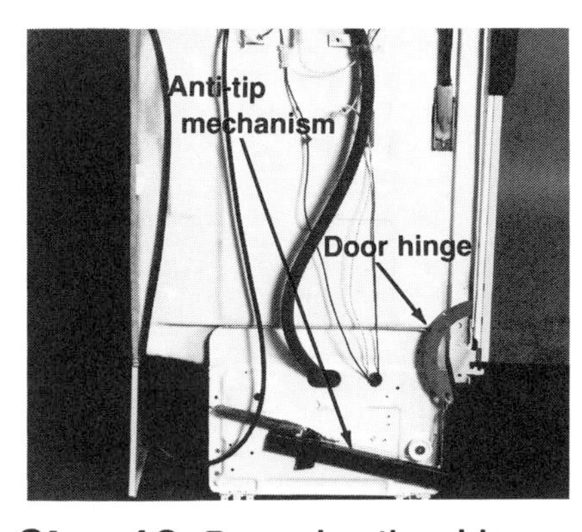

Step 16: Removing the side panel of a convertible dishwasher exposes the door hinge and spring assembly, as well as the anti-tip mechanism.

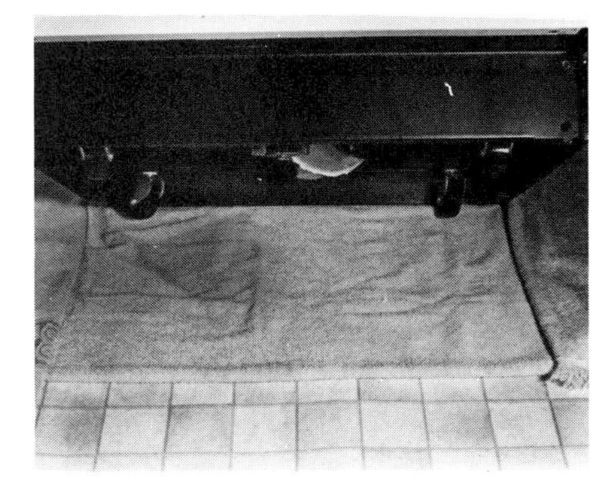

Step 17: Tilting dishwasher back. For access to hard-to-reach components under tub, prepare floor for water and lay convertible model over gently. Built-in dishwashers must first be disconnected from countertop, wiring and hoses before pulling out.

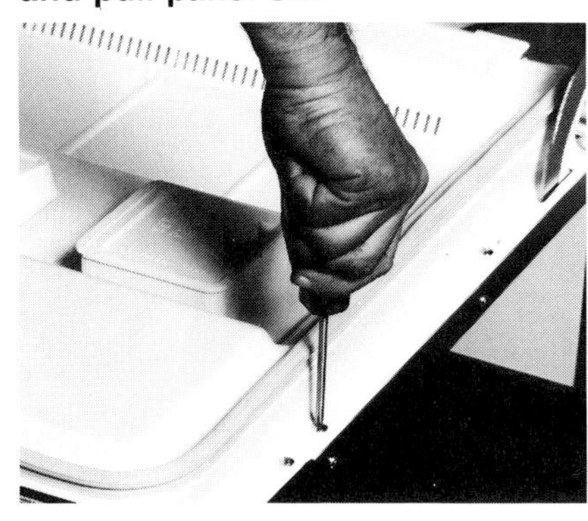

Step 18: After inspection and repair is completed, reassemble dishwasher and reconnect power supply.

Notes

Procedure 4

Repairing wiring and connections

Skill Level Rating:	Easy	Average	**Difficult**	Very Difficult

Power is carried to the components of the dishwasher by a network of insulated wires. These wires are connected to the timer, switches and other dishwasher components by various types of terminals. Virtually all dishwasher wires attach to terminals by means of push-on or plug-in connectors.

It's very important that the wiring is free from damage. Any cut that reduces the diameter of the wire reduces the amount of power it will carry. Also, the wire itself may overheat and eventually break at that point.

If terminals become dull and oxidized, they should be replaced. Any mating terminal, such as one located on the heating unit or a switch, should be polished until bright and shiny before a new wire is attached, to insure a good connection.

Whenever you service your dishwasher, be sure to note the position of any green ground wires in the area in which you are working. If it is necessary to replace any dishwasher wire or component, be certain that any green ground wire is correctly reconnected in its original position. This is vital in order to avoid danger of shock or short circuit.

CAUTION: If replacement wire is required, use only appliance wire having the same temperature and gauge rating as the wire you are replacing. This information is usually printed on the wire itself. If bell connectors are required, be sure to use the proper size for the gauge of wire being used.

Note: For installation reference, make note of how wires are connected. Use masking tape to mark wires or draw diagram of wiring connections on paper.

Damaged wires

Step 1: Be sure all dishwasher controls are turned OFF. Disconnect power supply at distribution panel. For convertible models, also unplug power cord from receptacle. Watch for sharp edges.

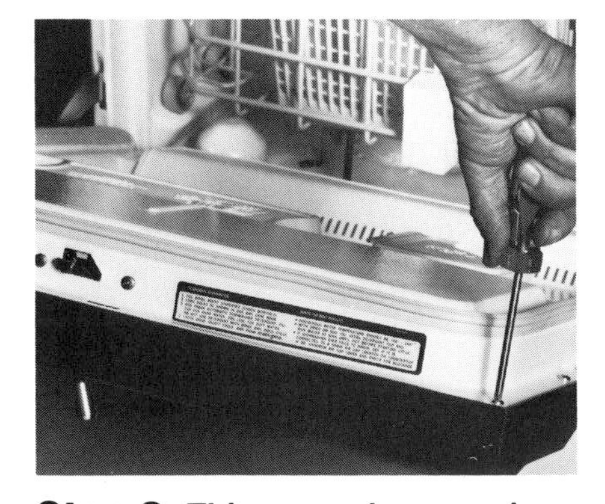

Step 2: This procedure requires the removal of service panels from your dishwasher. If you are unfamiliar with this process, please refer to Procedure #3: Removing Service Panels.

Step 3: Much of the dishwasher's internal wiring is connected with push-on terminals. Male and female portions of these terminals fit together snugly to make a solid connection.

Wiring and connections (continued)

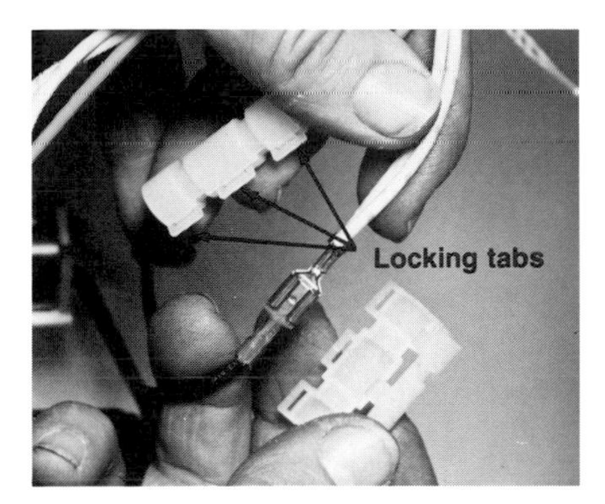

Step 4: Single push-on connectors often have covers to protect or insulate the connection. The cylindrical cover shown snaps open easily by depressing the locking tabs.

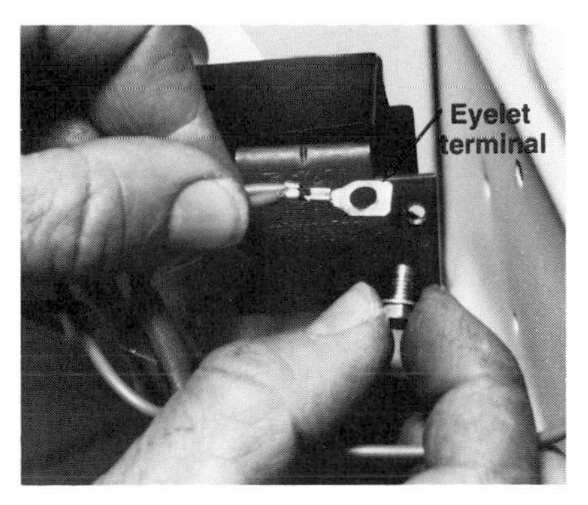

Step 5: Other internal dishwasher connections are made with eyelet terminals and screws. The green ground wires are often secured with this sort of terminal.

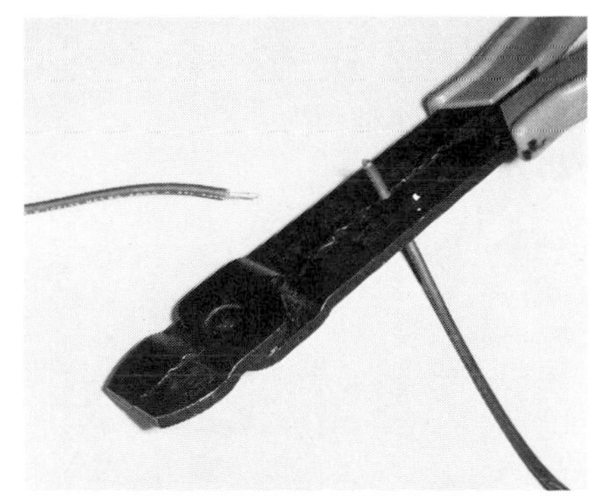

Step 6: To splice damaged wiring, remove insulation from the wire. Use wire stripper to avoid cutting into the conductor. Remove only enough insulation to allow you to make the connection or splice.

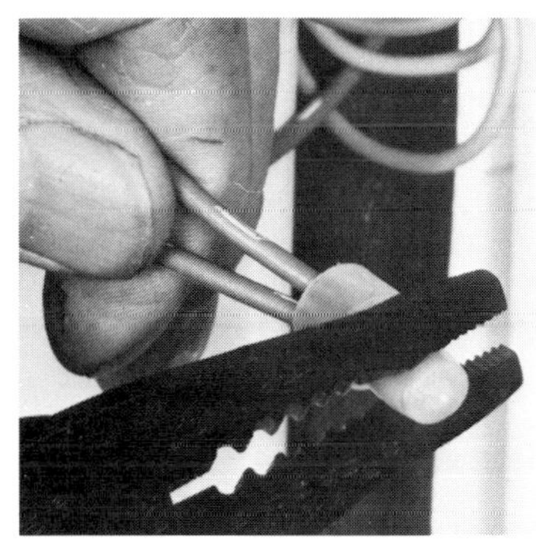

Step 7: To splice wiring, strip insulation back to bright and shiny wire. Twist strands together. Push on a bell connector and crimp to secure the splice. Be sure connector fully covers all bare wire.

Step 8: To replace a single terminal, such as those in Steps 4 and 5, cut off old terminal. Strip insulation from end of wire and twist strands together. Slip on new terminal and crimp with crimping tool to secure.

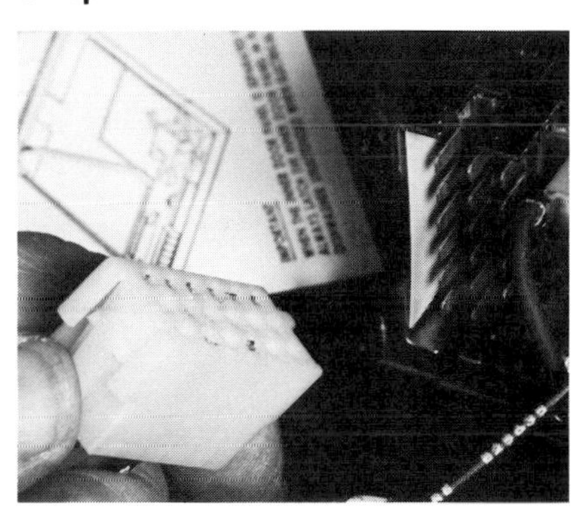

Step 9: Some dishwasher wiring is connected at a quick-disconnect terminal block. Inspect block for signs of distortion or discoloration. If block appears damaged, call a qualified service technician.

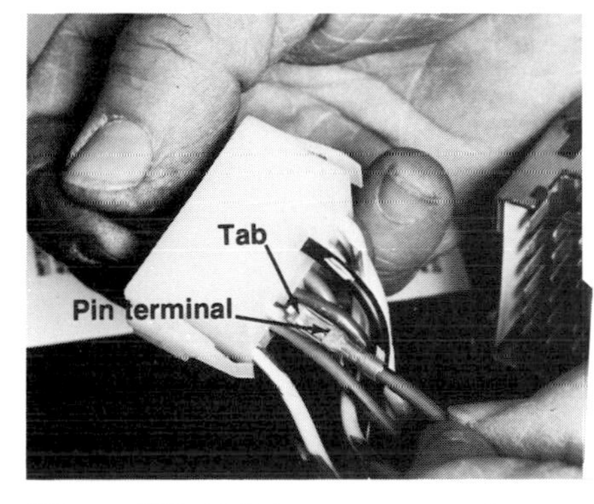

Step 10: If it is necessary to replace one wire of the terminal block, insert a small screwdriver or other long thin bladed tool into the terminal block hole. Depress the tab on the side of the metal pin, and withdraw pin terminal.

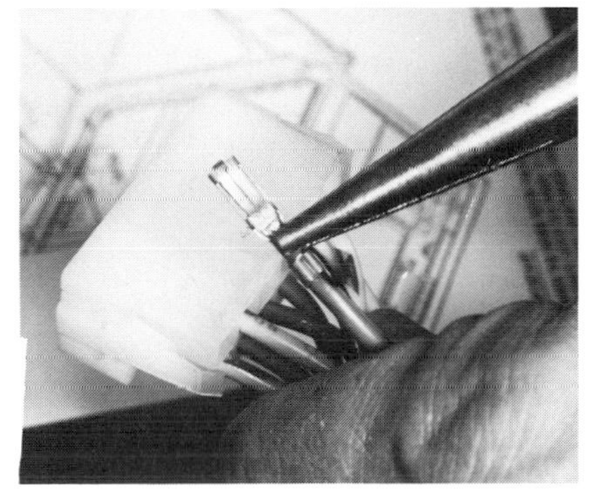

Step 11: Cut damaged wire and discard pin terminal. Strip insulation and insert bare wire into new terminal. Crimp with crimping tool. Insert new pin terminal into terminal block in same position from which old pin was removed.

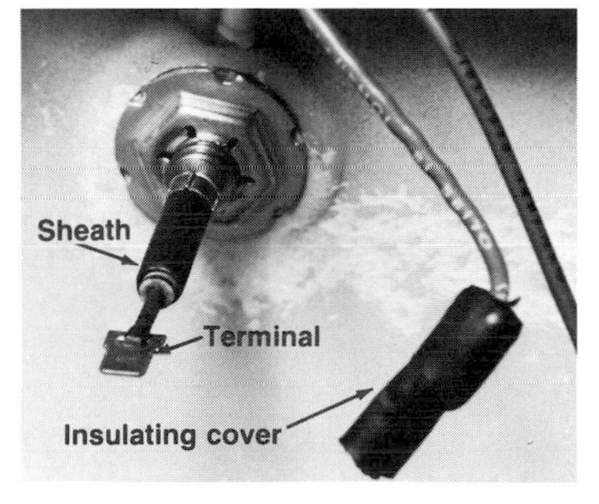

Step 12: When removing or replacing Calrod® heating unit, take care not to bend terminals. Damage to terminals may prevent proper connection or cause short circuit. Reassemble dishwasher and reconnect power supply.

Procedure 5
Loading dishwasher

Skill Level Rating:	**Easy**	Average	Difficult	Very Difficult

Many performance problems that commonly occur in dishwashers are not due to mechanical defects. Problems with poor washing results can often be solved without making repairs.

The first procedures in this manual are designed to help you eliminate performance problems before you begin checking and testing your dishwasher's components. To get the best results from your dishwasher, it is necessary to form good dishwashing habits. Correct loading is essential for good performance. If your dishwasher seems to run correctly, but does not get the dishes really clean, check to be sure you are loading the dishwasher properly. Your *Use and Care Book* will give you additional, detailed instructions for your particular dishwasher model.

Important Note: Do not clean furnace, air conditioner, or electrostatic air filters in your dishwasher. To do so will likely discolor your dishwasher tub.

Correct loading

Loading dishwasher (continued)

Step 1: For your personal safety, exercise caution when working with any electrical appliance.

Step 2: Prepare dishes properly. Tip or shake off large and hard food scraps. Remove large amounts of food, especially starchy foods. The soft food disposer will handle small amounts of soft food.

Step 3: Place dishes with dirty side facing water spray from wash arm and Power Tower™ sprayer. Don't "nest" dishes so that water cannot reach the outer item.

Step 4: Bottom wash arm is the most forceful. Place heavily soiled items such as pots and pans in lower rack, facing down. Do not block entire lower rack. Don't place items in upper rack above pans in lower rack.

Step 5: Don't block the Power Tower™ sprayer by loading tall items next to it. Keep the front of the lower rack clear so that water can reach the detergent dispenser, located on the door.

Step 6: Wash action is gentler on the upper rack. Use this for glasses, cups and smaller odd-shaped items. Place any plastic items securely so that they cannot fall onto the Calrod® heating unit.

Step 7: Place flatware in silverware basket, handles up. Do not allow spoons to "nest". Distribute evenly and remove any items that may fall through bottom of basket.

Procedure 6

Checking water and detergent

Skill Level Rating:	Easy	Average	Difficult	Very Difficult

Water and detergent are major factors in good dishwasher performance. Water pressure, hardness and temperature all play vital roles in getting your dishes clean. The correct detergent, in proper amounts, is equally important for good dishwashing results. The hardness of the water in your area will affect the amount of detergent needed to get your dishes clean.

Note: Some dishwashers with a Sani Cycle or Temperature Sensor feature energize the Calrod® heating element during some cycles to heat water to the proper temperature for getting dishes clean.

Three-level wash system

Water and detergent (continued)

Step 1: For your personal safety, exercise caution when working with any electrical appliance.

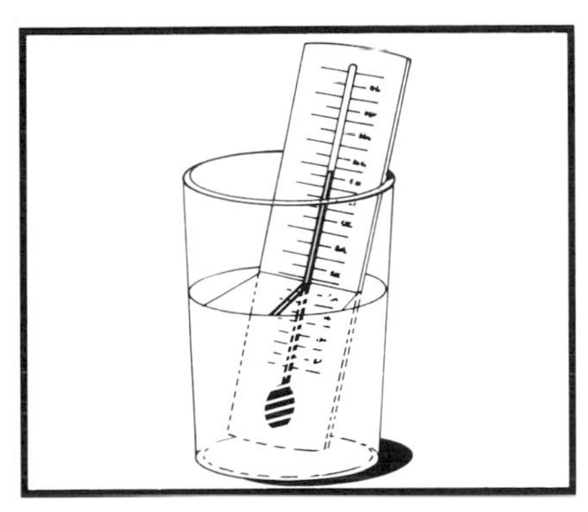

Step 2: Check the temperature of the water coming into the dishwasher tub. Place a candy or meat thermometer in a glass and fill the glass with hot water from the faucet nearest the dishwasher. Let the water run until the temperature stops rising.

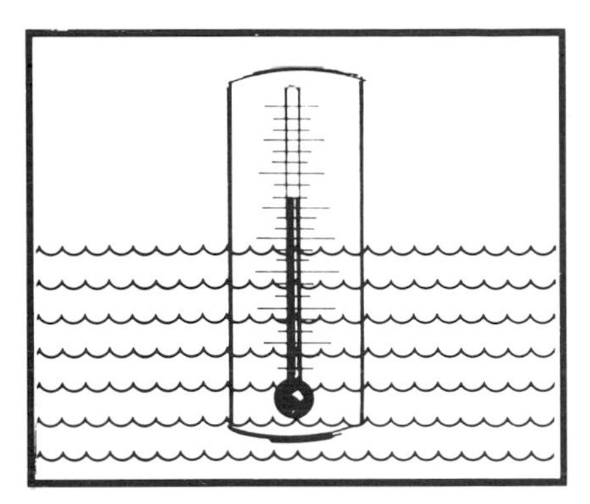

Step 3: Most dishwashers require 140°-150°F water. Some later models with a water heat feature require a minimum of 120°F. Check your *Use and Care Book* for water temperature requirement and adjust water heater setting, if necessary.

Step 4: Schedule dishwashing when there is an ample supply of hot water. Wash dishes before baths, showers or laundry. Or wait to give the water heater time to recover.

Step 5: Use detergent intended specifically for automatic dishwashers. Other detergents can damage your machine. Make sure detergent is fresh and dry. Old, caked detergent will not wash well. Do not use liquid detergent.

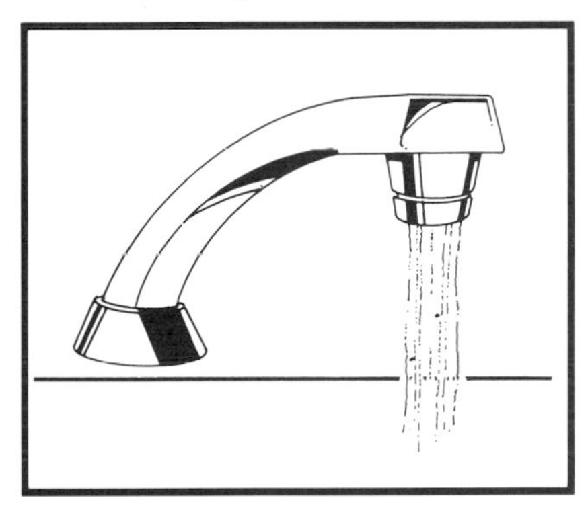

Step 6: Ask your water company about local water conditions. With very hard water, more detergent may be required for good results. If the water is soft, or if you use a water softener, use less detergent.

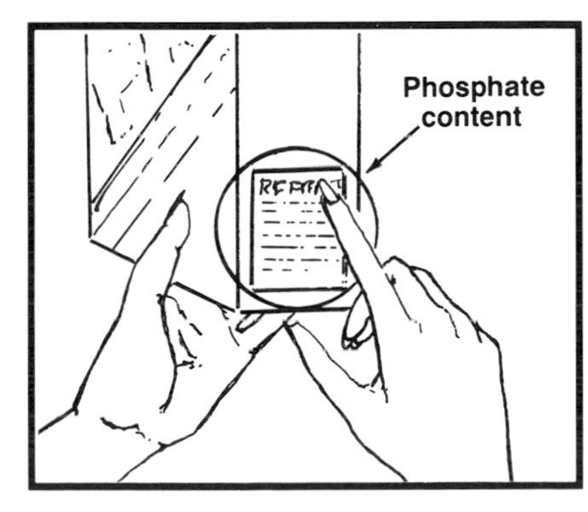

Step 7: Check your detergent's phosphate level. 12.9% is fully phosphated. If the phosphate level is 8.7% or less, it may be necessary to use more detergent or to add detergent to both dispenser cups, especially if water is very hard.

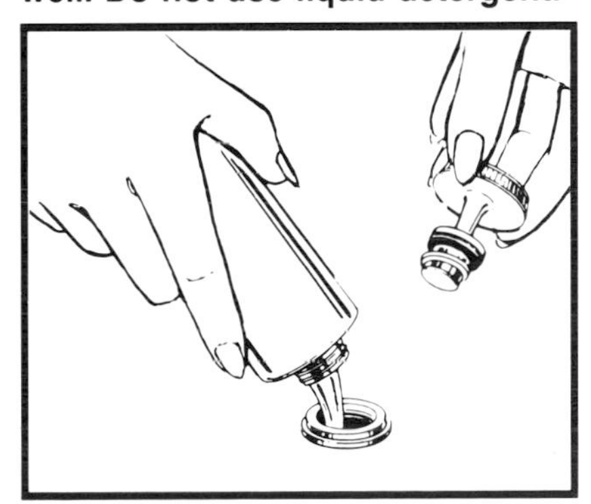

Step 8: Using a rinse agent will make water flow off dishes faster for quicker drying and fewer spots. If your dishwasher has a rinse agent dispenser, be sure to fill it, but avoid overfilling, as this will cause leaking down the inner door panel.

Procedure 7

Inspecting air gap and drain lines

Skill Level Rating:	Easy	**Average**	Difficult	Very Difficult

Plumbing problems can be responsible for poor dishwashing performance. Drainage problems can be caused by a blocked house drain or a clogged dishwasher drain hose. If wash results are poor, or if too much water remains in the tub after washing, check the drain and hose, as well as the air gap. (A small amount of water remaining in the dishwasher sump is normal.)

The air gap is a plumbing device often used with built-in dishwashers. It keeps water from backing up into the dishwasher if the house drain becomes clogged. If you have an air gap, check it periodically to prevent obstruction.

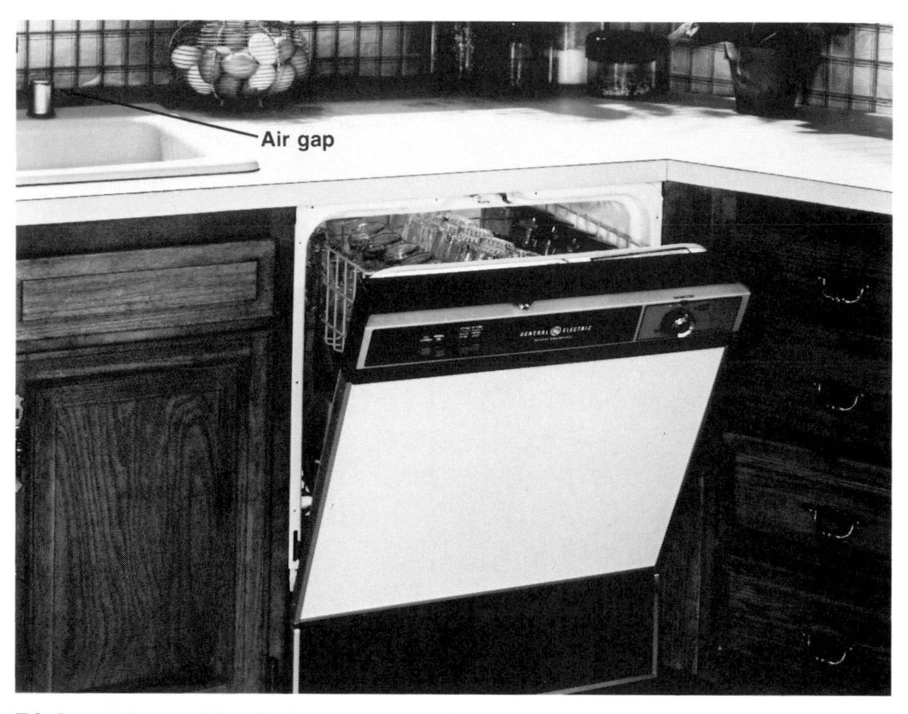

Dishwasher with sink-mounted air gap

Step 1: Dishwasher must drain completely before start of next fill. To check, let dishwasher fill, then turn timer to beginning of a drain period. Listen as water is pumped out. Sound should stop before next fill starts.

Step 2: Be sure all dishwasher controls are turned **OFF**. Disconnect power supply at distribution panel. For convertible models, also unplug power cord from receptacle. Watch for sharp edges.

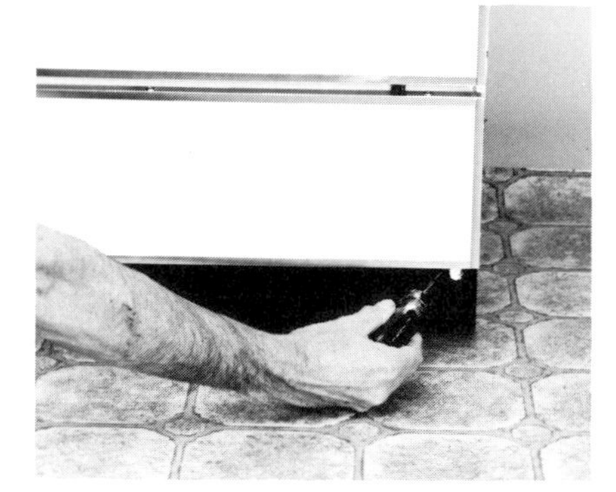

Step 3: This procedure may require removal of service panels from your dishwasher. If you are unfamiliar with this process, please refer to Procedure #3: Removing Service Panels.

Air gap and drain lines (continued)

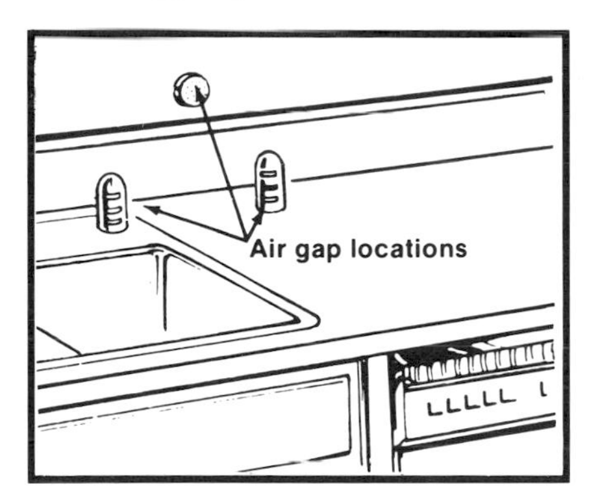

Step 4: The air gap, if you have one, is usually located on the counter, sink, or wall above the dishwasher. Check it if your dishwasher is not draining well.

Step 5: For most air gaps, lift off chrome cover and unscrew plastic cap. Check for clogs and accumulated foreign material. Clean air gap if necessary.

Step 6: Check at kitchen sink to be sure house drain is not clogged. If dishwasher drains into a disposer, be sure disposer is empty before running the dishwasher.

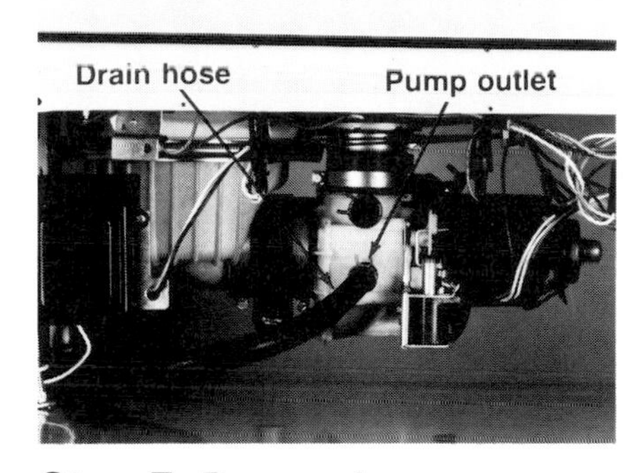

Step 7: Remove lower access panel and check drain hose for kinks or sharp bends. Begin near pump outlet and follow hose, straightening kinks. Problems can also result from defective drain valve. See Procedure #14.

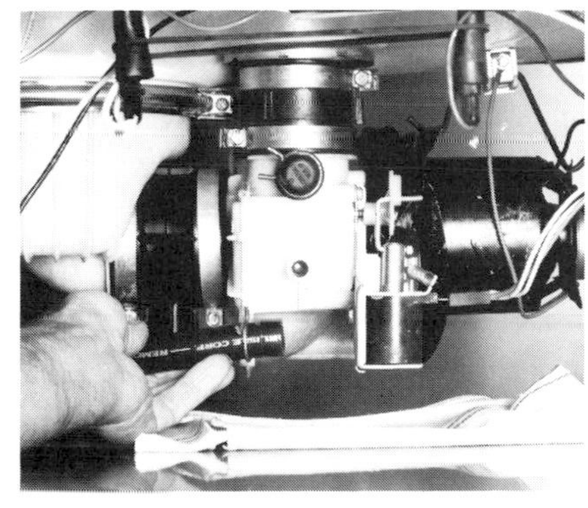

Step 8: Remove drain hose if necessary to clear obstruction. Replace if collapsed or permanently kinked. Disconnect hose at pump outlet. Catch draining water with towel or shallow pan.

Step 9: For built-in models, follow hose to house drain or disposer and disconnect. For convertible models, remove top and side panels. Disconnect hose at unicouple. For instructions, refer to Procedure #27: Unicouple.

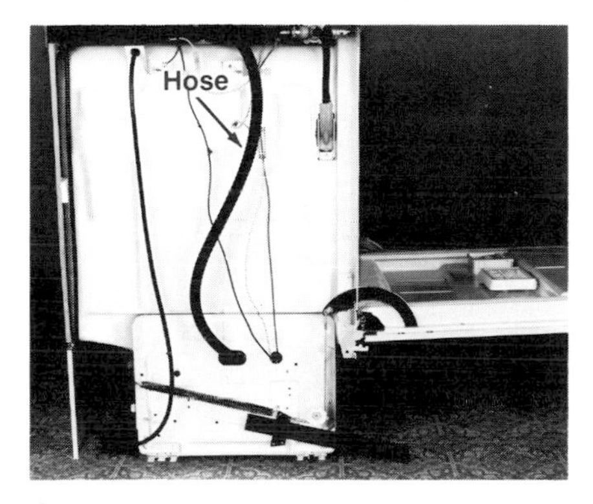

Step 10: Replace hose, positioning same as original installation. Reconnect at house drain or unicouple, and at pump outlet, clamping tightly to prevent leakage.

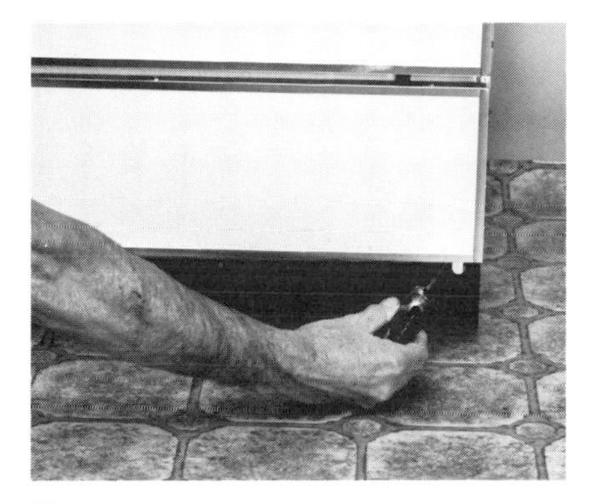

Step 11: Reassemble dishwasher and reconnect power supply.

Procedure 8

Inspecting and replacing door latch mechanism

Skill Level Rating: | Easy | Average | **Difficult** | Very Difficult |

The door latch is essential to the operation of your dishwasher. Latching the door handle lever closes a switch which allows electrical current to flow to the timer. All other dishwasher components are controlled by the timer.

If the door latch switch is open, the dishwasher will not operate. The latch switch cannot be activated while the dishwasher door is open. There is a safety mechanism which prevents the dishwasher from being operated accidentally with the door open. However, if the door latch switch contacts should become stuck in the closed position, dishwasher operation will not stop when the door is opened during the cycle.

Door latches on different dishwasher models will vary somewhat in shape and in method of mounting, but inspection and repair procedures will be similar for all models.

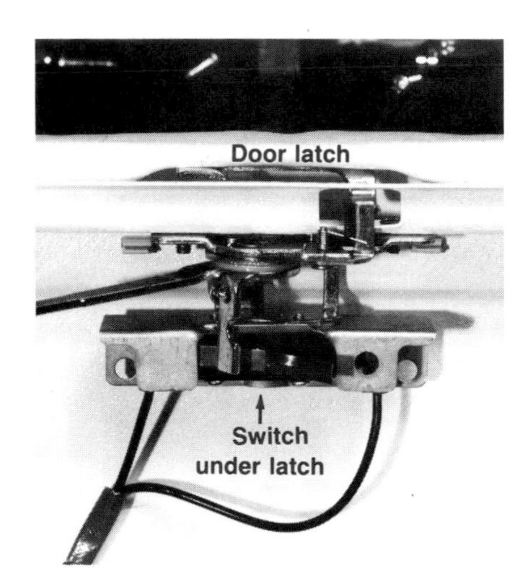

Type A door latch mechanism

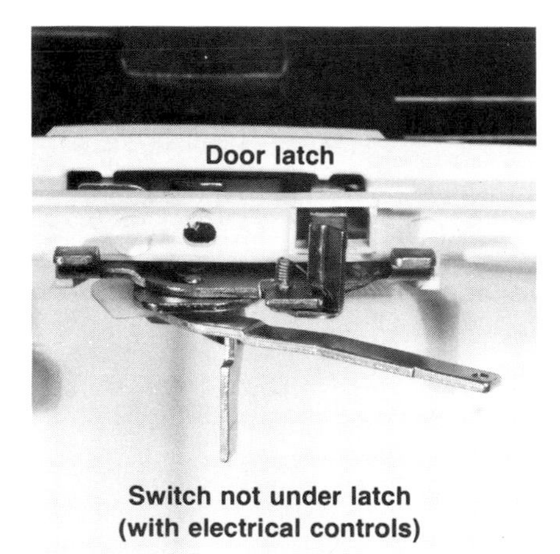

Type B door latch mechanism

Step 1: Be sure all dishwasher controls are turned **OFF.** Disconnect power supply at distribution panel. For convertible models, also unplug power cord from receptacle. Watch for sharp edges.

Step 2: This procedure requires the use of an ohmmeter. For instructions on how to use an ohmmeter, please refer to Tools and Testing Equipment, page 95.

Step 3: This procedure requires removal of service panels from your dishwasher. If you are unfamiliar with this process, please refer to Procedure #3: Removing Service Panels.

Door latch mechanism (continued)

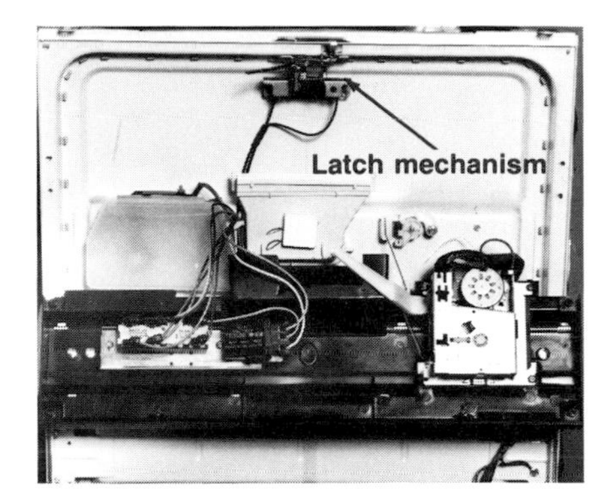

Step 4: On most models, tip control panel escutcheon down for access to latch mechanism. On some models with PermaTuf® interior, separate door panels. Latch is on inner door panel. Switch is on outer door panel.

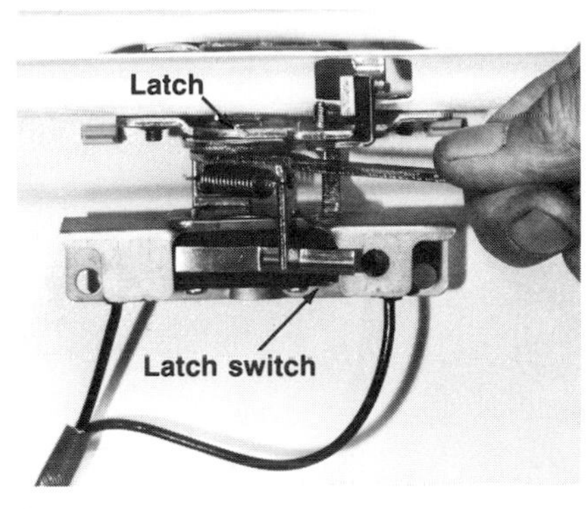

Step 5: Visually inspect latch for bent, broken or missing parts. Move latch lever by hand and lubricate any parts which seem to be binding with a light grease. Replace latch if damaged.

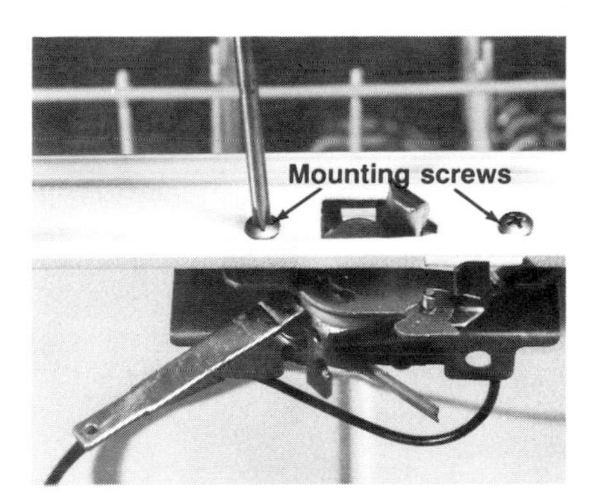

Step 6: To replace damaged latch, open dishwasher door and remove mounting screws on top. On models with removable PermaTuf® inner door panel, latch simply snaps into place without use of mounting screws.

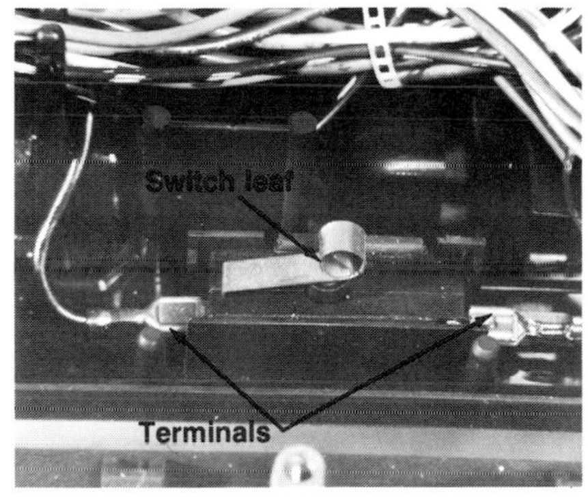

Step 7: Inspect latch switch terminals for loose or broken wires. On most models, switch is mounted beneath latch mechanism. On models with removable PermaTuf® inner door panel, switch is located on outer door panel, as shown above.

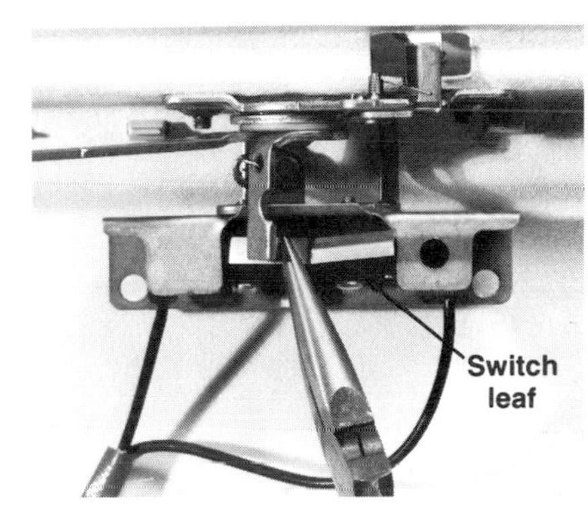

Step 8: Close latch and listen for click as switch closes. On models with removable PermaTuf® inner door panel, depress switch leaf by hand. Switch leaf can be bent slightly for better contact.

Step 9: Test switch with ohmmeter at R x 1. Remove leads and place probes on terminals. With latch open, needle should not move. Depress switch leaf. Needle should sweep upscale to indicate continuity. If no continuity, replace switch.

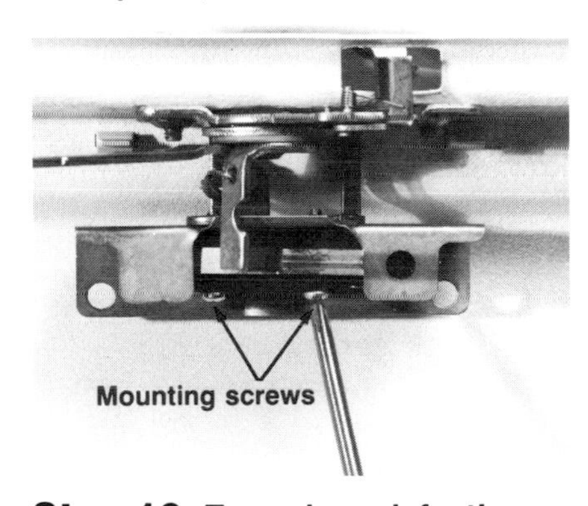

Step 10: To replace defective latch switch, disconnect wire leads. (For installation reference, make note of how wires are connected.) Remove mounting screws. Install new switch and reconnect leads.

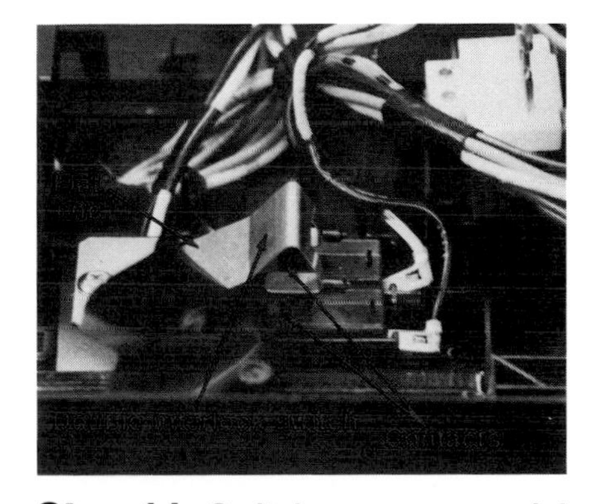

Step 11: Switch on some models snaps in place with flat end of switch leaf on left. Some models have two switches paired together that can be replaced independently. Be sure each arm of actuator is properly positioned over contact.

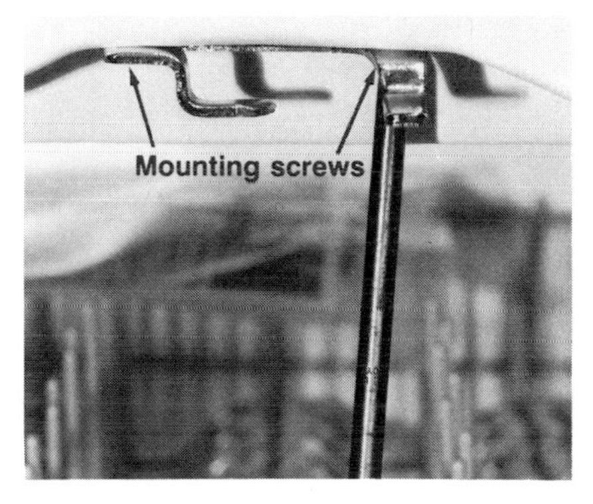

Step 12: To stop leaks around door, adjust latch strike on tub. Loosen screws and slide strike toward rear of tub. Adjust to tighten door, but not enough to make latch hard to close. Tighten screws.

Procedure 9

Inspecting and replacing timer

Skill Level Rating:	Easy	Average	Difficult	**Very Difficult**

The timer for your dishwasher consists of a timer motor and a variety of switches which automatically control every phase of the dishwasher's operation. The timer motor runs at a constant speed, like a clock. As it advances through the selected cycle, the timer's internal switches open and close in a precise sequence. As each switch closes, it completes a circuit to a dishwasher component. When a pre-set period has elapsed, the timer opens the switch again and shuts off power to that component.

Timers vary somewhat with different dishwasher models. On some models, each wire is attached to a separate external terminal. On other models, all wiring is attached to a terminal block. This procedure covers inspection procedures for both types of timers and covers replacement for the terminal-block timer.

All outgoing wires from the timer are color-coded. By referring to your dishwasher's circuit diagram, you can trace the path of electrical current from the timer to any component.

The timer is a very reliable mechanism. If you have a problem with your dishwasher, it is best to eliminate all other possible causes before attempting to test or replace the timer.

CAUTION: Testing the timer requires a high degree of skill in reading circuit diagrams. If you are not an accomplished handyman, call a qualified service technician for this repair.

If testing shows an external-terminal timer to be defective, call a qualified service technician. Replacement of this type of timer may require modification of wiring in order to install a substitute timer.

External-terminal timer

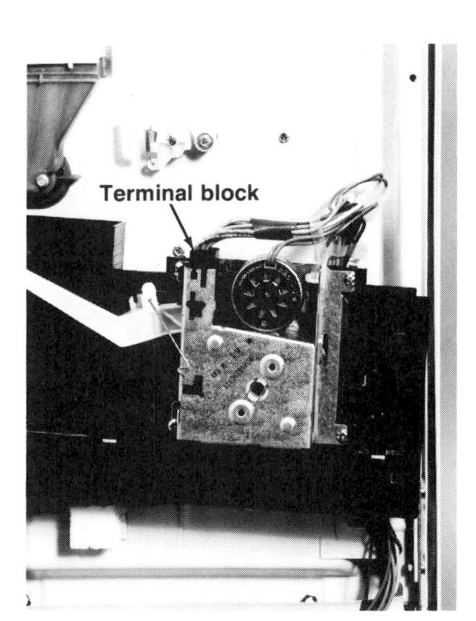

Terminal block timer

Timer (continued)

Step 1: Be sure all dishwasher controls are turned **OFF.** Disconnect power supply at distribution panel. For convertible models, also unplug power cord from receptacle. Watch for sharp edges.

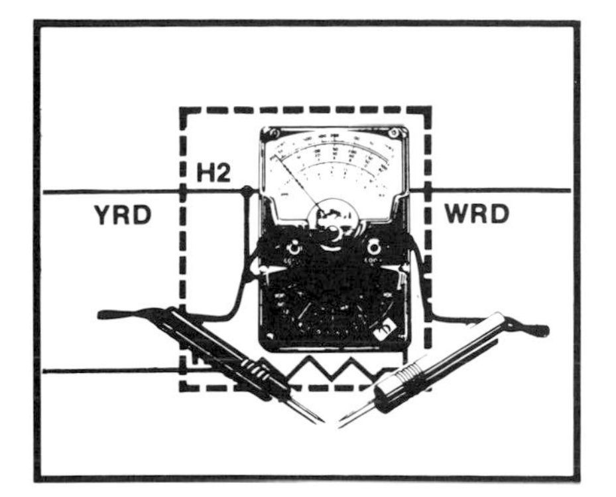

Step 2: This procedure requires the use of an ohmmeter and the ability to read a circuit diagram. For instructions, please refer to Tools and Testing Equipment, pages 95-98.

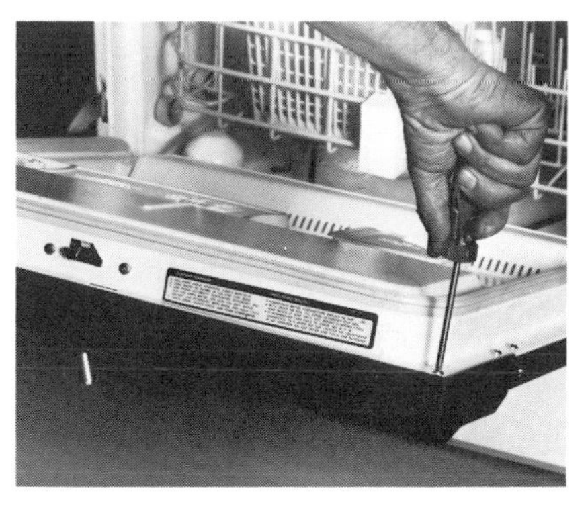

Step 3: This procedure requires the removal of service panels from your dishwasher. If you are unfamiliar with this process, please refer to Procedure #3: Removing Service Panels.

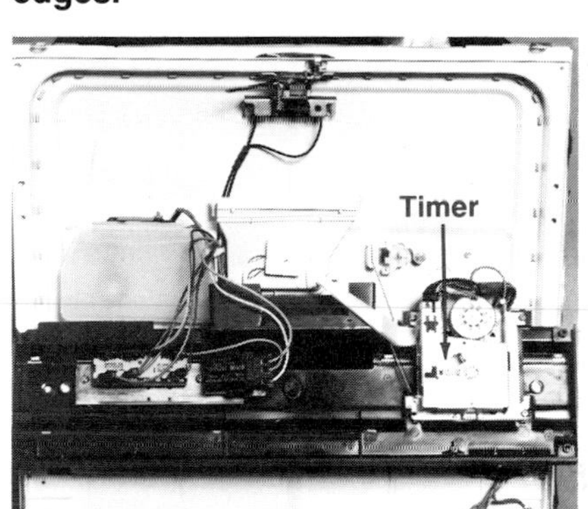

Step 4: On most models, tip control panel escutcheon down to reveal timer. On other models, remove outer door panel. Remove mounting screws and turn timer if necessary to check for loose or broken wires.

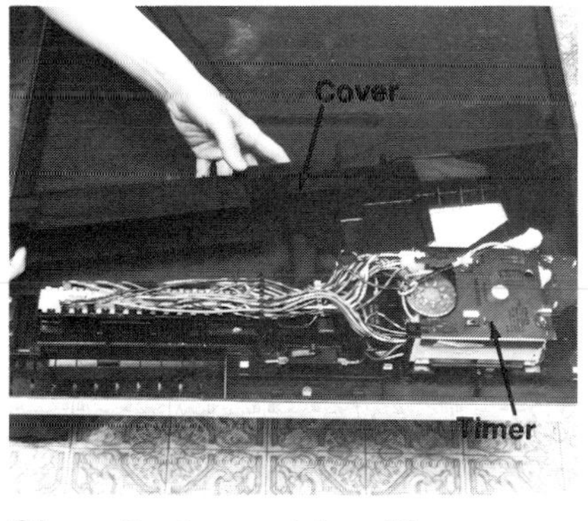

Step 5: On models with removable PermaTuf® inner door panel, remove retaining screws and lift inner door panel. Remove cover on outer portion of door to expose timer.

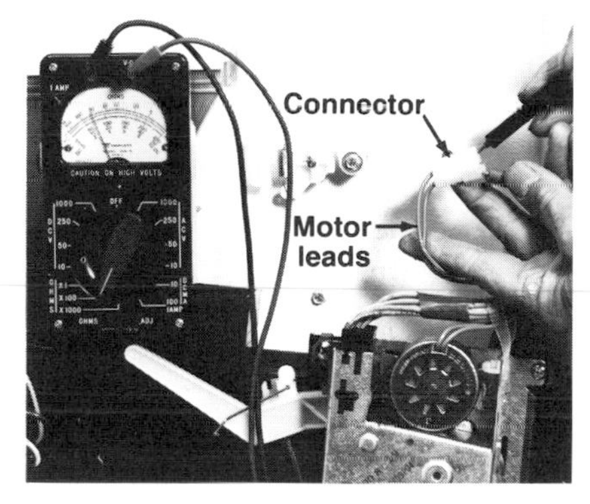

Step 6: Timer Motor. Disconnect timer motor leads at connector. With ohmmeter at R x 100, place probes on motor terminals. Needle should sweep partially upscale. If no continuity, replace timer.

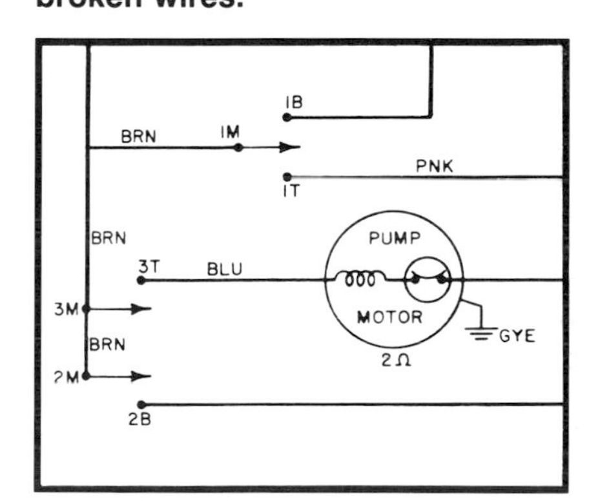

Step 7: Refer to dishwasher's circuit diagram to see which timer contacts close to activate a component. On this sample diagram, contacts 3M (brown lead) and 3T (blue lead) close to energize the pump motor.

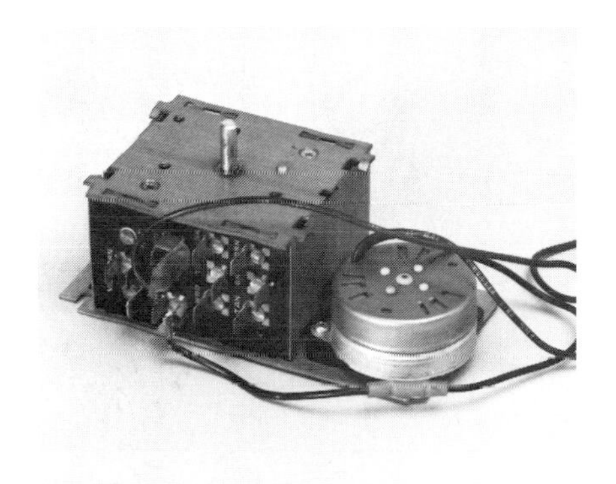

Step 8: External-terminal timers may vary somewhat in shape. However, testing procedures are similar for any timer with external terminals.

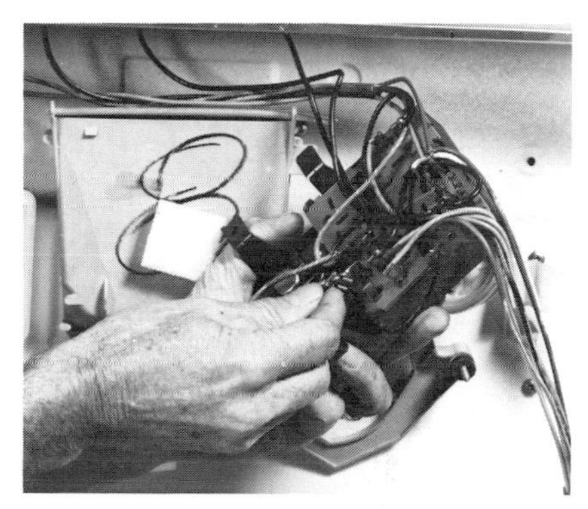

Step 9: External-terminal timer. Locate color-coded terminals which close to activate a component. Disconnect one lead. With ohmmeter at R x 1, place a test probe on each terminal.

Timer (continued)

Step 10: Refer to circuit diagram bar chart to see when component should be activated during dishwashing cycle. Contacts should be closed at these times. Turn timer dial slowly through full cycle.

Step 11: Ohmmeter needle should sweep upscale whenever timer contacts should be closed. Test each set of timer contacts. If any test shows failure, contact qualified service technician for replacement.

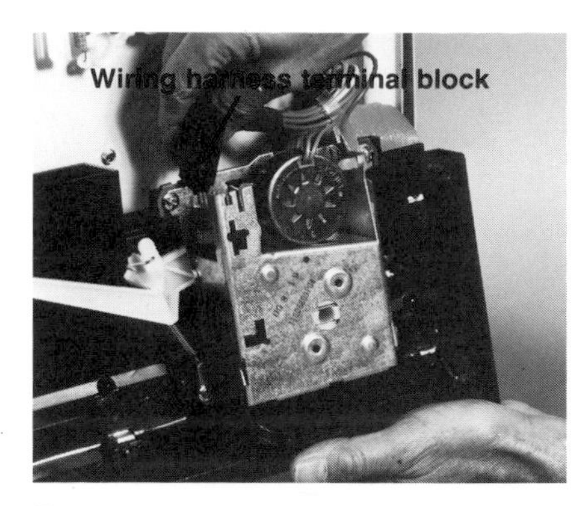

Step 12: Terminal-block timer. Remove wiring harness terminal block and examine. Check that wiring harness terminals are positioned securely in terminal block.

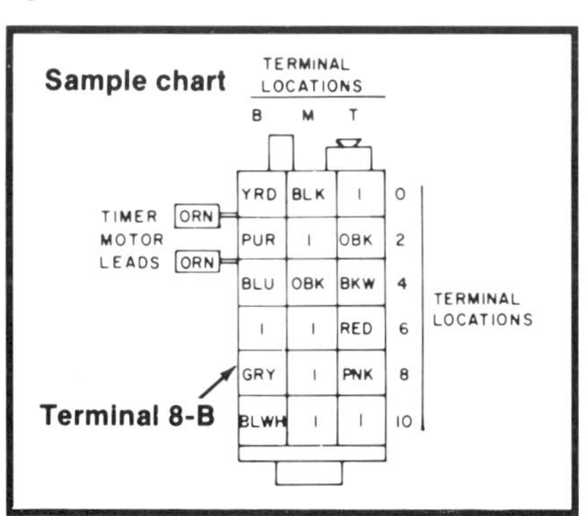

Step 13: Refer to circuit diagram and timer terminal location chart to determine which terminals close to activate a component. Terminals are coded by letter and number.

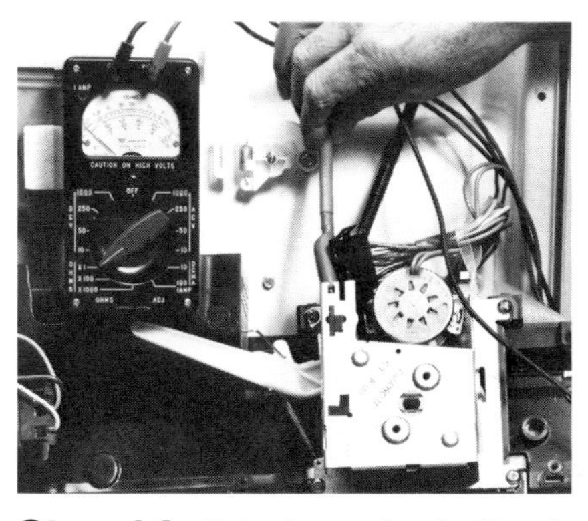

Step 14: Set ohmmeter to R x 1. Place one test probe on each timer terminal. Turn timer dial slowly through full cycle.

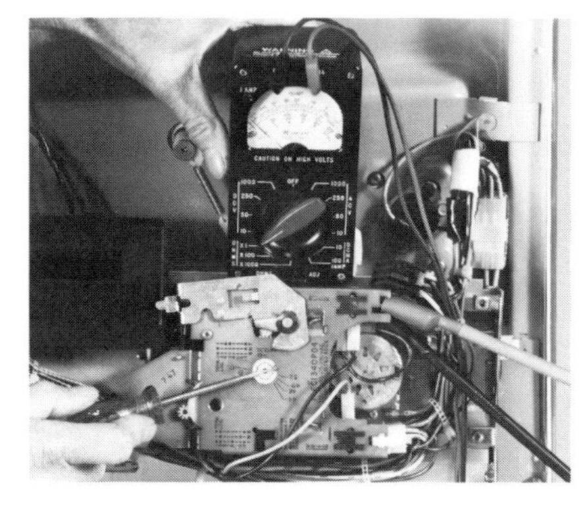

Step 15: If dishwasher has no timer dial knob, turn timer from back with a screwdriver. Insert blade into slot in timer hub and use as a lever to turn timer through cycle.

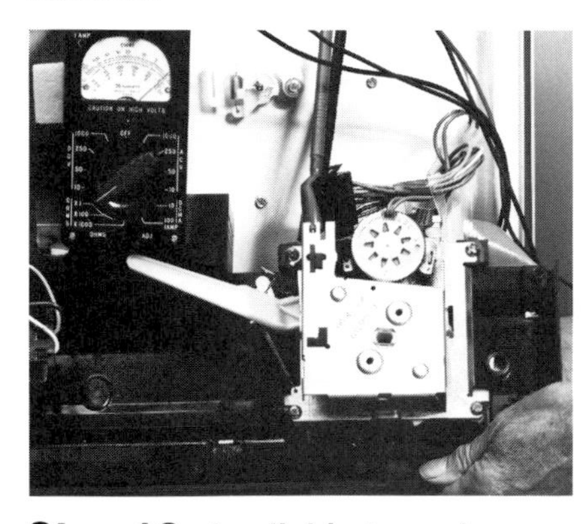

Step 16: As dial is turned, ohmmeter needle should sweep upscale whenever timer contacts should be closed. Repeat test for each set of contacts. If test shows failure, replace timer.

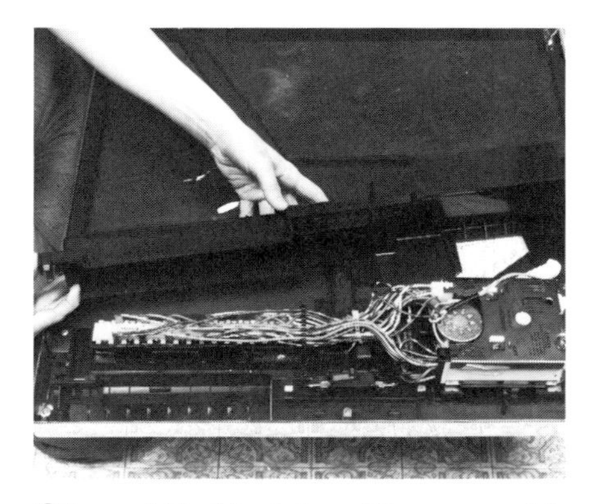

Step 17: Models with removable inner door panel (some models with PermaTuf® interiors). If timer jams after tripping detergent dispenser, check timer trip lever. Remove cover on outer door panel.

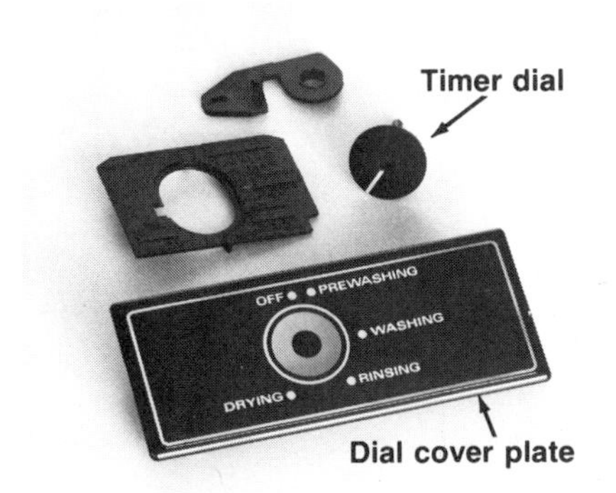

Step 18: Remove timer dial knob, if any. On models without knob, pry off dial cover plate on control panel. Remove dial and other parts, noting how they are installed.

Timer (continued)

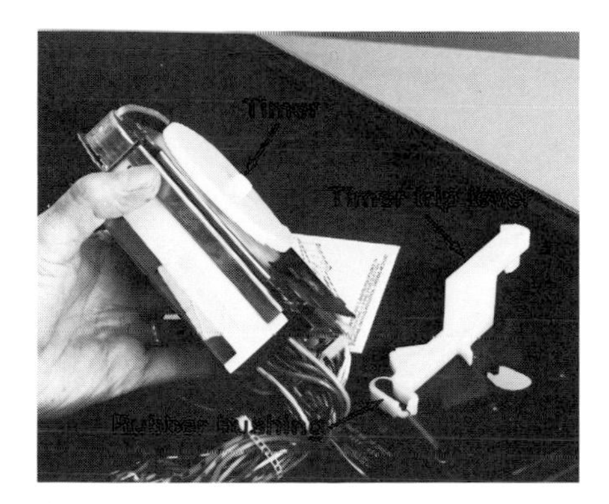

Step 19: Remove timer mounting screw, bend holding tab and lift timer up. Inspect rubber bushing on timer trip lever post. Replace if damaged or missing. Reassemble timer and dial.

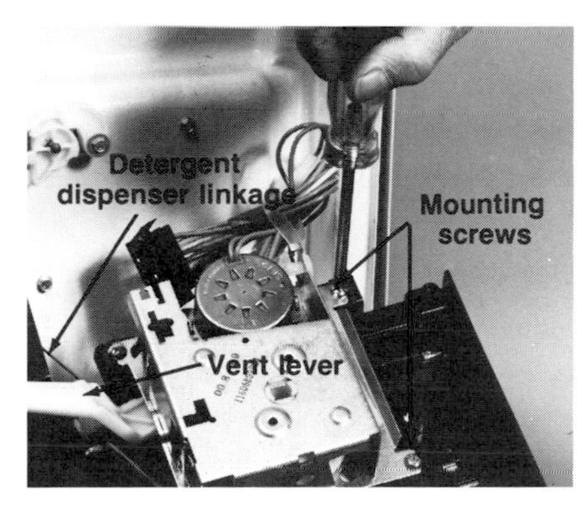

Step 20: To replace terminal-block timer, pull off dial knob, if any. Remove mounting screws. Detach other connections, such as detergent dispenser linkage or lever which opens vent cover.

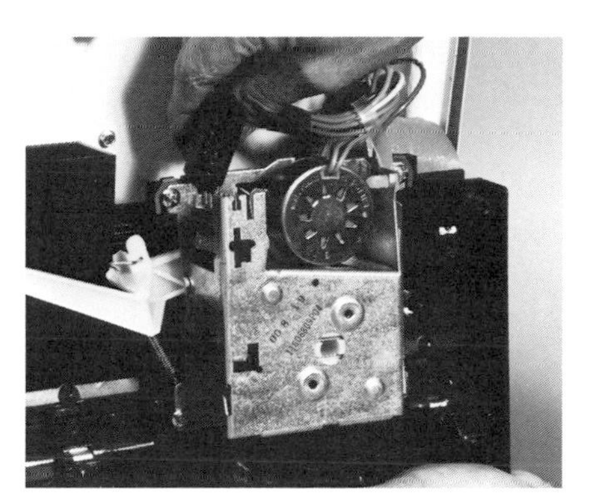

Step 21: Detach motor leads at connector (For installation reference, make note of how wires are connected.) Disconnect terminal block.

Step 22: Install new timer with mounting screws. Replace dial knob, if any. Push on terminal block. Reconnect motor leads and ground wire.

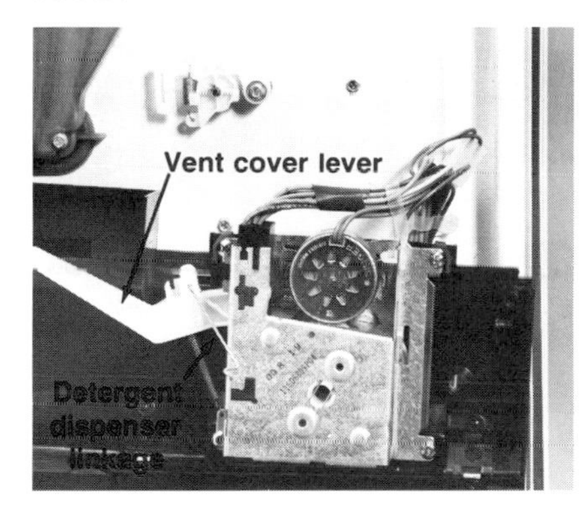

Step 23: Reconnect any mechanisms, such as vent cover trip lever or detergent dispenser linkage, same as original installation. Turn timer through full cycle to check that mechanisms are activated properly.

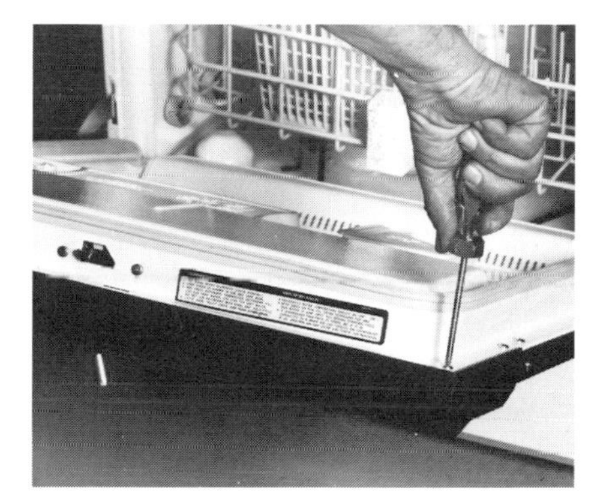

Step 24: Reassemble dishwasher and reconnect power supply.

Procedure 10

Inspecting and replacing pushbutton switches

Skill Level Rating:	Easy	Average	Difficult	**Very Difficult**

Most dishwashers are equipped with pushbutton switches to allow you to select from a variety of dishwasher cycles. When a pushbutton is depressed, its internal circuitry changes the way various components are energized by the timer. For example, when the Energy Saver Dry pushbutton is selected, the timer advances through the end of the cycle without energizing the Calrod® heating unit.

Often an inoperative pushbutton switch will give outward indication that it has failed. Look for loose or overheated terminals. Also, mechanical malfunctions within the switch can prevent the pushbutton from operating correctly. A switch which is jammed or mechanically inoperative should be replaced.

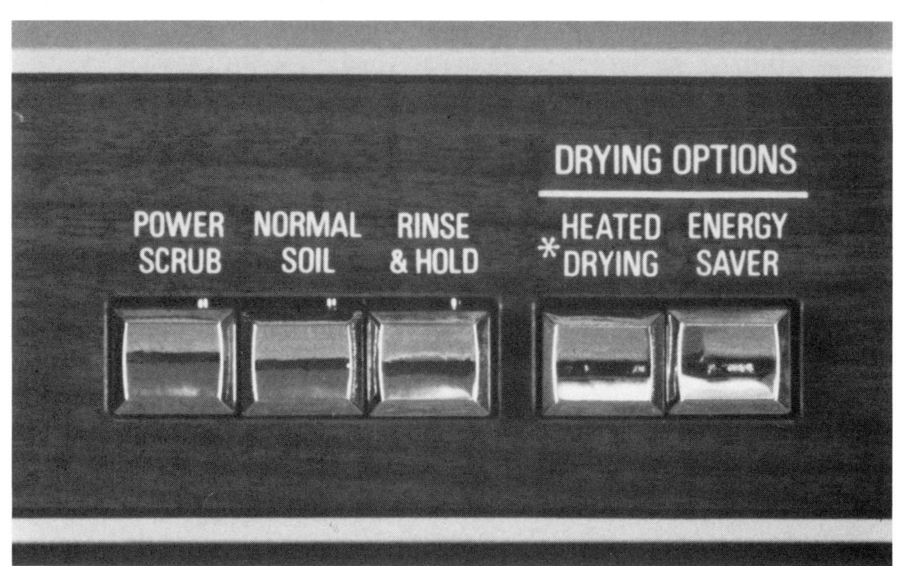

Pushbutton switches

Pushbutton switches (continued)

Step 1: Be sure all dishwasher controls are turned **OFF.** Disconnect power supply at distribution panel. For convertible models, also unplug power cord from receptacle. Watch for sharp edges.

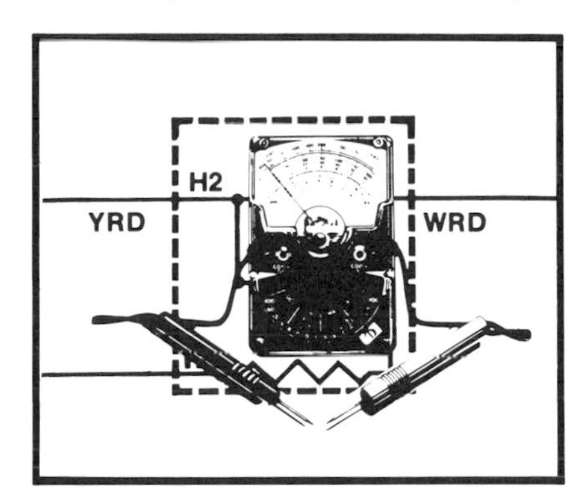

Step 2: This procedure requires the use of an ohmmeter and the ability to read a circuit diagram. For instructions, please refer to Tools and Testing Equipment, pages 95-98.

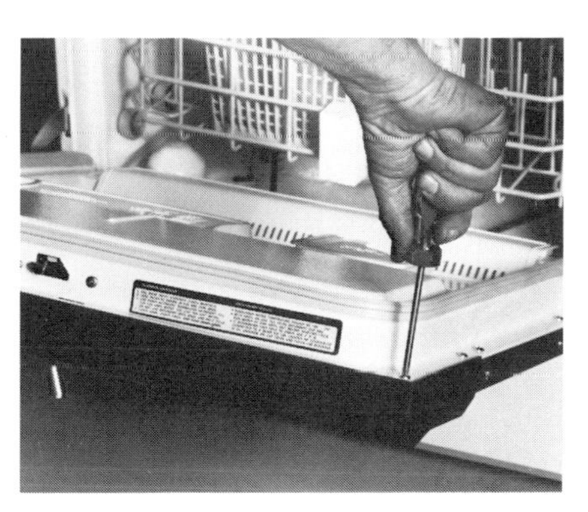

Step 3: This procedure requires the removal of service panels from your dishwasher. If you are unfamiliar with this process, please refer to Procedure #3: Removing Service Panels.

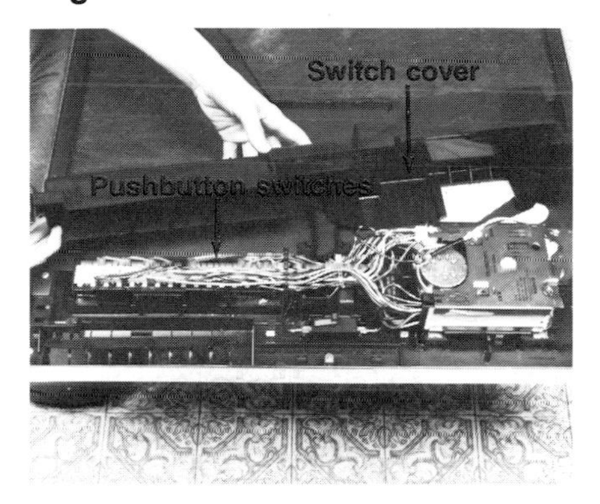

Step 4: For most models, tip control panel escutcheon down for access to pushbutton switches. On models with removable PermaTuf® inner door panel, separate door panels and lift cover on outer door panel.

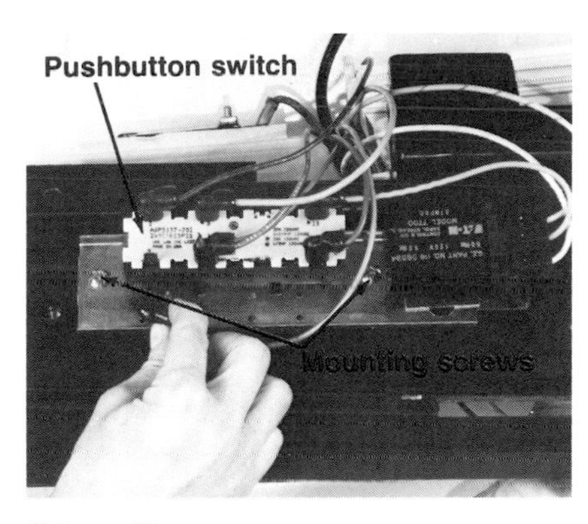

Step 5: Inspect for loose or broken wires. Remove leads from each pair of terminals before testing and replace after testing to assure proper reconnection.

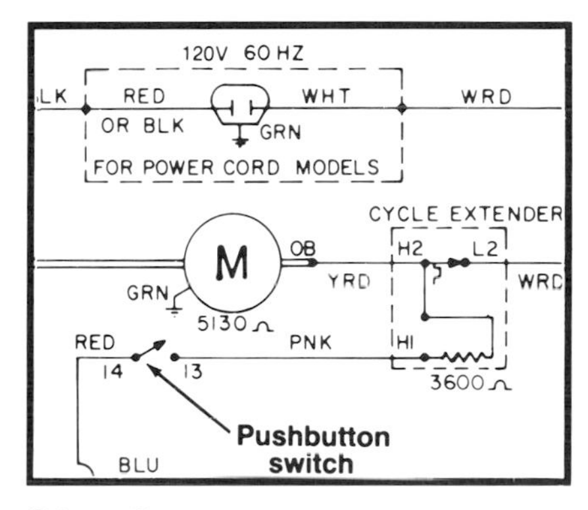

Step 6: Refer to your dishwasher's circuit diagram. It will show which contacts should be closed for each pushbutton setting. Switch terminals are coded by color or number to correspond to the circuit diagram.

Step 7: Depress one pushbutton. With ohmmeter at R x 1, place probes on appropriate terminals. Needle should sweep upscale to indicate continuity. If no continuity, replace switch. Repeat test for each pushbutton.

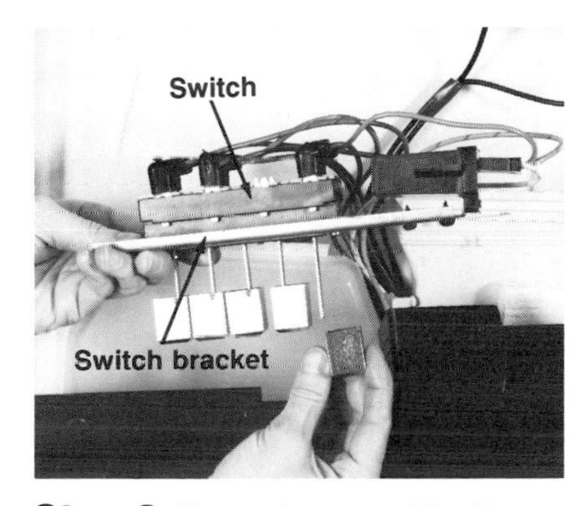

Step 8: To replace pushbutton switch, remove mounting screws and detach switch bracket from dishwasher. Pull pushbuttons off. To assure proper re-installation, keep pushbuttons in order.

Step 9: Remove screws securing switch to bracket. Install new switch and replace pushbuttons. Transfer leads from old switch to same terminals on new switch one at a time. Reassemble dishwasher and reconnect power supply.

Procedure 11

Inspecting and replacing cycle extender switch

Skill Level Rating:	Easy	Average	**Difficult**	Very Difficult

The cycle extender switch is used on many dishwashers to extend the wash period 18-20 minutes for 1) extra cleaning in heavy duty cycles (e.g., POTSCRUBBER, Power Scrub, and "Pots and Pans") or 2) raising the water temperature when needed during water-heat cycles.

The cycle extender switch is in the circuit that provides power to the timer motor. When energized, a resistor in the switch heats and opens the switch, stopping the timer motor. The dishwasher continues to operate while the timer motor is off, but the timer does not advance to end the cycle. As the resistor cools, the switch closes and restores power to the timer motor.

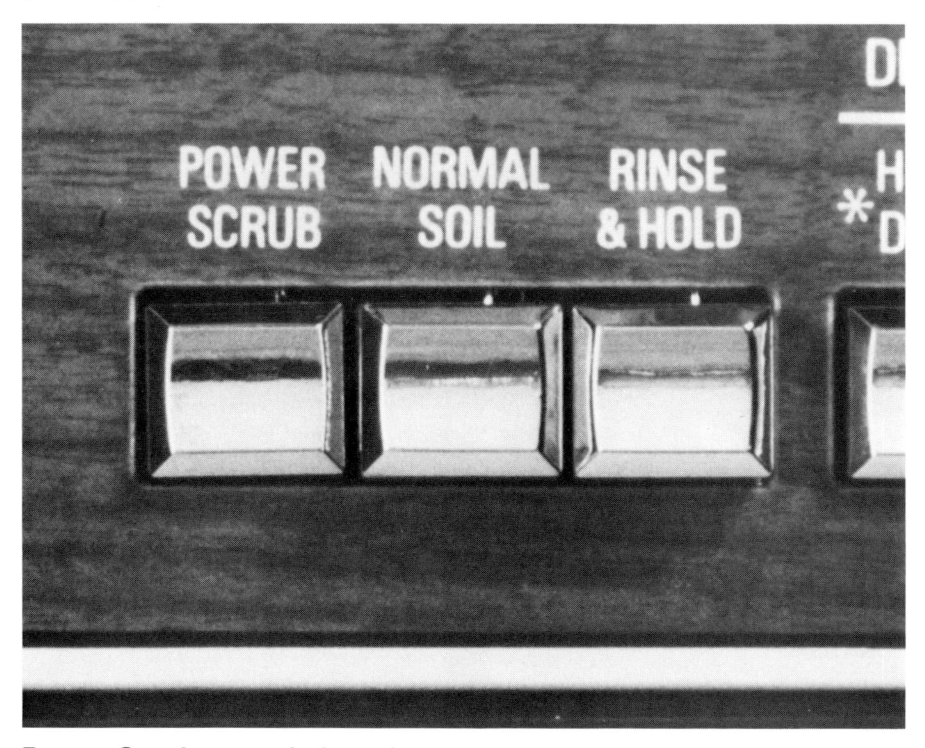

Power Scrub extended wash cycle

Cycle extender switch (continued)

Step 1: Be sure all dishwasher controls are turned **OFF.** Disconnect power supply at distribution panel. For convertible models, also unplug power cord from receptacle. Watch for sharp edges.

Step 2: This procedure requires the use of an ohmmeter. For instructions on how to use an ohmmeter, please refer to Tools and Testing Equipment, page 95.

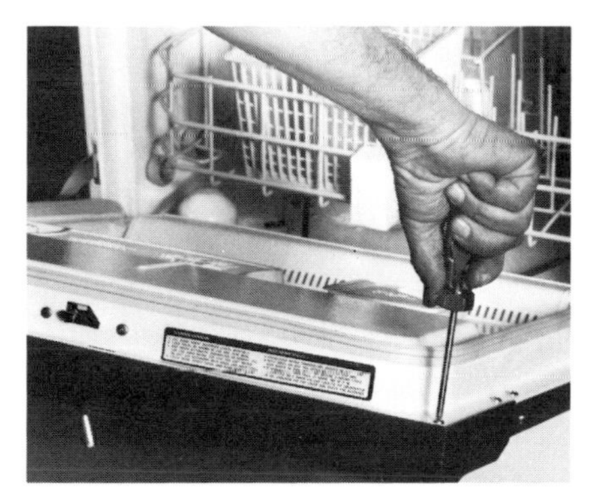

Step 3: This procedure requires removal of the control panel escutcheon from your dishwasher. If you are unfamiliar with this process, please refer to Procedure #3: Removing Service Panels.

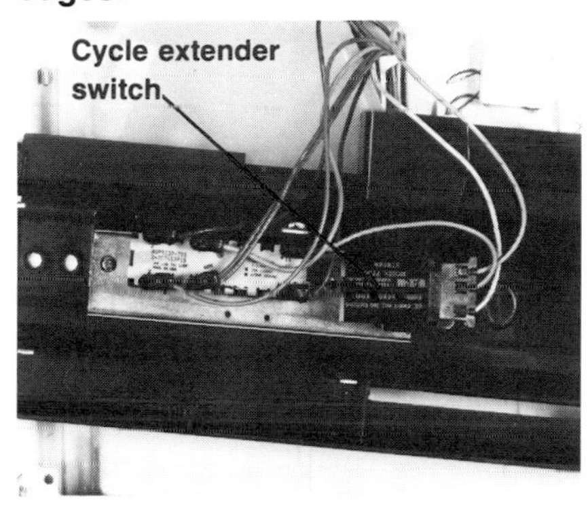

Step 4: Tip control panel escutcheon down. If dishwasher has a cycle extender switch, it will be near center, between pushbutton switches and timer. Inspect it visually for loose or broken wires.

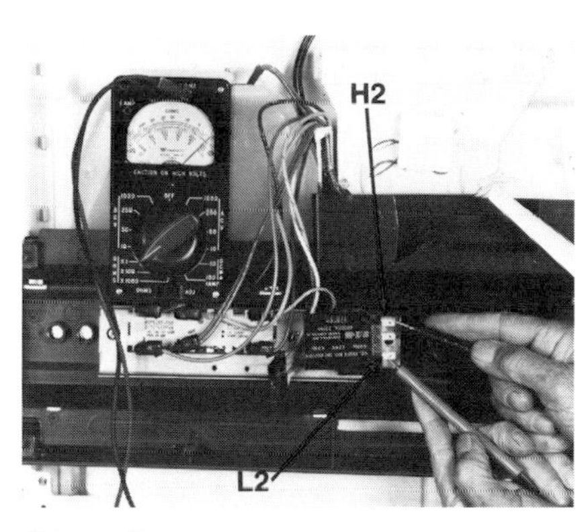

Step 5: Remove leads from switch. With ohmmeter at R x 1, place one probe on switch terminal marked H2 and the other probe on terminal L2. Needle should sweep upscale to indicate continuity.

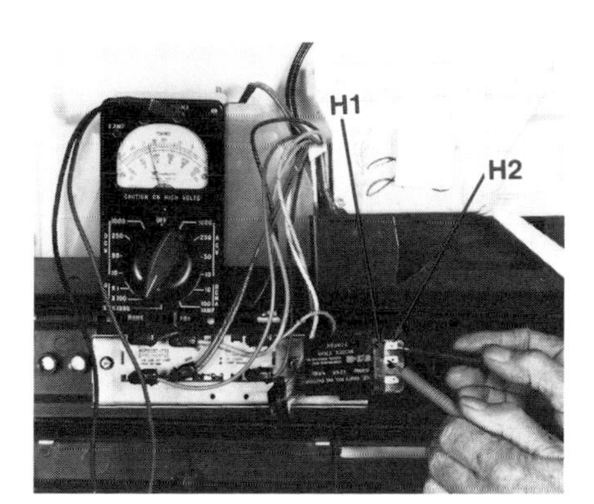

Step 6: With ohmmeter at R x 100, place one probe on switch terminal H1 and the other probe on terminal H2. Needle should sweep partially upscale to indicate continuity. If either test shows no continuity, replace switch.

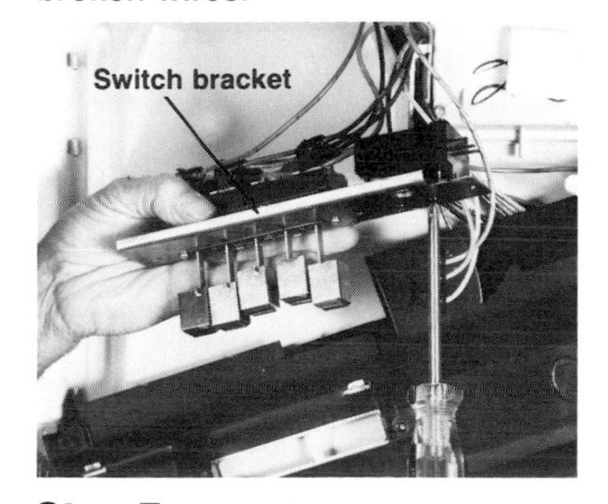

Step 7: To replace switch, detach leads. Remove screws that secure switch to panel. If switch is mounted on a bracket, remove bracket mounting screws and pull bracket out for access to switch screws. Install new switch and reconnect leads.

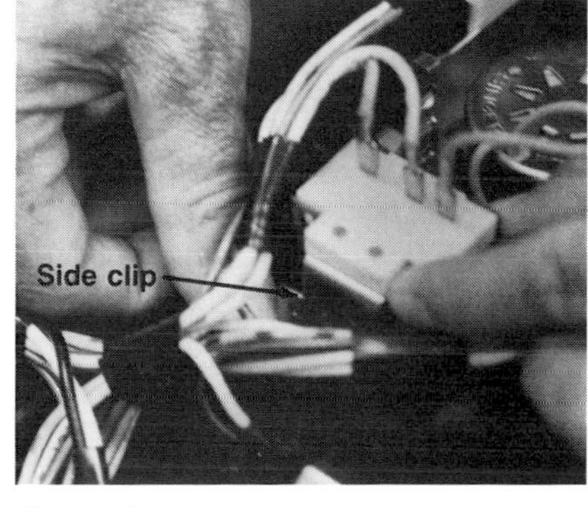

Step 8: On some models, switch is secured with side clip, not screws. Pull up gently on switch to remove.

Step 9: Reassemble dishwasher and reconnect power supply.

Procedure 12

Inspecting and replacing water inlet valve

Skill Level Rating: | Easy | Average | **Difficult** | Very Difficult |

The water inlet valve controls the flow of water into the dishwasher. A solenoid coil attached to the valve housing creates a magnetic field when energized. This magnetic pull opens a plunger inside the valve which allows water to flow through the valve into the dishwasher.

Water fill is controlled by the timer, which opens the water inlet valve for a specified time. Under normal conditions, the dishwasher tub should fill to approximately 1/2 inch under the Calrod® heating unit. Open dishwasher after any fill to check that water level is normal.

A malfunctioning water inlet valve solenoid may allow the dishwasher to fill only intermittently. In this case, water will enter the dishwasher during the early portions of the cycle, but the dishwasher will fail to fill during the final rinse periods. This problem can best be diagnosed by operating the dishwasher and listening for entering water during each fill.

CAUTION: To prevent burns from hot water, turn off the water at the house shut-off valve before removing the water inlet hose from built-in dishwashers.

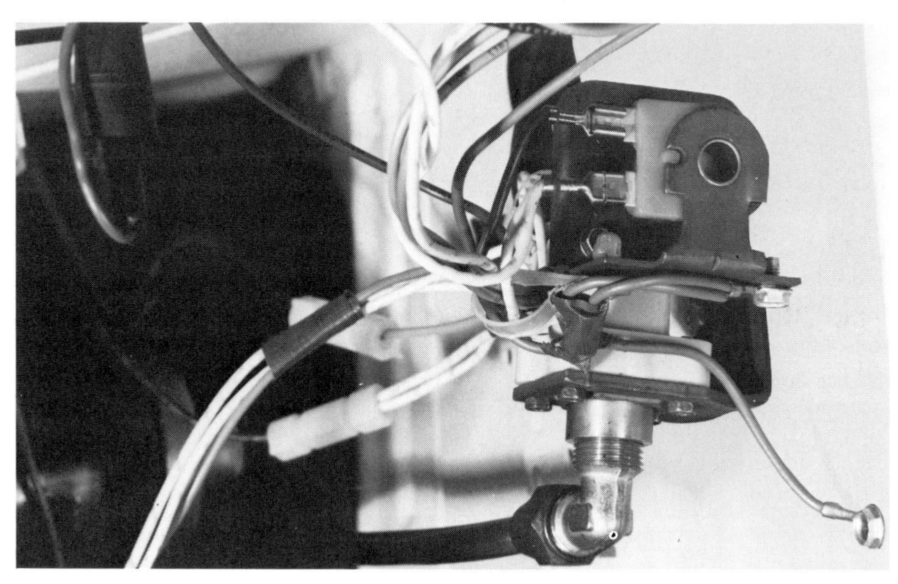

Water inlet valve

Step 1: Be sure all dishwasher controls are turned **OFF**. Disconnect power supply at distribution panel. For convertible models, also unplug power cord from receptacle. Watch for sharp edges.

Step 2: This procedure requires the use of an ohmmeter. For instructions on how to use an ohmmeter, please refer to Tools and Testing Equipment, page 95.

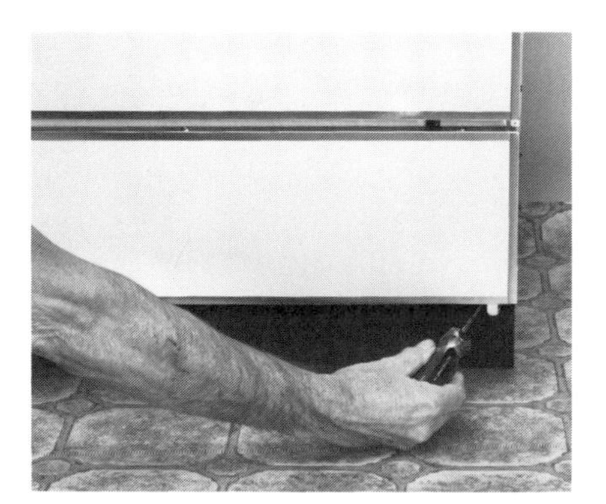

Step 3: This procedure requires removal of service panels from your dishwasher. If you are unfamiliar with this process, please refer to Procedure #3: Removing Service Panels.

Water inlet valve (continued)

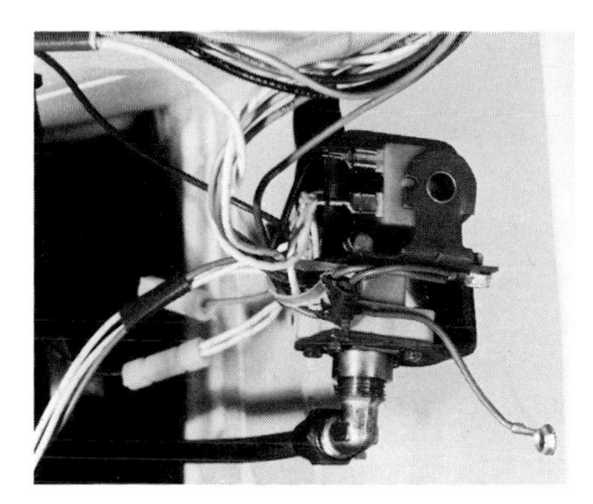

Step 4: Built-in dishwasher. Remove lower access panel and locate water inlet valve where incoming water line is attached. Inspect visually for loose or broken wires or cracks in valve body.

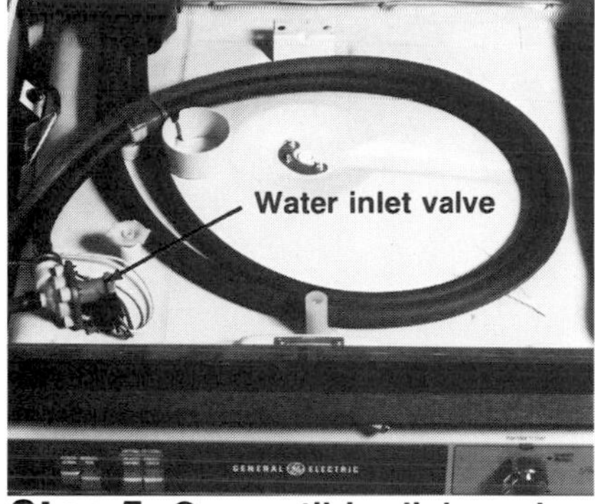

Step 5: Convertible dishwasher. Locate valve and inlet hose attachment. Some models have inlet valve inside top panel. Other models have inlet valve near right rear leg. Access these valves by removing lower access panel. Check wires and valve body.

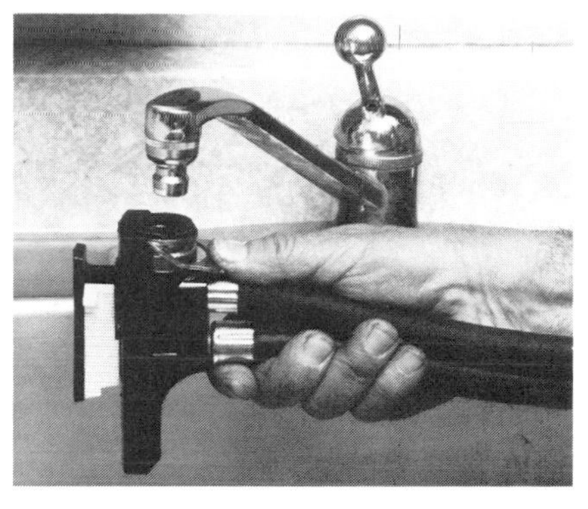

Step 6: To inspect water valve, shut off water supply to dishwasher. For built-in models, use valve located under adjacent sink, if any, or shut off entire house supply. Detach faucet coupling of convertible model.

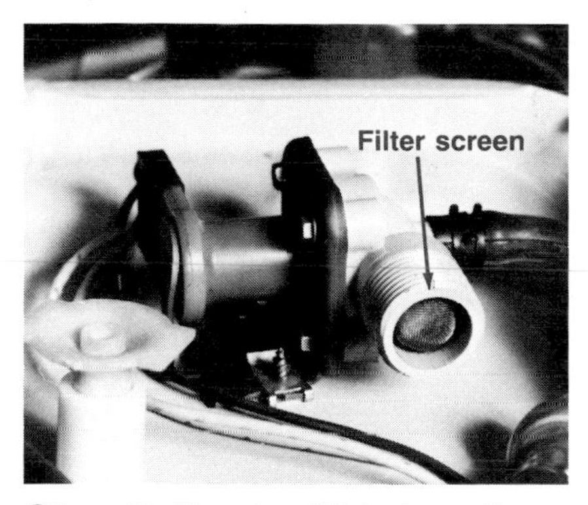

Step 7: If water fill is less than normal, detach water inlet hose and expose filter screen. Clean or replace screen, if necessary. Reconnect water line. Photo shows older convertible model. Other models have valve in dishwasher bottom.

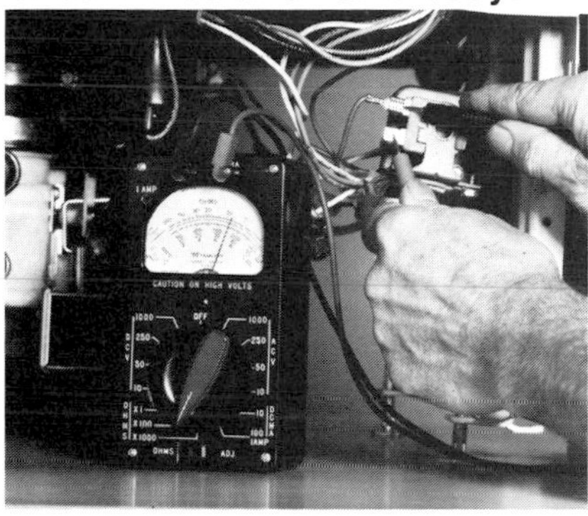

Step 8: Test water valve solenoid with ohmmeter at R × 100. Remove cover, if any, and detach one lead. Place test probes on water valve terminals. Needle should sweep upscale to indicate continuity. If no continuity, replace valve.

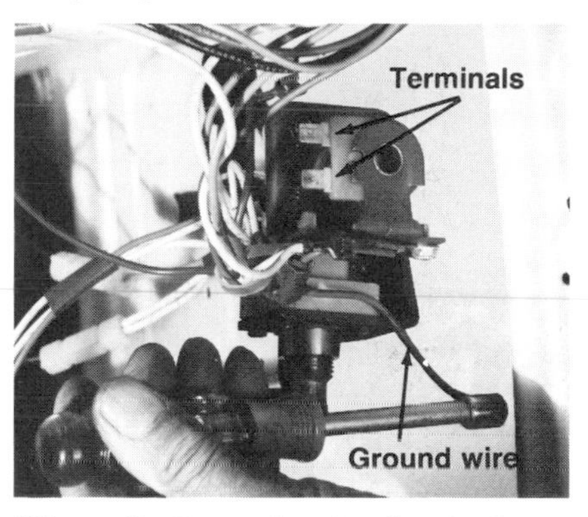

Step 9: Detach wire leads from water inlet valve terminals. Detach green wire. (For installation reference, make note of how wires are connected.)

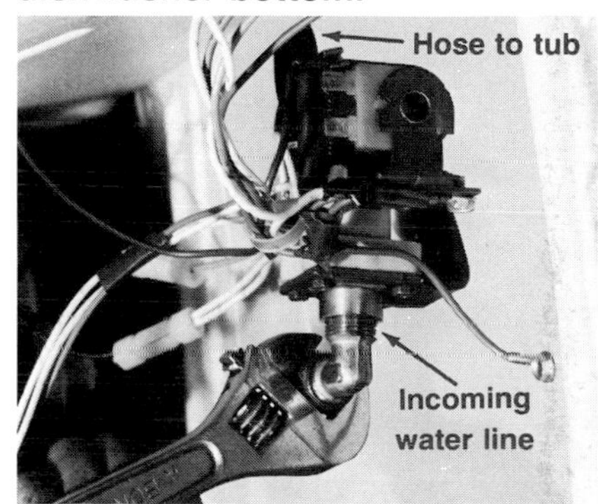

Step 10: Built-in dishwasher. Remove brass flare or compression fitting and disconnect incoming water line. Detach hose that runs from water valve into dishwasher tub. Transfer adapter from old valve to new valve.

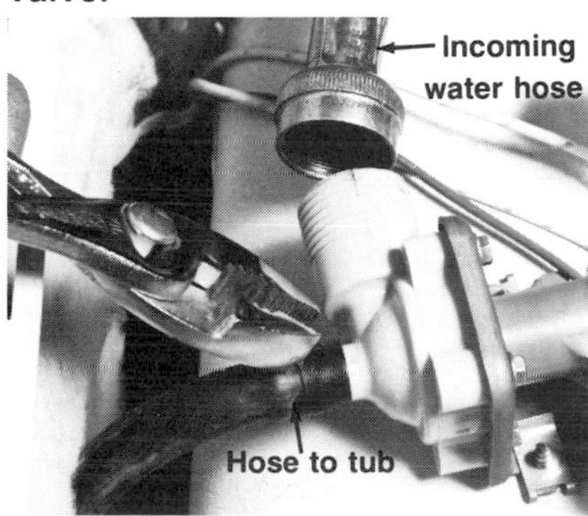

Step 11: Convertible dishwasher. Disconnect incoming water supply hose. Remove clamp and detach smaller hose running into dishwasher tub. Photo shows older model which has valve in top. Newer models have valve in dishwasher bottom.

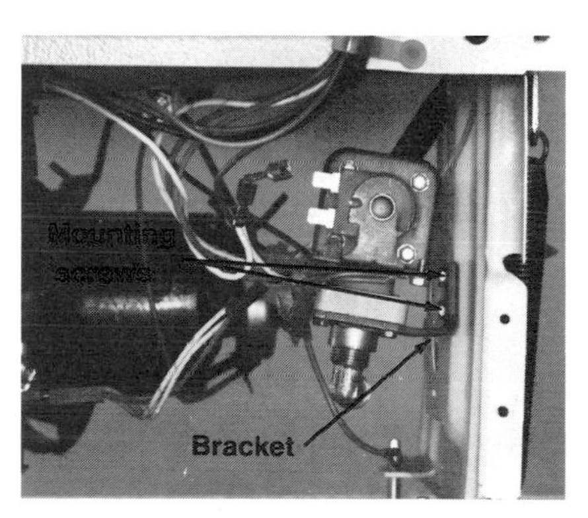

Step 12: Remove screws that secure water valve bracket to tub. Install new valve. Reconnect leads and water lines. Reassemble dishwasher and reconnect water and power supply.

Procedure 13
Inspecting and replacing float switch

Skill Level Rating:	Easy	Average	**Difficult**	Very Difficult

The float switch is designed to prevent accidental overfilling of the dishwasher. If water in the tub rises above a pre-set level, the float rises and the float switch opens, stopping the flow of power to the water inlet valve coil. When this circuit is broken, the water inlet valve closes and shuts off the incoming water. In some models, the float switch also causes the water to pump out automatically by closing an additional switch that energizes the drain valve solenoid.

The float switch shuts the water off only in case of an electrical malfunction. If a mechanical defect or foreign object causes the water inlet valve to stick in the open position, the float switch will not prevent overfill from occurring.

The float switch should never cut off the water inlet valve solenoid during normal fill. If it does, it is not properly adjusted.

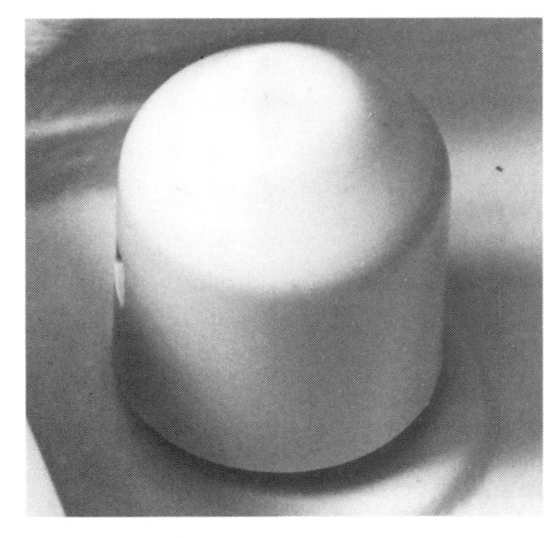

Float switch

Step 1: Be sure all dishwasher controls are turned **OFF**. Disconnect power supply at distribution panel. For convertible models, also unplug power cord from receptacle. Watch for sharp edges.

Step 2: This procedure requires the use of an ohmmeter. For instructions on how to use an ohmmeter, please refer to Tools and Testing Equipment, page 95.

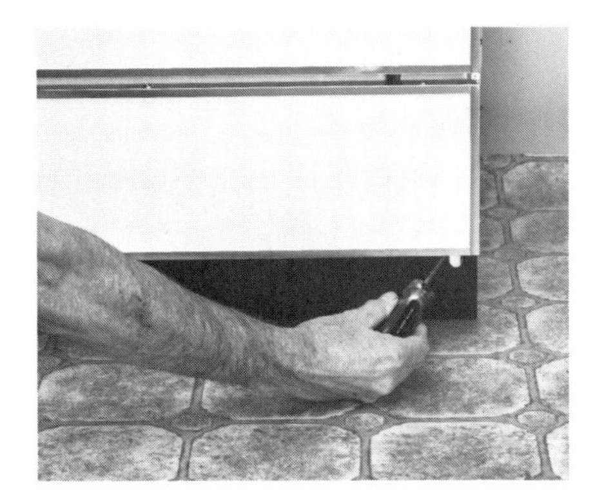

Step 3: This procedure requires removal of the lower access panel from your dishwasher. If you are unfamiliar with this process, please refer to Procedure #3: Removing Service Panels.

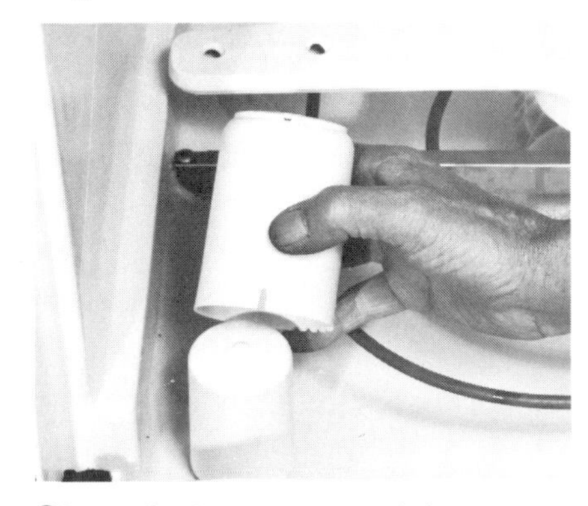

Step 4: On some models, cover must be removed in order to inspect float. Remove mounting screw and pull cover off. Inspect float visually for binding or obstructions.

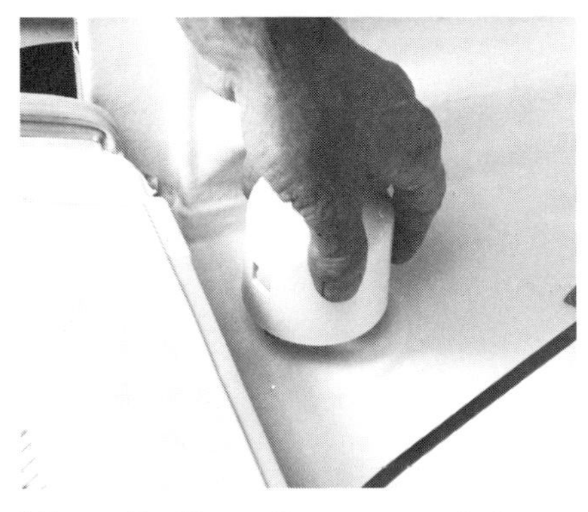

Step 5: Move float up and down by hand. If it does not move freely, check for binding or obstructions which may be causing the problem. Replace float if damaged or defective.

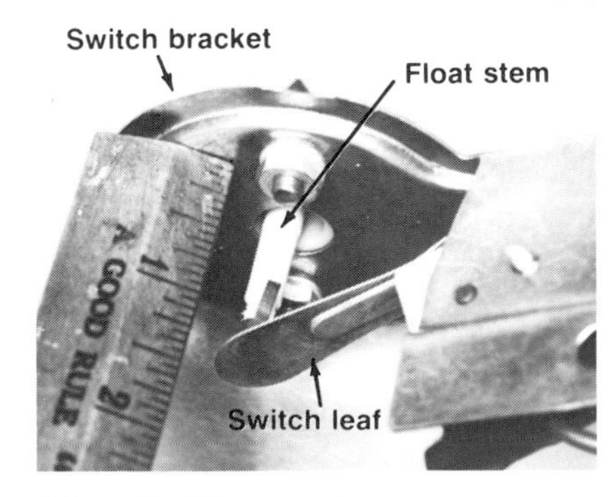

Step 6: Remove lower access panel and locate switch directly under float. Hold ruler against bottom of switch bracket, as shown.

Float switch (continued)

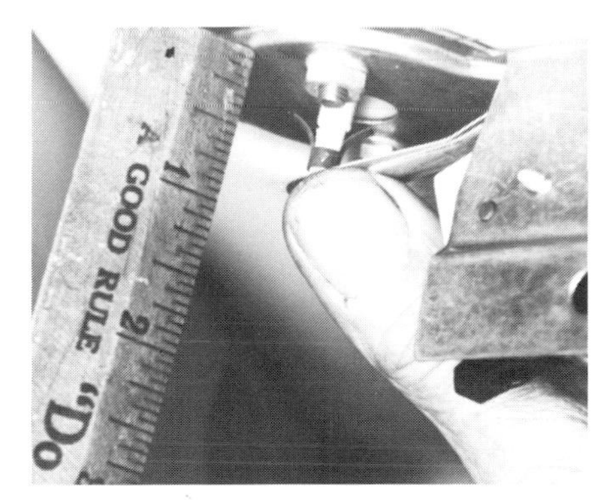

Step 7: Push switch leaf up until switch clicks. This should occur between 9/16" and 11/16" from switch bracket. To adjust, bend switch leaf slightly at end near float stem.

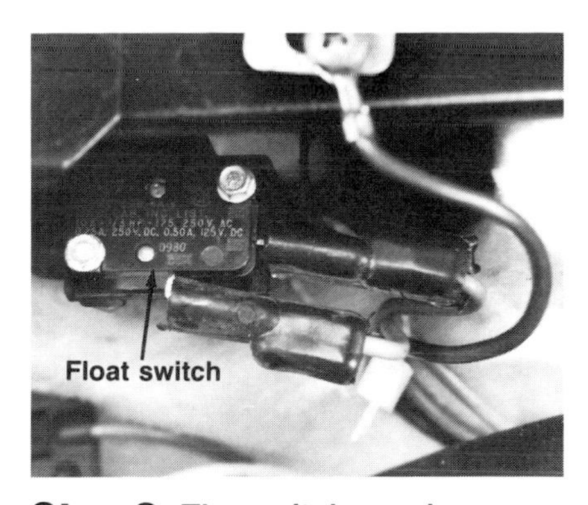

Step 8: The switch used on dishwashers with PermaTuf® interior and covered float does not require adjustment.

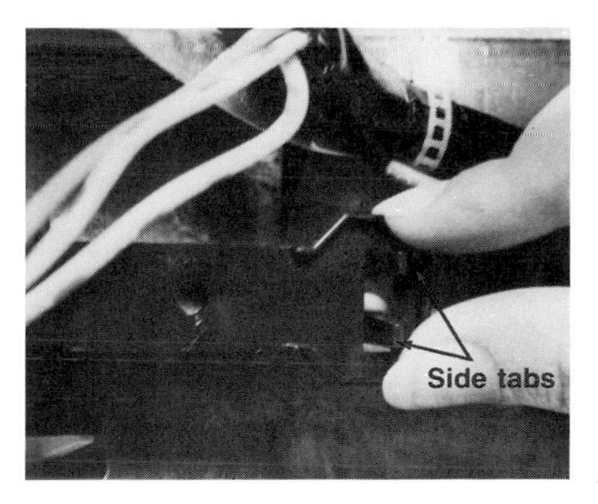

Step 9: Float switch on some models is mounted inside plastic housing. Depress side tabs to open cover.

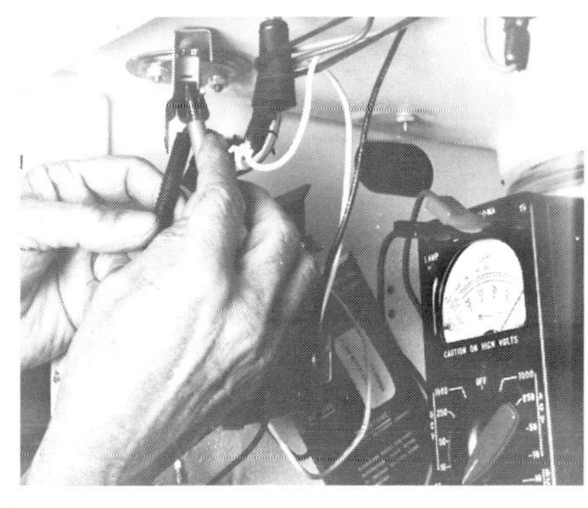

Step 10: To test switch, detach wire leads. With ohmmeter at R x 1, place one test probe on each terminal. With float resting on tub bottom, needle should sweep upscale to indicate continuity.

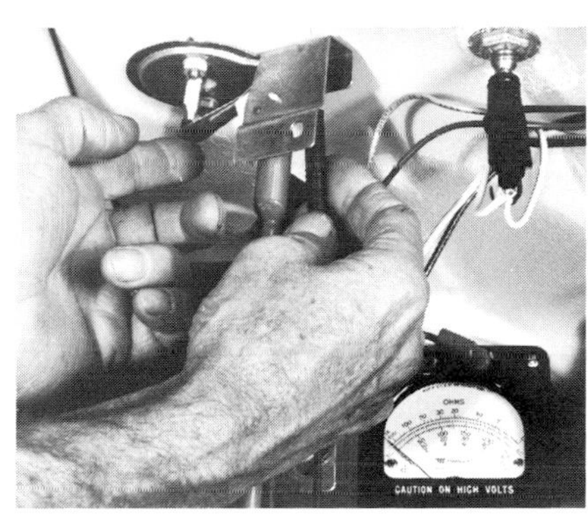

Step 11: With test probes still attached to terminals, push up on switch leaf. Ohmmeter needle should drop back to show no reading. If either test shows failure, replace float switch.

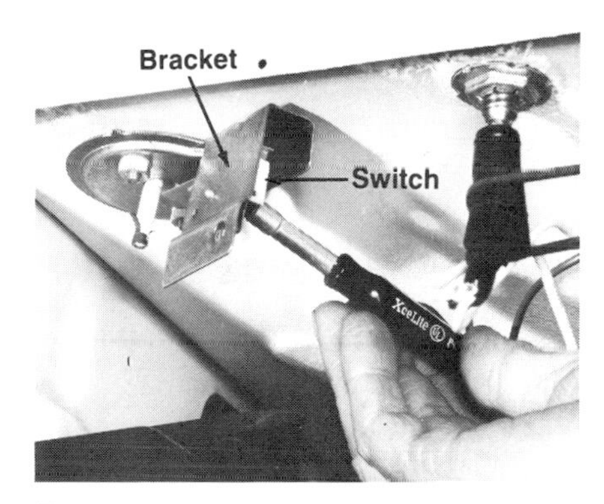

Step 12: To remove switch, detach wire leads, noting how wires are connected. For some models, use nutdriver to remove screws which hold switch to bracket. Attach new switch to bracket and reconnect leads. Check switch and adjust, if needed, as in Steps 6 and 7.

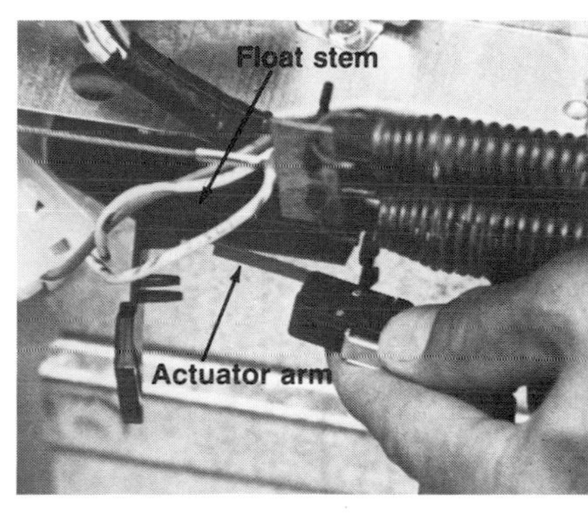

Step 13: On models where switch is inside housing, gently pull switch out from side to remove. When replacing new switch, make sure actuator arm is properly placed under float stem.

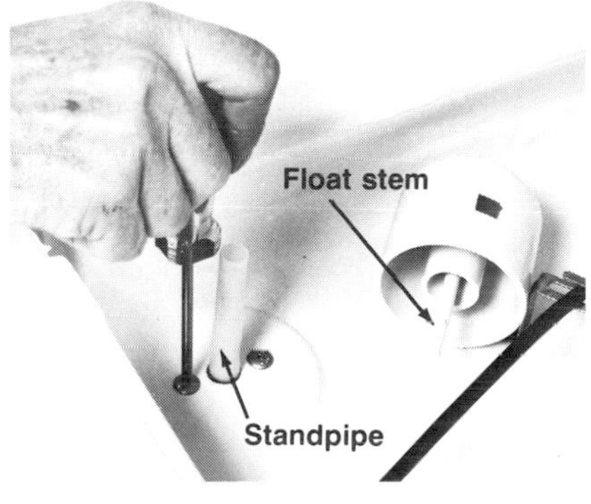

Step 14: To replace damaged or leaky float, remove any float cover. Lift float off standpipe. On some models, float is secured by a clip on end of float stem, removed from under dishwasher tub. Remove mounting screws.

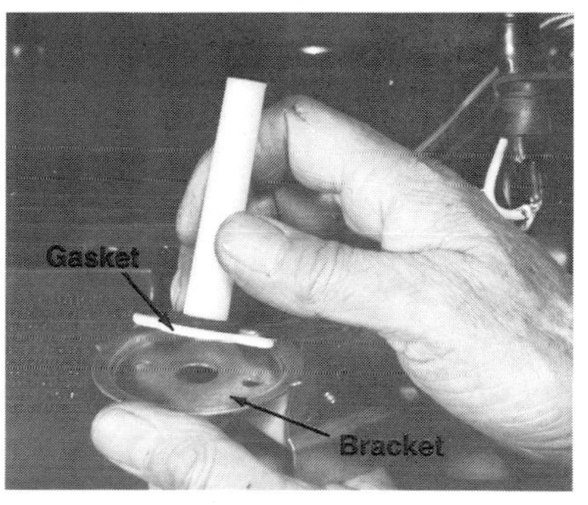

Step 15: Remove bracket and standpipe from under dishwasher tub. Replace assembly, if damaged. To stop leakage, replace gasket at base of standpipe and reassemble float system.

Procedure 14

Inspecting and replacing drain valve solenoid

Skill Level Rating:	Easy	Average	**Difficult**	Very Difficult

Inside the pump housing of your dishwasher is a drain valve which changes position to direct water flow through the pump. In its normal position, the valve is vertical, blocking the drain opening so that water flows from the pump through a connector boot into the water spray system inside the dishwasher tub.

During the drain portions of the cycle, a solenoid coil mounted near the pump housing is activated by the timer. The solenoid coil creates a magnetic field which exerts a strong downward pull on a metal plunger. As the plunger moves downward, it moves a gate arm which is attached to the drain valve. This causes the drain valve to move to a horizontal position, blocking the water spray system and opening the pump outlet to drain the tub.

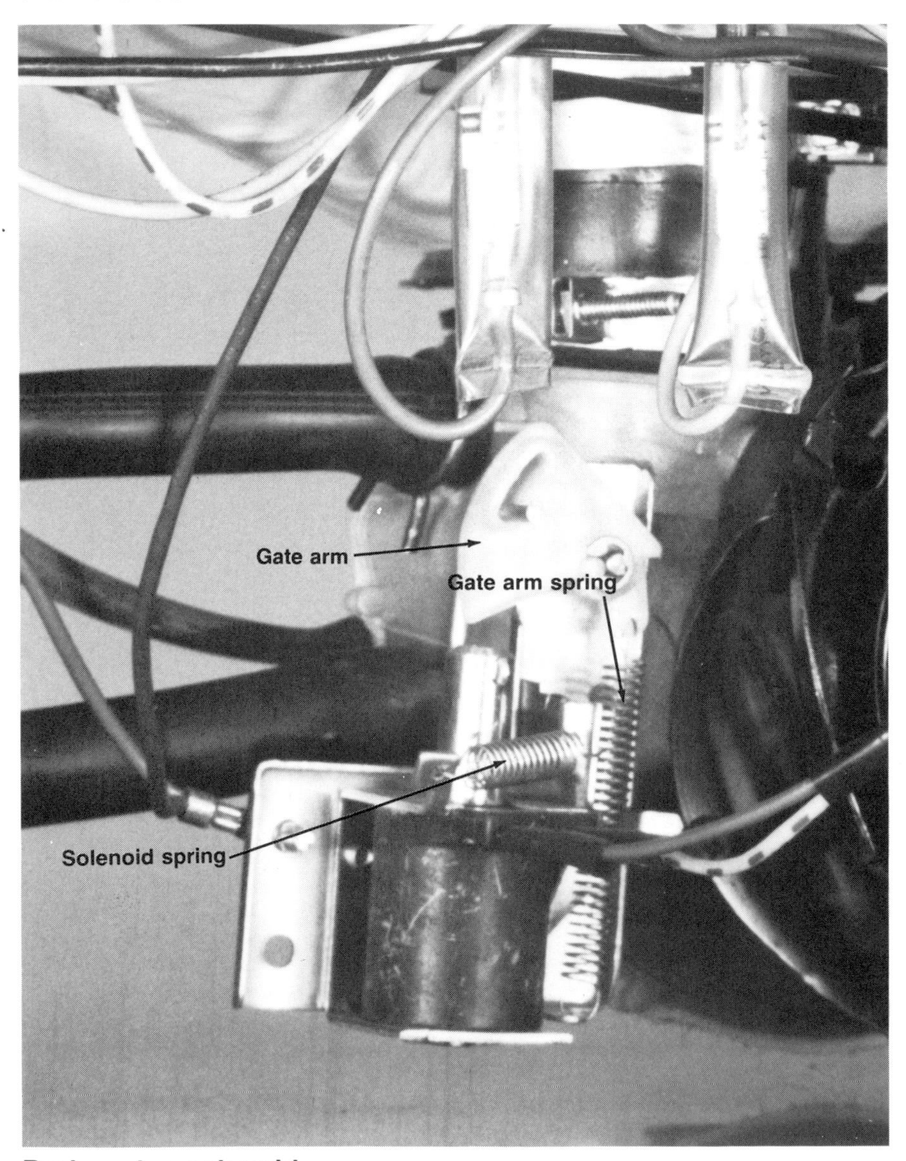

Drain valve solenoid

Drain valve solenoid (continued)

Step 1: Be sure all dishwasher controls are turned **OFF.** Disconnect power supply at distribution panel. For convertible models, also unplug power cord from receptacle. Watch for sharp edges.

Step 2: This procedure requires the use of an ohmmeter. For instructions on how to use an ohmmeter, please refer to Tools and Testing Equipment, page 95.

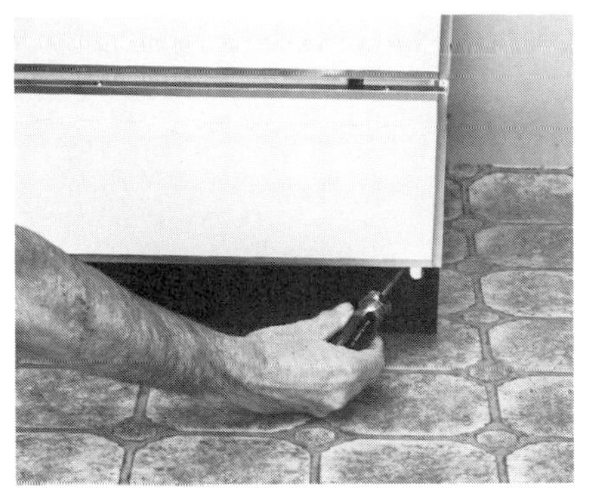

Step 3: This procedure requires removal of the lower access panel from your dishwasher. If you are unfamiliar with this process, please refer to Procedure #3: Removing Service Panels.

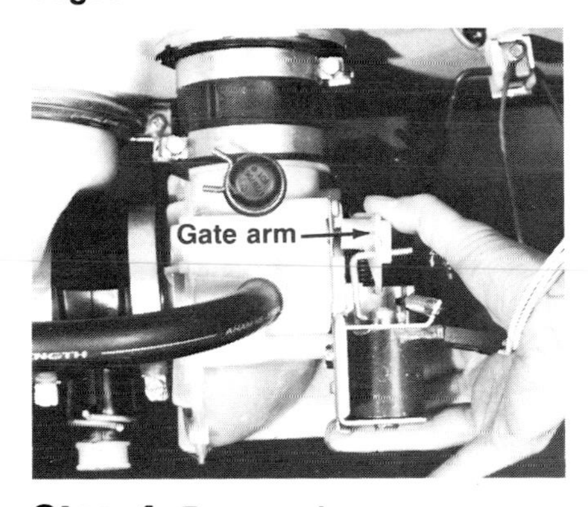

Step 4: Remove lower access panel and locate solenoid near front of pump. Move gate arm mechanism by hand. Check that mechanism moves freely up and down. Replace any missing or broken springs.

Step 5: Remove drain hose from pump outlet to inspect drain valve inside pump. Move gate arm and watch to see that valve moves freely and that no foreign object interferes with movement of valve.

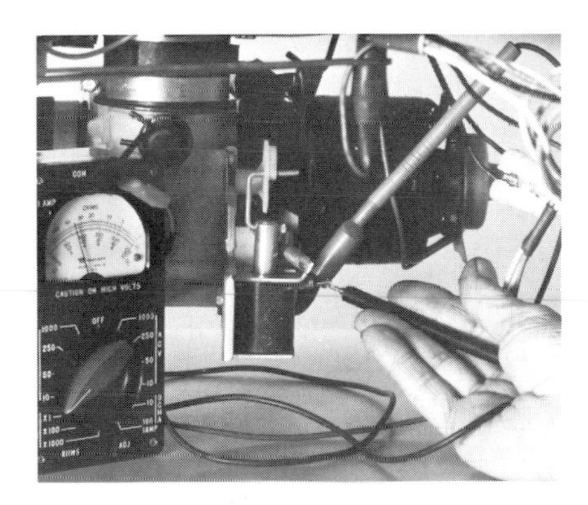

Step 6: Test solenoid with ohmmeter at R x 1. Disconnect leads and place test probes on solenoid terminals. Needle should sweep upscale to indicate continuity. If no continuity, replace solenoid.

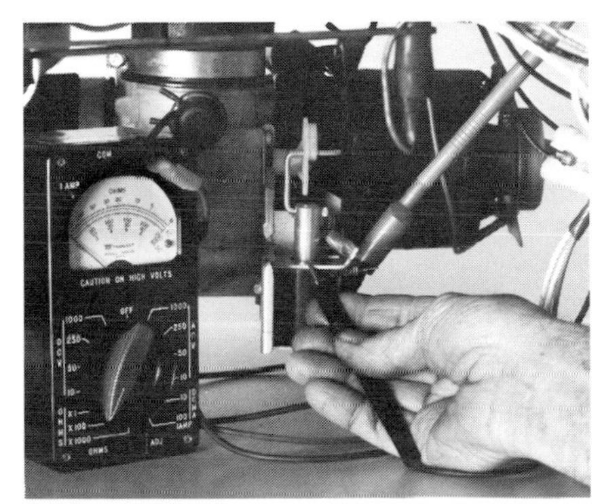

Step 7: Check drain valve solenoid for ground with ohmmeter set at R x 100. Place one test probe on a terminal and other probe on metal solenoid frame. Repeat test for other terminal. If needle moves upscale, solenoid is grounded and should be replaced.

Step 8: To replace drain valve solenoid, remove mounting screws and detach solenoid spring and leads. (For installation reference, make note of how springs and wires are connected.) Install new solenoid and reconnect spring and leads.

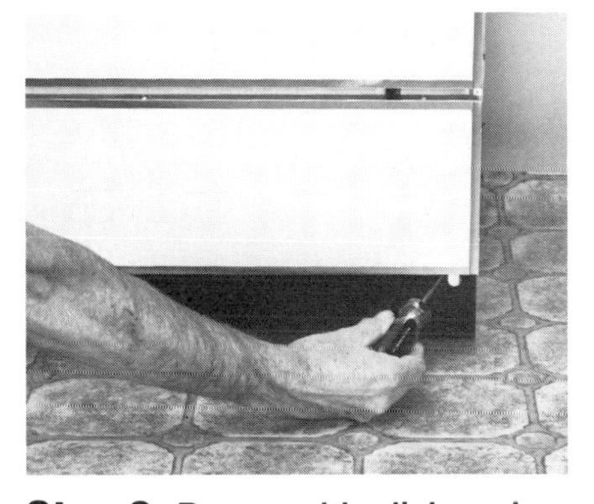

Step 9: Reassemble dishwasher and reconnect power supply.

Procedure 15

Inspecting and replacing motor/pump assembly

Skill Level Rating: | Easy | Average | Difficult | **Very Difficult** |

The motor and pump on your dishwasher form one complete assembly. The simple motor has only one winding. The motor powers the pump, which constantly recirculates water during the wash cycle, and also pumps the water out at the end of each wash or rinse period.

Water enters the tub from an inlet on the side and is pulled into the pump through a sump in the bottom of the tub. From the sump, water moves through a boot connector to the pump inlet. A soft food cutter at this point pulverizes most soft food particles, and a trap catches particles which are too large or heavy to pass through the pump. The pump impeller then forces the water up through a second boot connector into the wash arm and Power Tower™ sprayer. The pressure of the water causes the wash arm and Power Tower™ sprayer to revolve and spray water evenly throughout the dishwasher tub.

During the drain period, water continues to move through the sump and into the pump housing. The motor and pump run just as before, but the drain valve operates to block the entrance into the dishwasher tub and to divert the water into the drain hose.

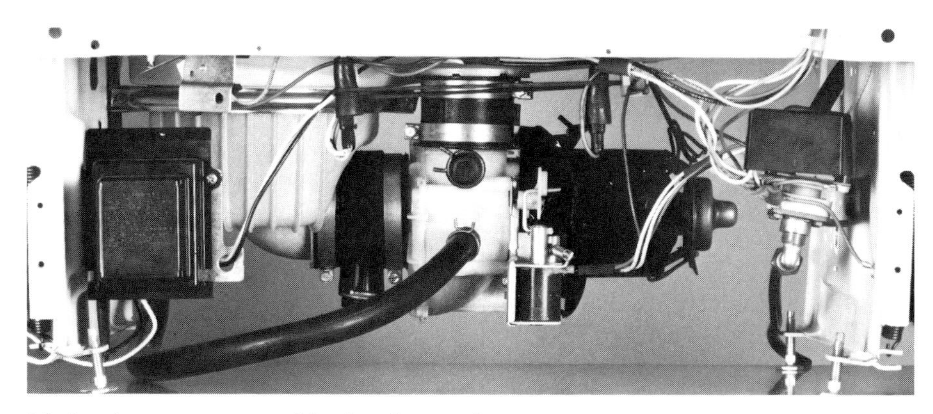

Motor/pump assembly horizontal mount

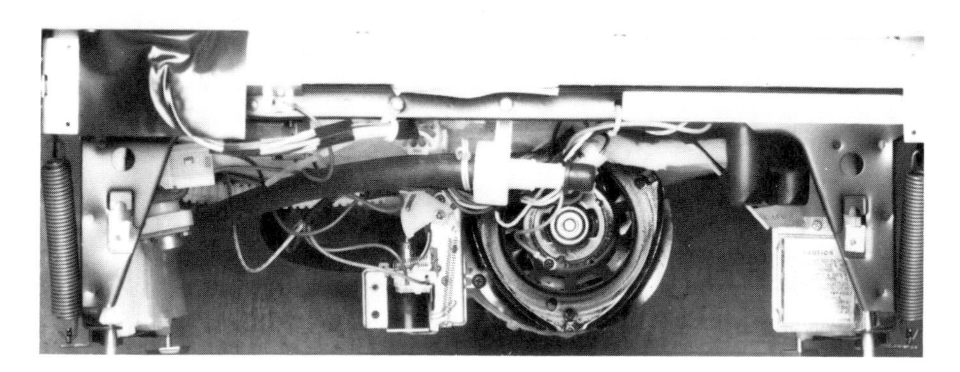

Motor/pump assembly vertical mount

Motor/pump assembly (continued)

Step 1: Be sure all dishwasher controls are turned **OFF**. Disconnect power supply at distribution panel. For convertible models, also unplug power cord from receptacle. Watch for sharp edges.

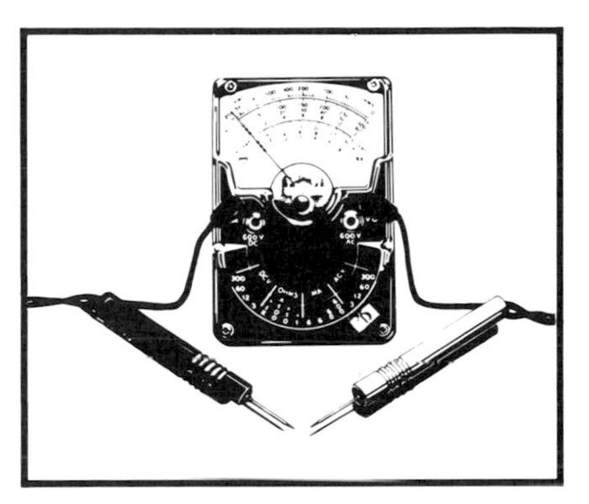

Step 2: This procedure requires the use of an ohmmeter. For instructions on how to use an ohmmeter, please refer to Tools and Testing Equipment, page 95.

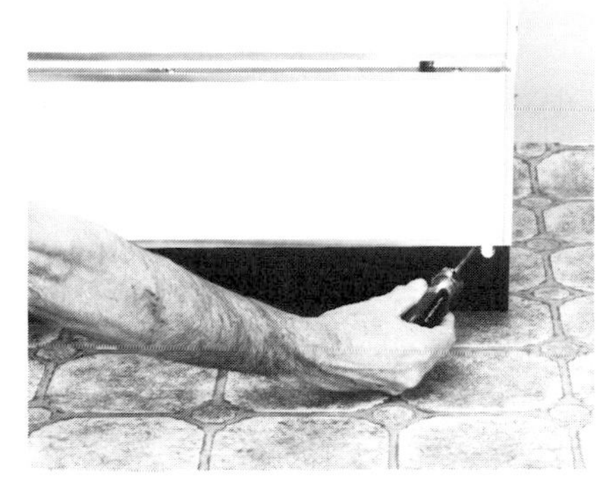

Step 3: This procedure requires removing the lower access panel from your dishwasher. If you are unfamiliar with this process, please refer to Procedure #3: Removing Service Panels.

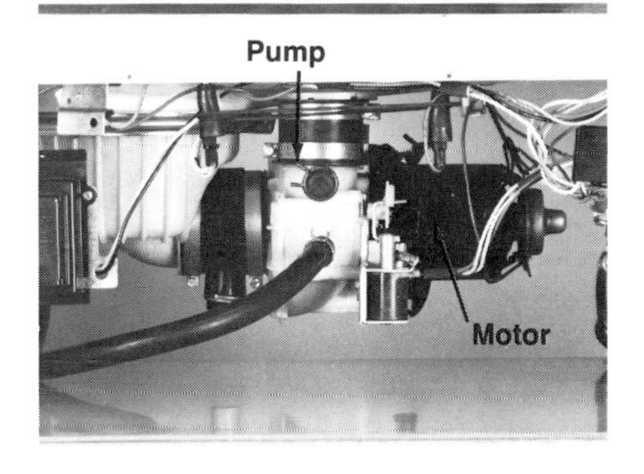

Step 4: Remove lower access panel. If leakage is a problem, check visually for loose clamps, split hose or cracks in pump housing. Replace any defective components.

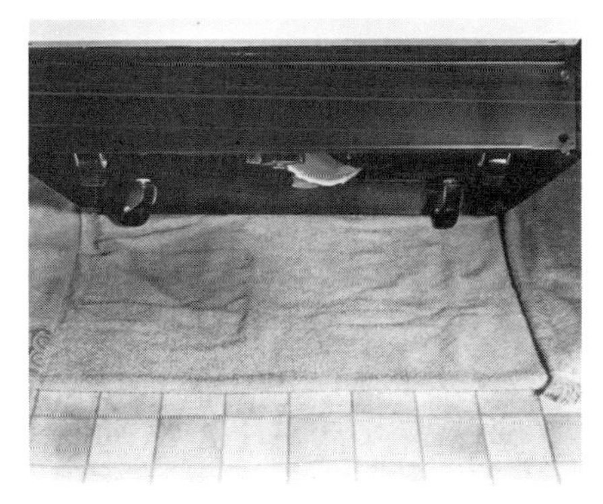

Step 5: If your motor/pump assembly is mounted front to back instead of side to side, you may have to tilt dishwasher back to replace it. If you are unfamiliar with this process, please refer to Procedure #3: Removing Service Panels.

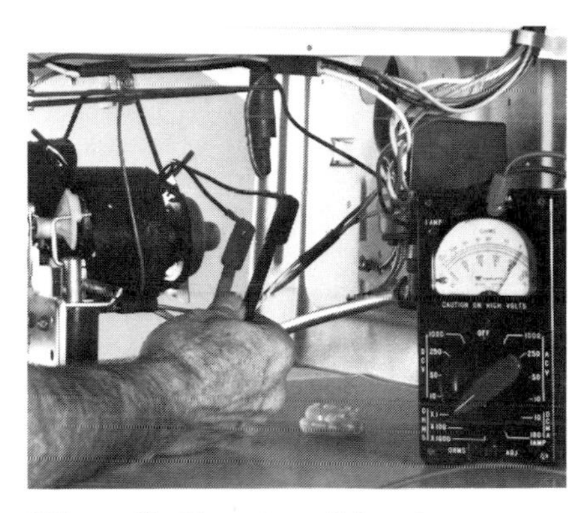

Step 6: If motor did not run or hum when turned on, detach leads. With ohmmeter at R x 1, place one probe on each terminal. Needle should sweep upscale. If no continuity, replace motor/pump assembly.

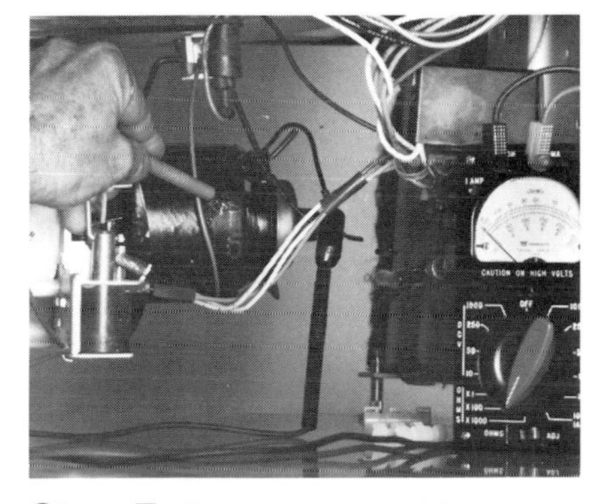

Step 7: Test ground with ohmmeter at R x 100. Place probe on bare metal or motor housing. Place other probe on each terminal in turn. If needle moves upscale, motor is grounded. Replace assembly.

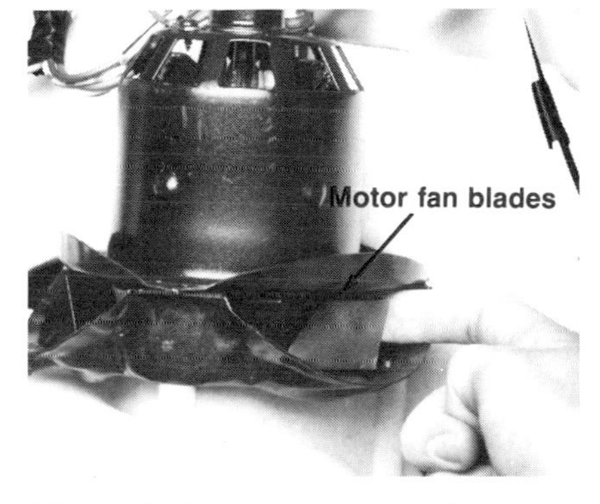

Step 8: If motor hummed but would not run when turned on, check for binding. Turn motor fan blades by hand.

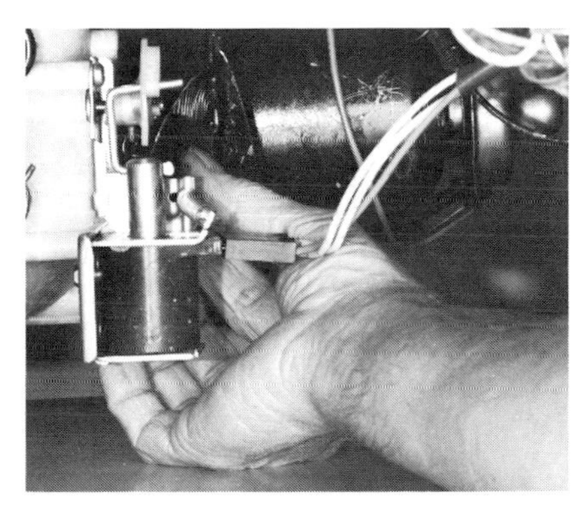

Step 9: If turning blades by hand does not clear binding, disassemble and inspect motor/pump assembly for foreign objects or stuck seal.

Motor/pump assembly (continued)

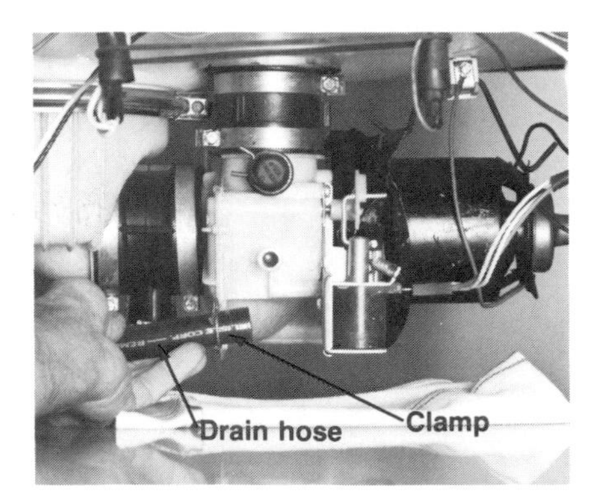

Step 10: Remove water from tub sump with sponge. Disconnect drain hose, catching remaining water with towel or pan.

Step 11: Detach motor and solenoid leads. (For installation reference, make note of how wires are connected.) Loosen screw on clamp nearest pump on each boot connector. Loosen clamps.

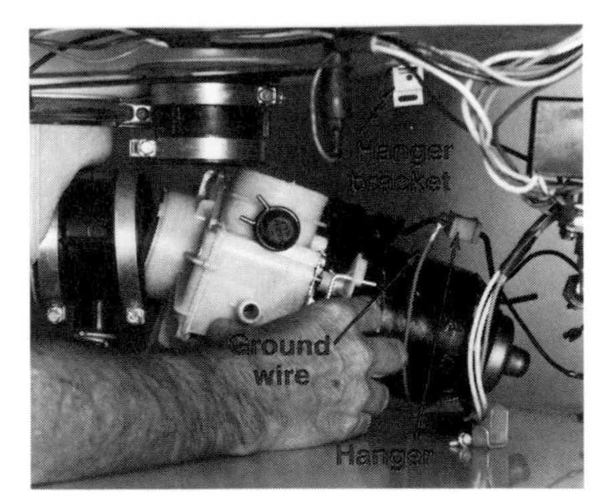

Step 12: Remove screw on motor hanger bracket, detach ground wire and pull hanger free. Hanger may be attached to tub bottom or suspended from a strap. Pull motor down and away from bottom connectors.

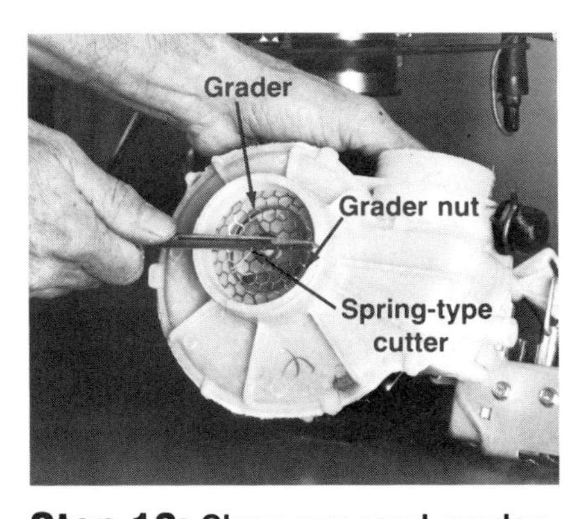

Step 13: Clean exposed grader. Replace cutter if binding or broken. Cutter may be spring or blade type. For spring cutter, remove grader nut by turning clockwise, using flat-sided screwdriver as a lever.

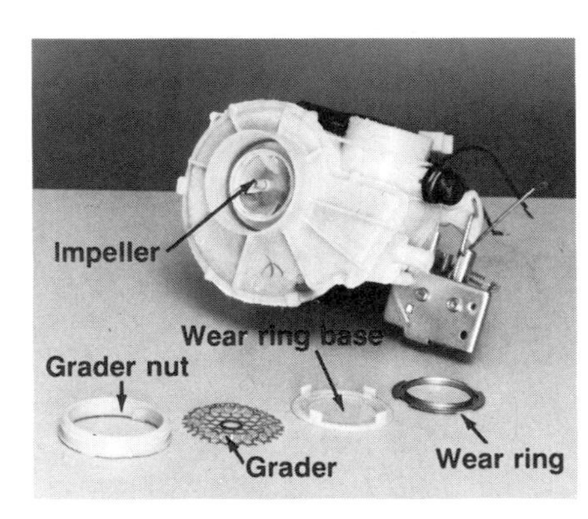

Step 14: Pull grader off over spring cutter. Lift out wear ring and wear ring base. Check for foreign objects lodged between wear ring and impeller which may cause binding.

Step 15: Grasp lower edge of spring cutter with needle-nose pliers. Hold motor fan blades still. Turn spring clockwise until it clicks, then turn counterclockwise and pull outward to remove.

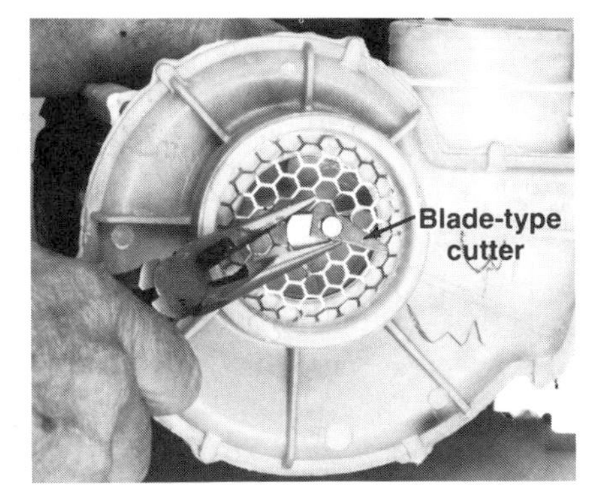

Step 16: For blade cutter, hold motor fan blades still. Grasp cutter shaft with pliers and turn counterclockwise to remove. Then remove grader nut, grader, wear ring and wear base. Check for foreign objects.

Step 17: Visually inspect pump impeller for cracks, chipping or other damage. Hold motor fan blades still and turn impeller counterclockwise with pliers to remove.

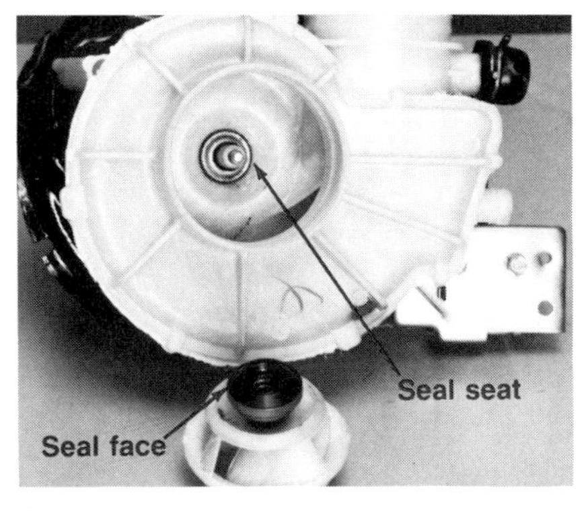

Step 18: If seal seat and face stick together, this may cause motor to bind. Stuck seal can usually be freed by turning motor fan blades by hand. Lubricate face of seal with a light grease if necessary.

Motor/pump assembly (continued)

Step 19: Inspect motor seal for damage that may allow leaks between pump and motor. Replace if necessary with new impeller/seal kit.

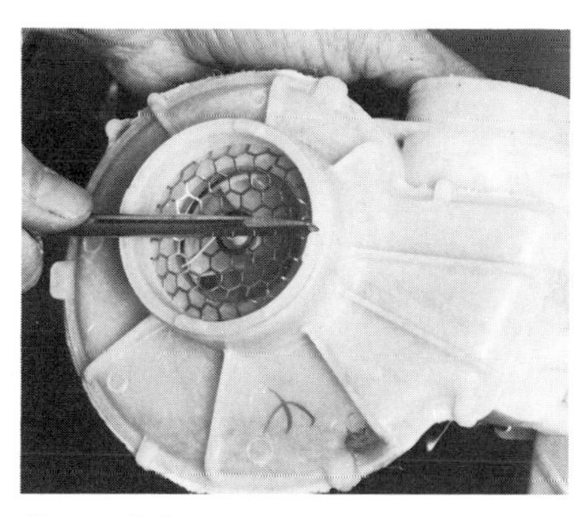

Step 20: To reassemble, turn impeller clockwise. Install wear ring, wear ring base, grader and grader nut. Tighten grader nut counterclockwise. Install spring or blade cutter by turning clockwise.

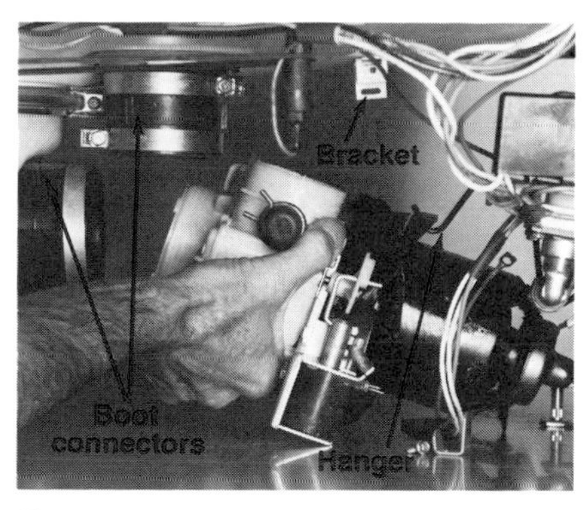

Step 21: For best results, replace complete motor/pump assembly if either component is defective. Install pump in boot connectors. Mount motor hanger to bracket, replacing ground wire under holding screw.

Step 22: Tighten clamps on boot connectors. Attach drain hose to pump outlet. Reconnect motor and solenoid leads. Reassemble dishwasher and reconnect power supply.

Inspecting and replacing wash system parts

Skill Level Rating:	Easy	Average	**Difficult**	Very Difficult

Inside your dishwasher, the wash system components spray water throughout the tub in constantly moving patterns. Water is forced by the pump into the wash arm in the bottom of the dishwasher and Power Tower™ sprayer. The water pressure raises the telescoping Power Tower™ sprayer, which on most models is attached to the top of the spray arm. From the tower, water sprays in a fan-shaped pattern for effective cleaning of dishes in the upper rack. Slots or holes in the wash arm and tower allow the water to escape in jets. Some of the jets are angled so that the pressure of escaping water causes the arm and tower to rotate.

The wash arm sprays water forcefully through the lower rack. There have been three types of wash arms used on GE/Hotpoint dishwashers, shown in exploded views below. The Multi-Orbit™ wash arm differs from standard wash arms in that it continually changes wash patterns, directing water up through the rack from different angles. A few models feature a dual wash arm design, with a second wash arm under the upper rack.

Note: Several types of wash systems are described in this procedure. Match the spray arm used on your dishwasher to one of the designs picture in this procedure. There have been many subtle variations in wash systems used on GE/Hotpoint dishwashers. Your wash arm may look like the design pictured and still differ slightly.

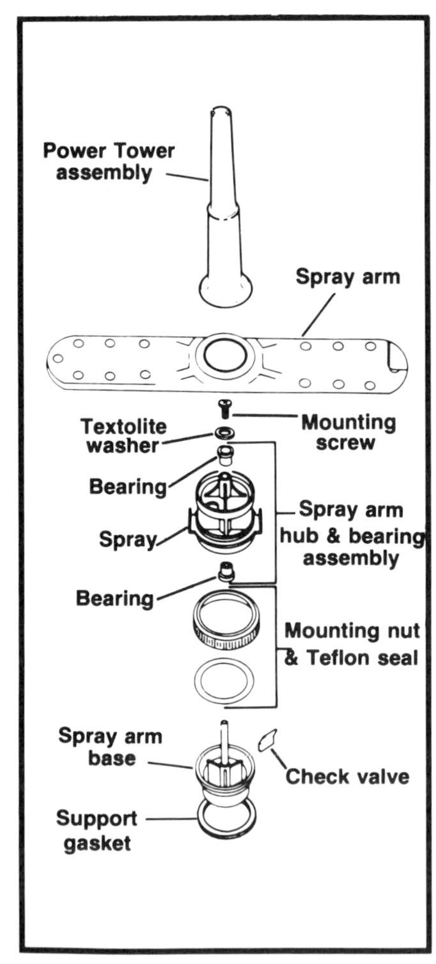

Standard wash arm--Type A

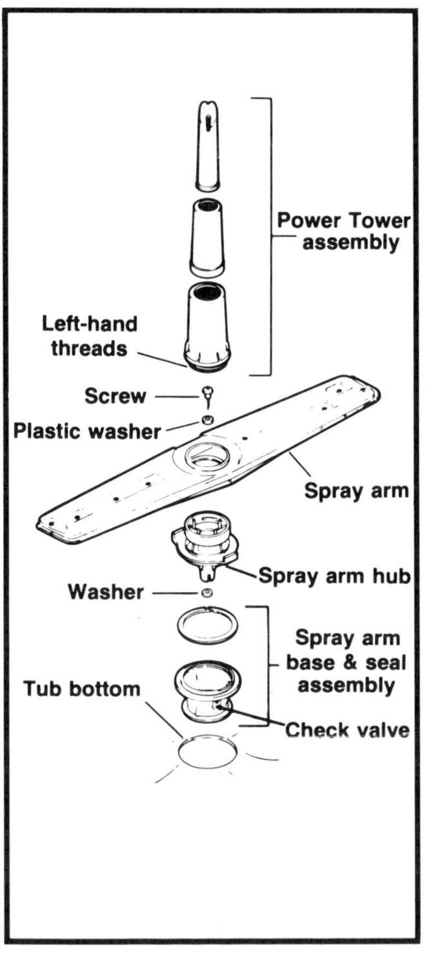

Standard wash arm--Type B

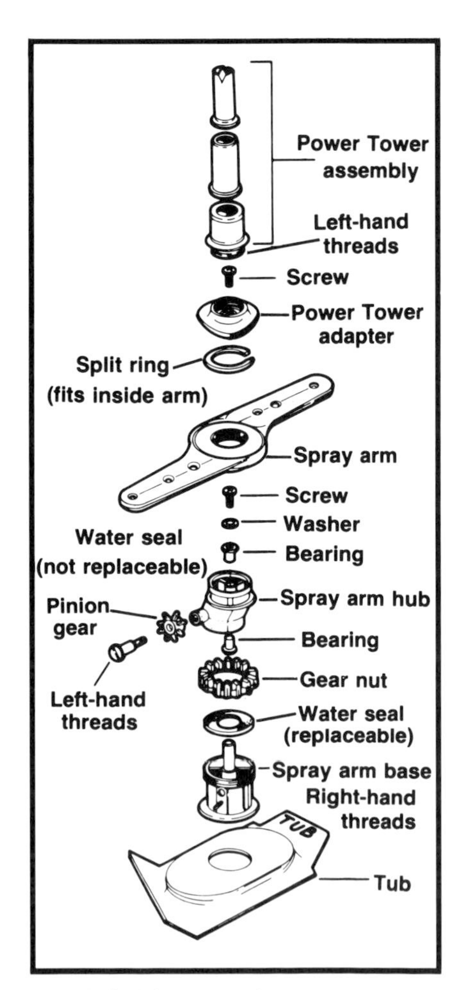

Multi-Orbit™ wash arm

Wash system parts (continued)

Step 1: Be sure all dishwasher controls are turned **OFF.** Disconnect power supply at distribution panel. For convertible models, also unplug power cord from receptacle. Watch for sharp edges.

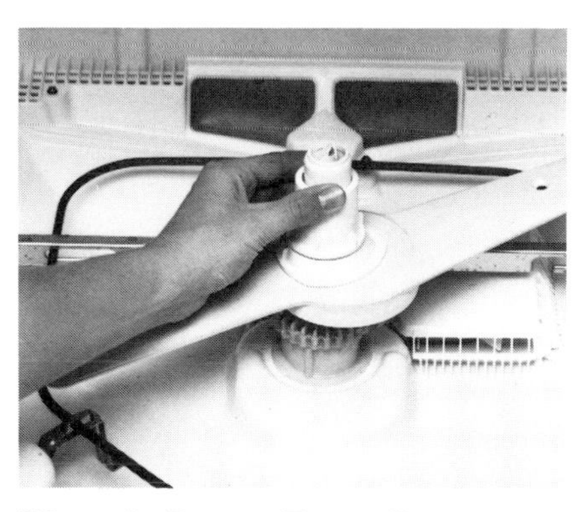

Step 2: Power Tower™ sprayer. Remove lower rack and inspect Power Tower™ sprayer on top of wash arm. If sprayer has disconnected and is lying in bottom of dishwasher tub, screw it counter-clockwise back onto top of wash arm.

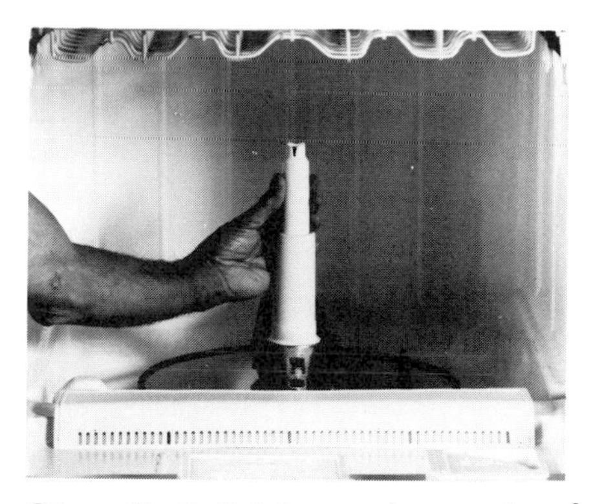

Step 3: Pull telescoping parts of Power Tower™ sprayer up to see that they move freely and to look for clogs. Unscrew Power Tower™ clockwise slightly to check for secure connection to wash arm. If threads are worn, replace hub as described in wash arm steps.

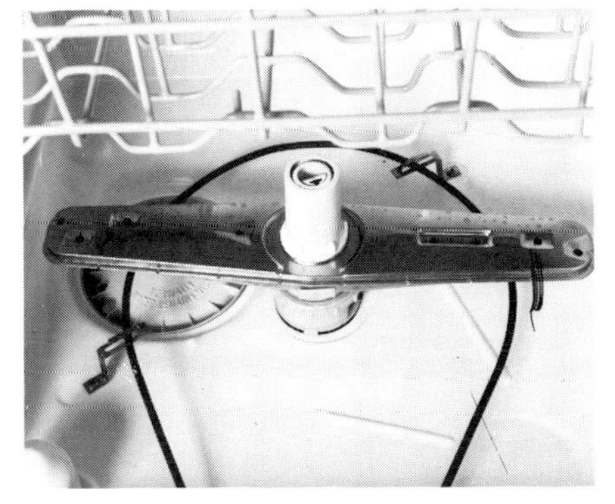

Step 4: Standard wash arm. Inspect wash arm for clogs. Rotate wash arm by hand to see if it moves freely. It should move up and down slightly. Hub inside arm may need new bearings if there is too much play.

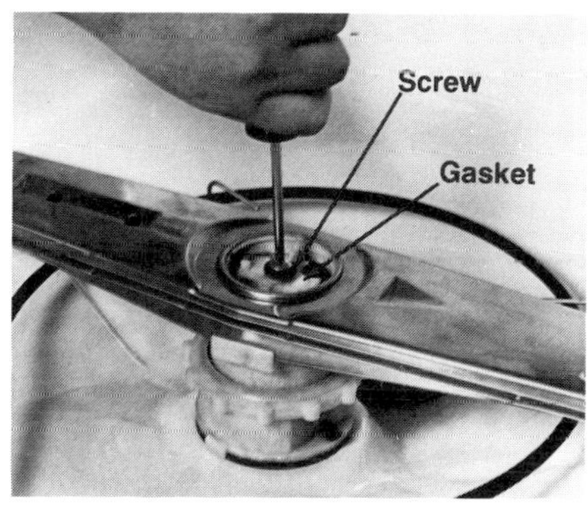

Step 5: To inspect wash arm further, unscrew Power Tower™ sprayer clockwise. Some models have a mounting screw and gasket that need to be removed before wash arm can be lifted off. When lifting arm off base, put your finger under the hub to hold in bearing or washer.

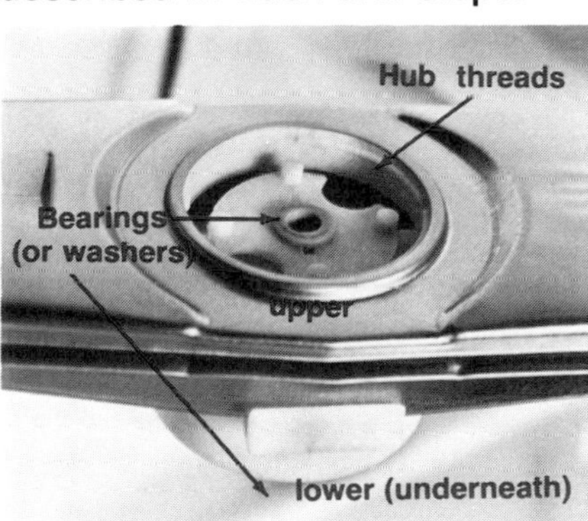

Step 6: Check upper and lower bearings on hub. Replace bearings (or washers) if worn or missing. Inspect threads on hub. Replace hub if threads are worn.

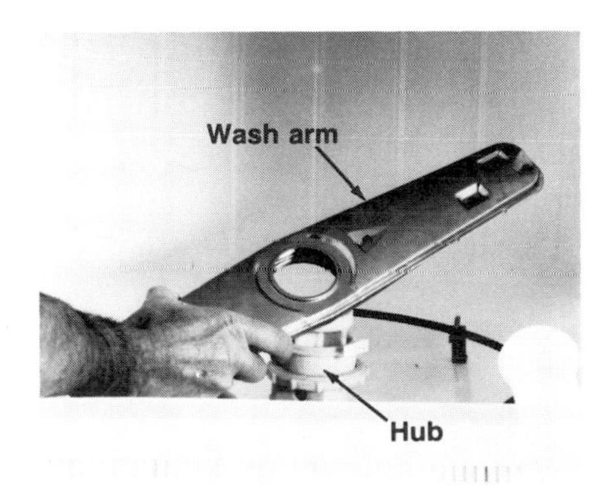

Step 7: Remove arm from hub if not already detached. Check wash arm for foreign objects. Snap new hub in from bottom, making sure bearings are properly seated.

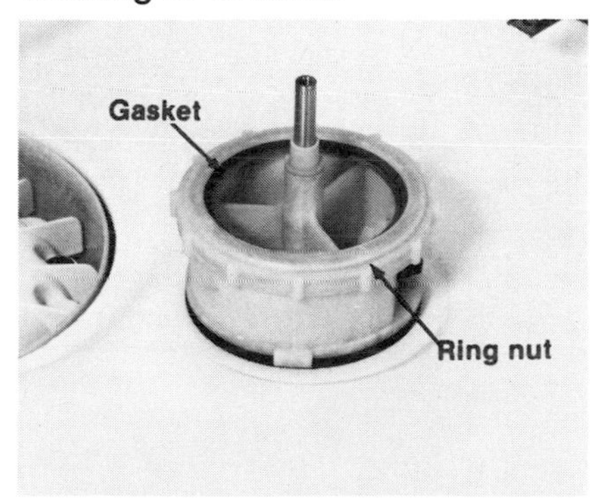

Step 8: Check gasket under large ring nut on spray arm base. Gasket must be in place and undamaged. Remove ring nut to replace gasket. If base is damaged or rod is broken off inside spray arm, replace base.

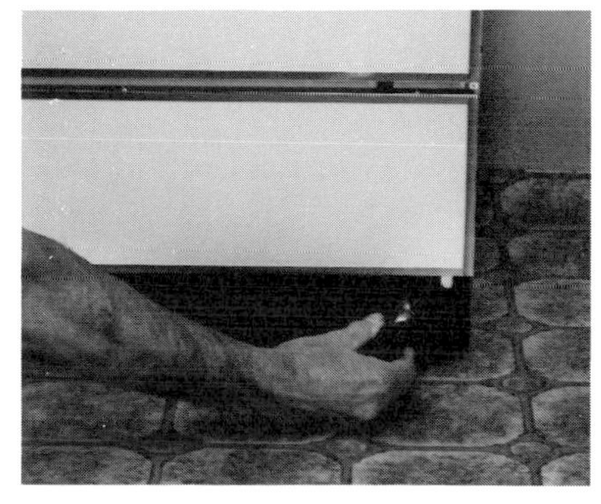

Step 9: Remove lower access panel or tilt dishwasher back, protecting floor for water leakage. If you are unfamiliar with this process, please refer to Procedure #3: Removing Service Panels.

Wash system parts (continued)

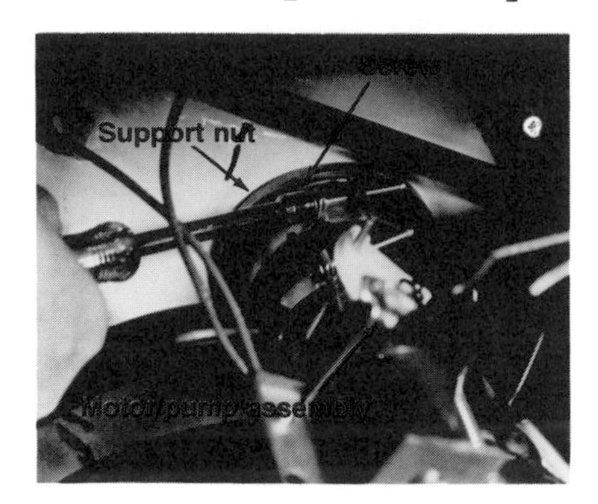

Step 10: Loosen but do not remove ring clamp connecting motor assembly boot to dishwasher tub.

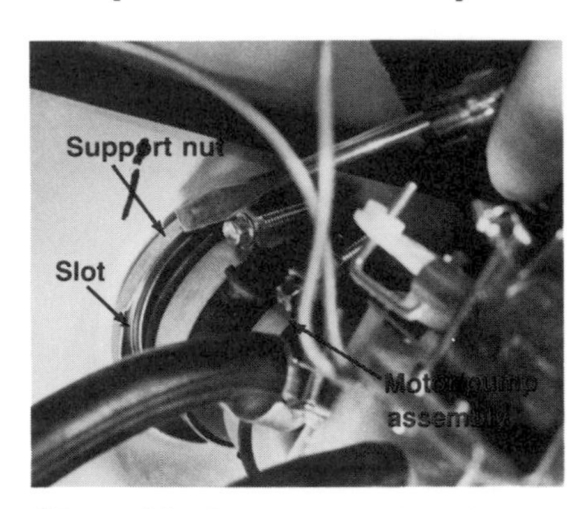

Step 11: Put screwdriver in slot of large support nut and exert pressure downward to loosen. You may have to tap with hammer.

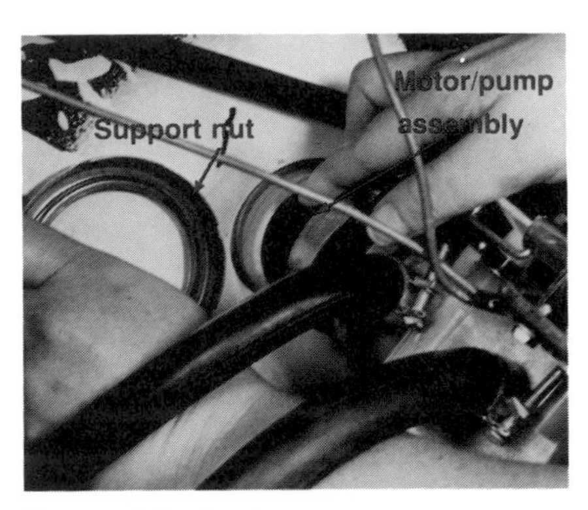

Step 12: Pull back on motor/pump assembly and remove support nut. Spray arm base should now be loose in tub.

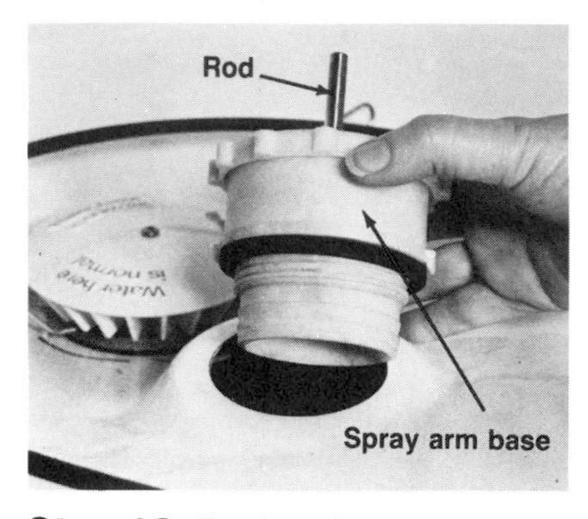

Step 13: Replace spray arm base and reconnect motor/pump assembly. Reassemble spray arm and hub, making sure holes in are on top when positioned back on base.

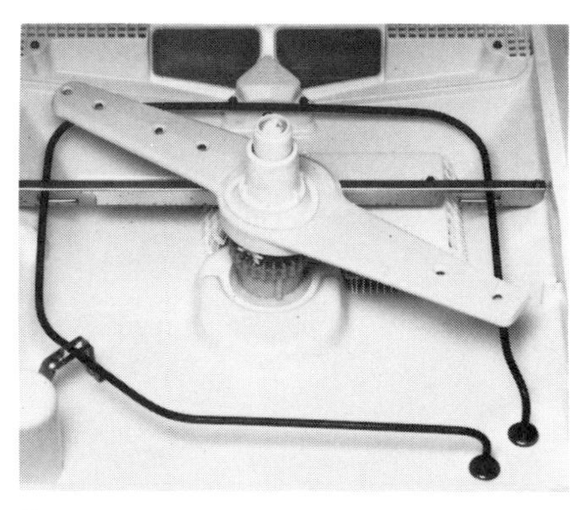

Step 14: Multi-orbit™ wash arm. Inspect wash arm for clogs. Rotate wash arm by hand to see if it moves freely. It should move up and down slightly. Hub inside arm may need new bearings if there is too much play.

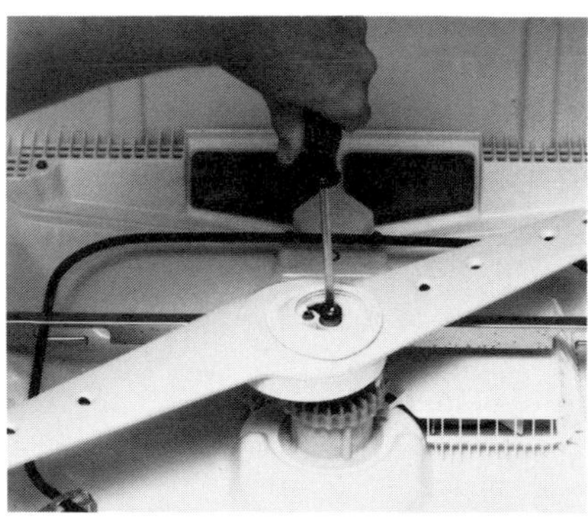

Step 15: To inspect wash arm and hub further, unscrew Power Tower™ sprayer clockwise and remove. Remove center screw and pull off wash arm and hub assembly.

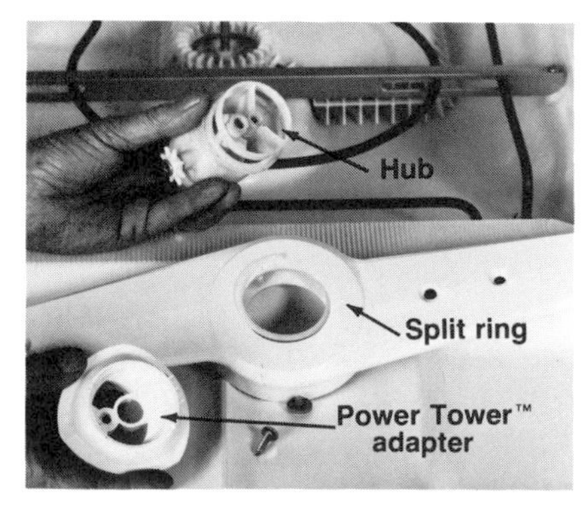

Step 16: Inspect all parts for damage or obstruction. Remove screw from Power Tower™ sprayer adapter. Detach adapter and hub from wash arm. Be sure split ring is in place inside wash arm. Replace hub if broken or threads are worn.

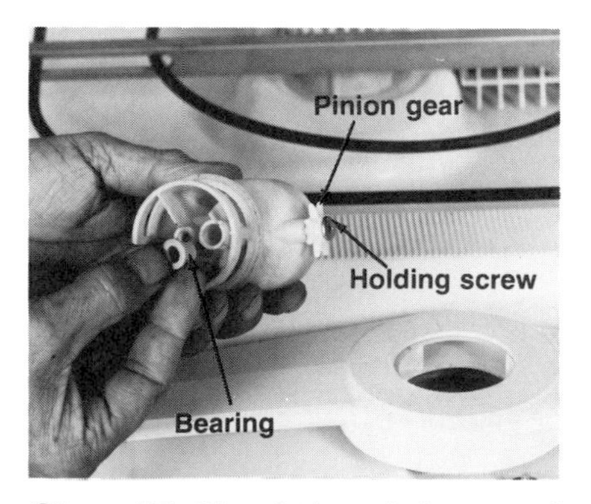

Step 17: Check that pinion gear is intact and in place. If damaged, remove holding screw to replace gear. Check bearings in top and bottom of hub. Replace bearings if worn or damaged.

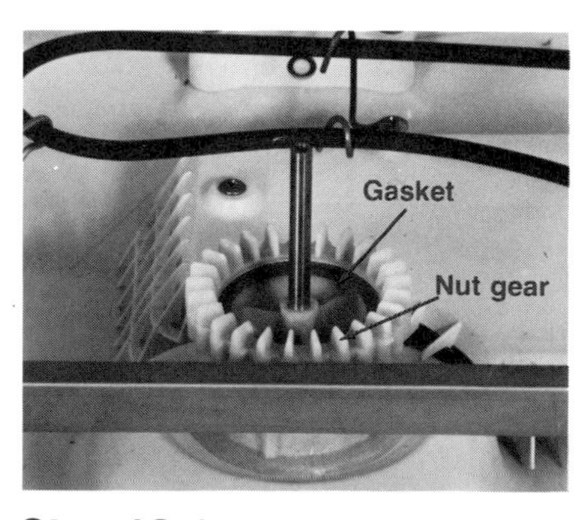

Step 18: Inspect nut gear for damage or foreign objects which may cause binding. Check to be sure gasket is in place and undamaged. Unscrew nut gear counterclockwise to replace damaged gasket.

Wash system parts (continued)

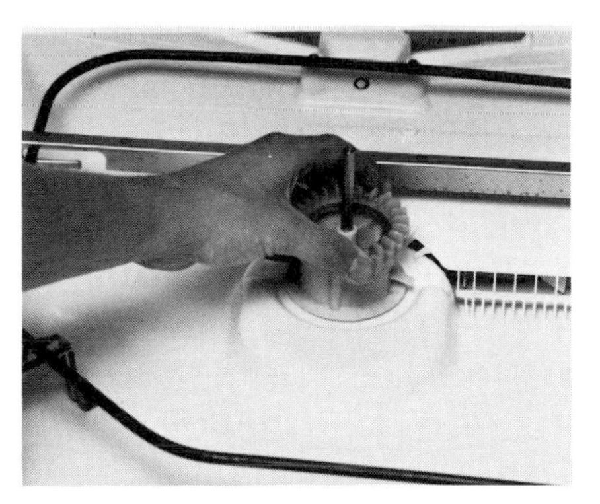

Step 19: If spray base or rod is damaged, remove and replace. On some models, you can simply unscrew base from bottom of dishwasher tub.

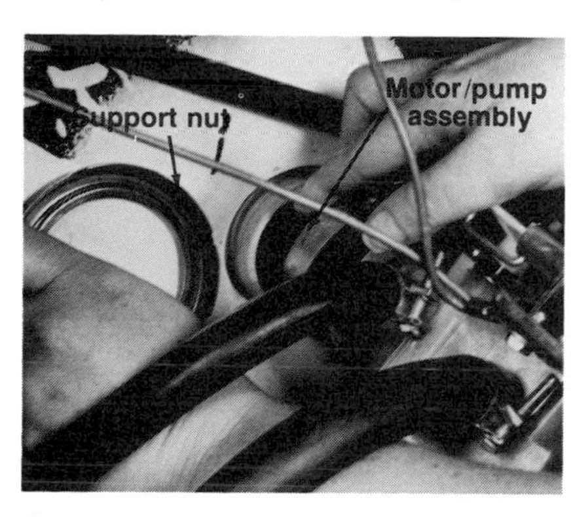

Step 20: If your base does not unscrew from the bottom, you will have to replace unit as described in Steps 9-13.

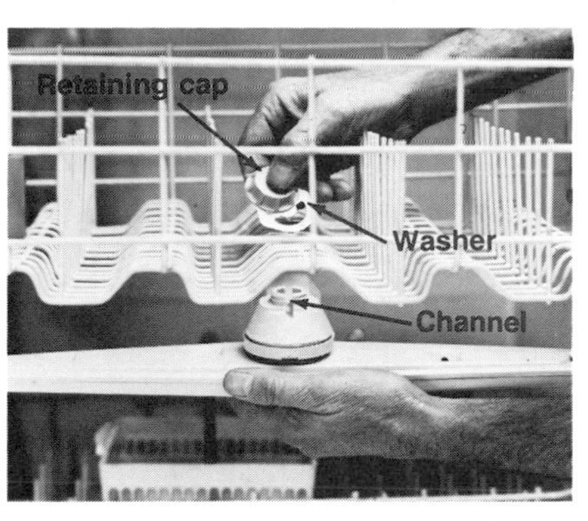

Step 21: Dual wash arms. To remove upper wash arm assembly from rack, unscrew retaining cap counterclockwise. Remove metal washer. Pull channel and wash arm forward and down.

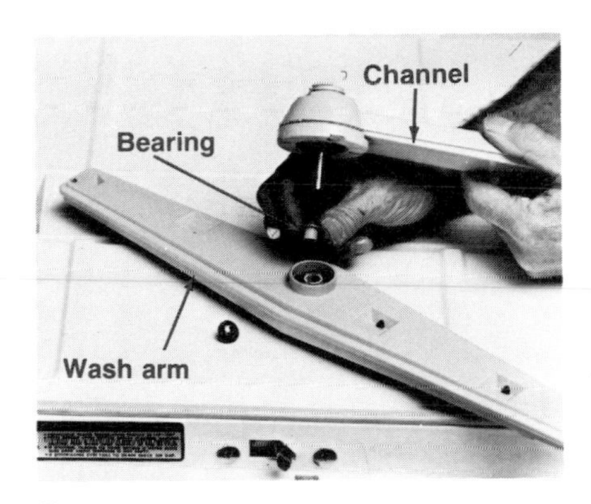

Step 22: Remove center screw and detach upper wash arm from channel. Inspect parts for damage or clogging. Check bearings in top and bottom of wash arm. Replace bearings if worn.

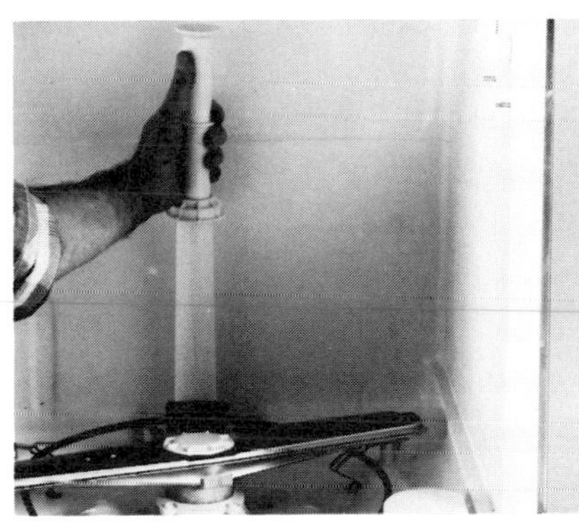

Step 23: Pull up telescoping parts of coupling tube at rear of dishwasher tub. They should move freely to connect with upper wash arm channel. Replace any damaged or binding parts.

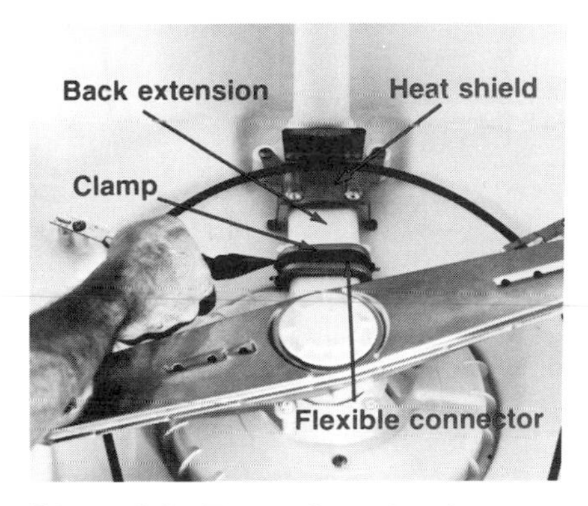

Step 24: To replace back extension and coupling tube, remove screws and detach heat shield. Bend tabs on rear clamp at flexible connector and detach clamp. Lift out extension and coupling tube.

Step 25: To inspect lower wash arm assembly, screw retaining cap clockwise and remove. Pull off wash arm. Detach hub same as described in Step 7. Inspect gasket and check for foreign objects.

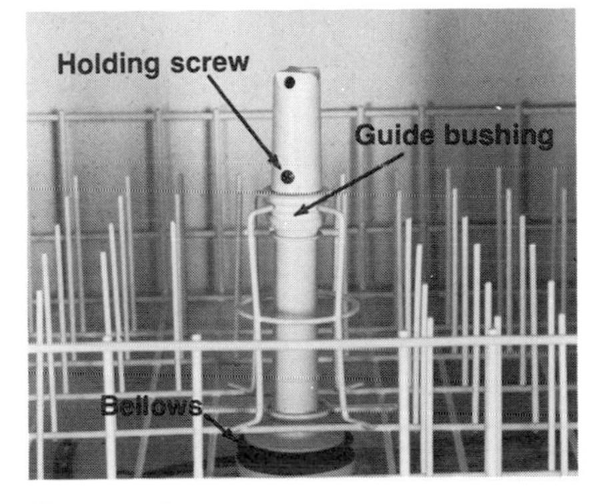

Step 26: Wash tower on rack. Snap guide bushing up or down in rack to adjust contact with bellows. Flexible bellows expands with water pressure and must contact tower to cause it to revolve with wash arm.

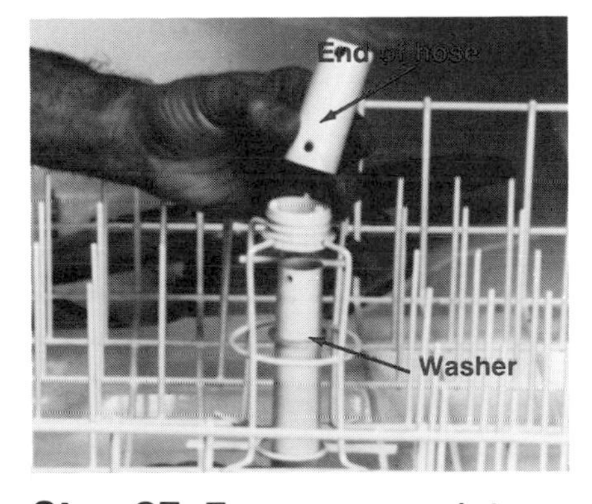

Step 27: To remove wash tower from rack, remove holding screw. Separate halves and remove from guide bushing. Examine parts for damage or clogs. Make sure washer is in place when reassembling.

Wash system parts (continued)

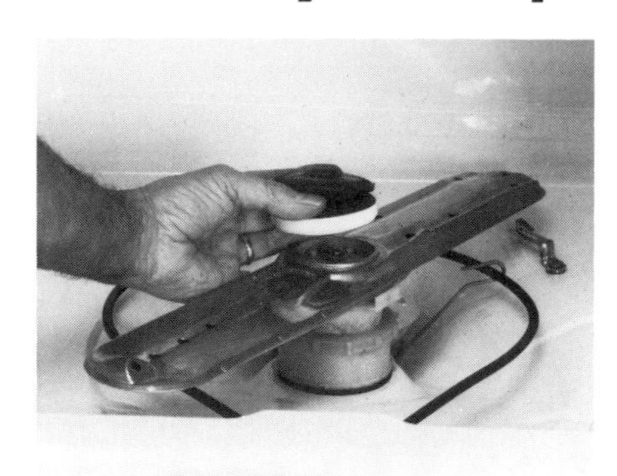

Step 28: Screw bellows clockwise to remove from wash arm hub. Replace bellows if damaged or deteriorated. Pull off wash arm. Detach hub and inspect same as in Steps 5-7.

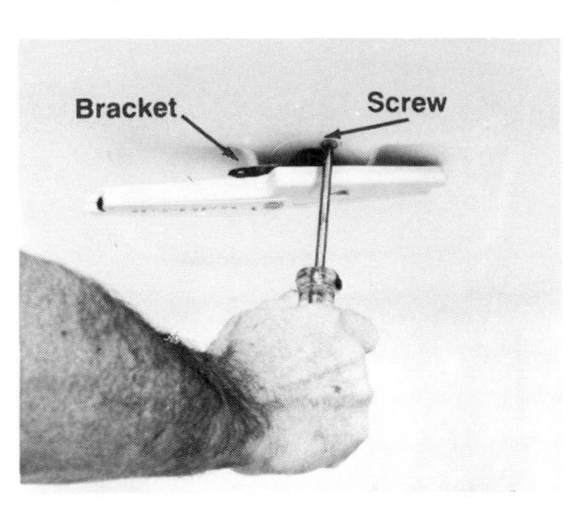

Step 29: Power Shower® spray arm. To remove Power Shower® spray arm, remove one screw and loosen other. Turn bracket away from hole. Replace screw before removing second screw to secure nut strip on outside of tub.

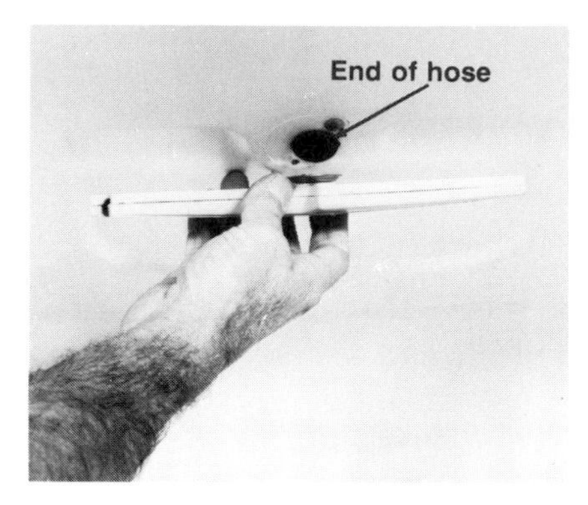

Step 30: Remove second screw and detach Power Shower® spray arm. Inspect for damage or clogging. Check flared end of hose that extends into tub for cracks or deterioration. Replace any damaged parts.

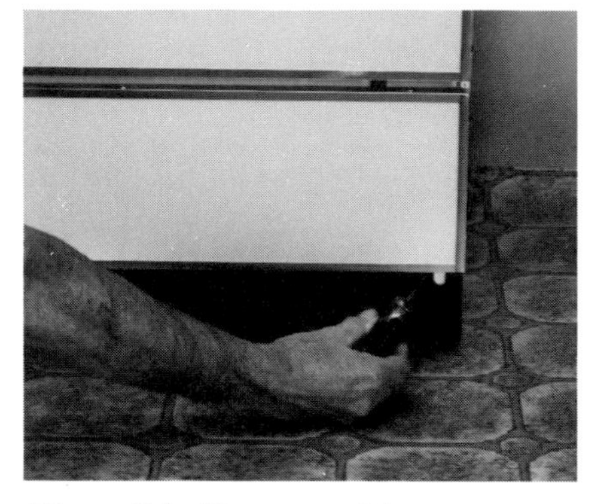

Step 31: Reassemble dishwasher and reconnect power supply.

Notes

Procedure 17

Inspecting and replacing single or dual cup detergent dispenser

Skill Level Rating: | Easy | **Average** | Difficult | Very Difficult |

The detergent dispenser located inside the dishwasher door must be filled with detergent before each wash. At the proper point in the wash cycle, the dispenser opens automatically to release detergent into the dishwasher tub.

Some dishwashers have an open cavity as well as a covered cup for detergent. Normally, detergent is placed in the covered cup, which is opened mechanically during the main wash portion of the cycle. For extra wash effectiveness, detergent can also be placed in the open cavity. This detergent is released immediately when the dishwasher door is closed.

Some dishwashers have dual detergent cups, both of which have covers. Each cup is opened mechanically at a pre-determined point during the cycle. Like the single covered cup models, each cup is activated by a lever which is tripped by a cam on the dishwasher timer. The inspection and replacement procedure is similar for both single-cup and dual-cup assemblies.

Note: There are two types of detergent dispensers used on GE and Hotpoint dishwashers. This procedure covers standard single or dual-cup dispensers. Molded-type dispensers, found on some models with Perma-Tuf® interiors, are covered in Procedure #18. This manual does not cover dispensers used on electronic models, as these should be repaired an authorized GE service technician.

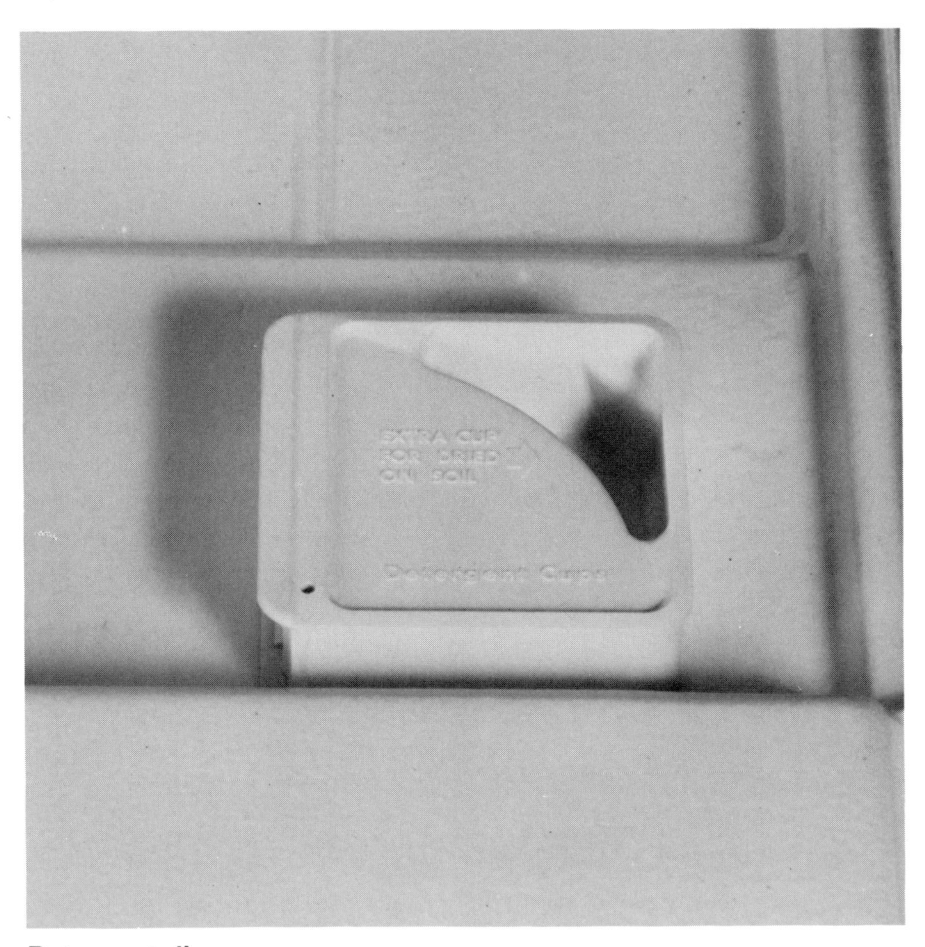

Detergent dispenser cup

Single and dual cup detergent dispenser (continued)

Step 1: Be sure all dishwasher controls are turned **OFF**. Disconnect power supply at distribution panel. For convertible models, also unplug power cord from receptacle. Watch for sharp edges.

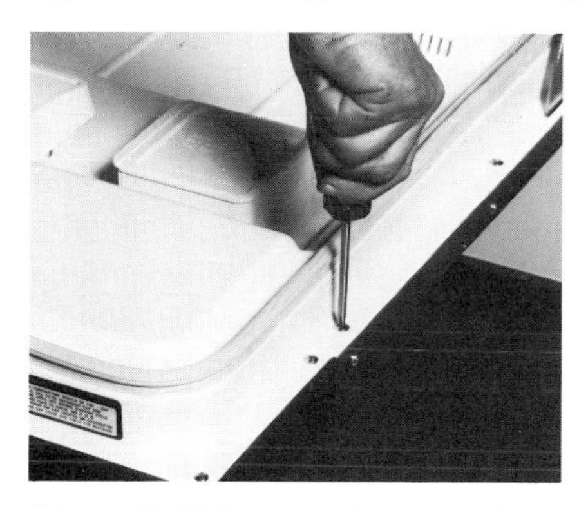

Step 2: This procedure requires removal of the outer door panel from your dishwasher. If you are unfamiliar with this process, please refer to Procedure #3: Removing Service Panels.

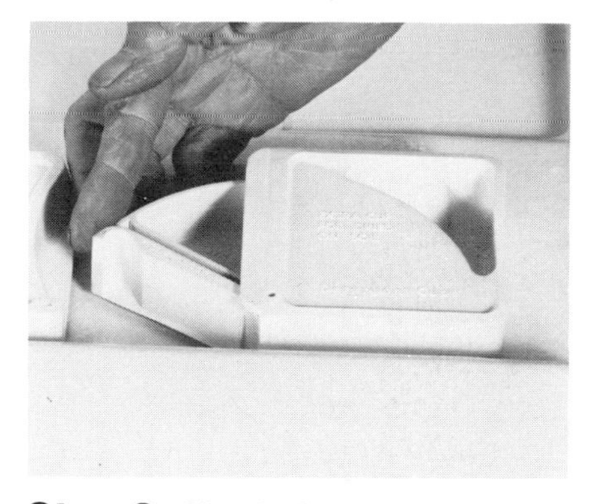

Step 3: Check detergent cup for caked detergent. Open and close cup by hand to see if it is warped or binding. Close cup and turn control knob, if any, to see if it springs open.

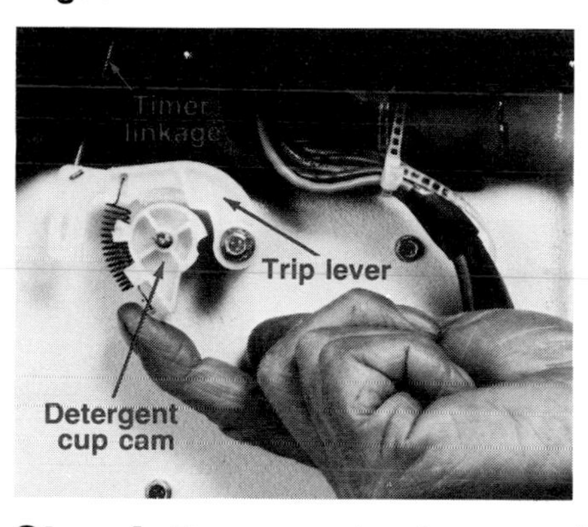

Step 4: Remove outer door panel and visually check mechanism for broken or binding parts, broken springs or linkage. Check that all moving parts move freely.

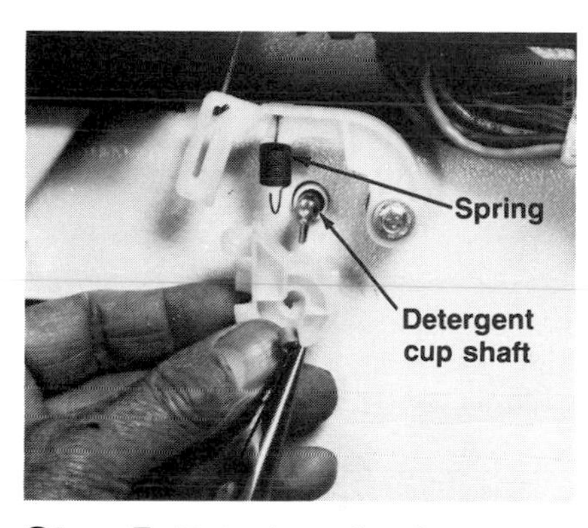

Step 5: Detach spring from detergent cup cam. Remove screw or holding clip that secures cam to detergent cup shaft. Pull cam off and pull out roll pin that secures shaft.

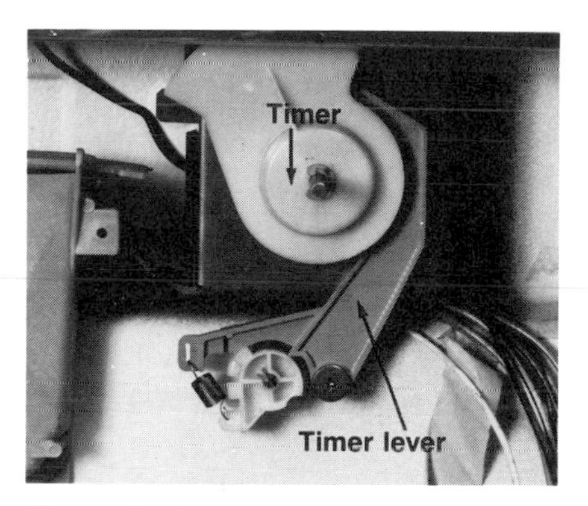

Step 6: On some models, detergent cup is tripped by a lever from the timer. These models do not use a wire linkage, but other details of inspection and replacement are similar.

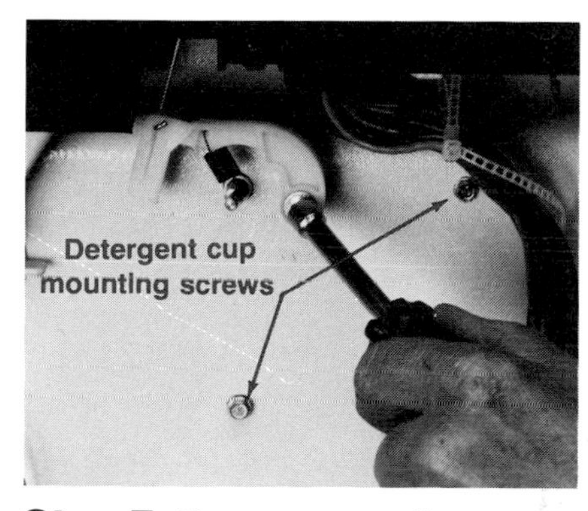

Step 7: Remove mounting screw that secures the detergent cup to the door panel. Remove holding screw from trip lever. Pull detergent cup assembly off from inside dishwasher.

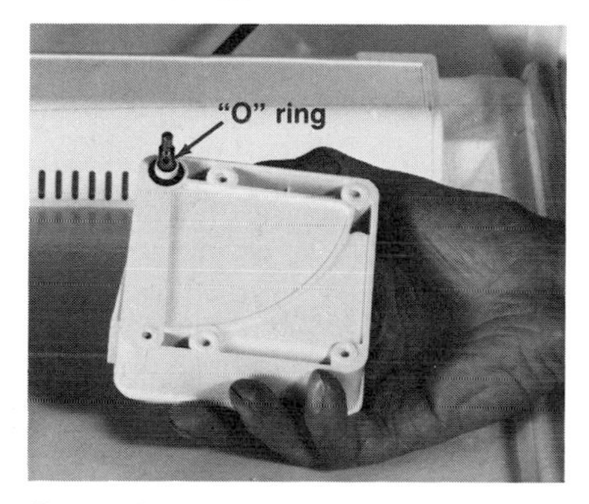

Step 8: Replace cup assembly, being sure to install "O" ring on detergent cup shaft to prevent leaks. Tighten mounting screws and install trip lever.

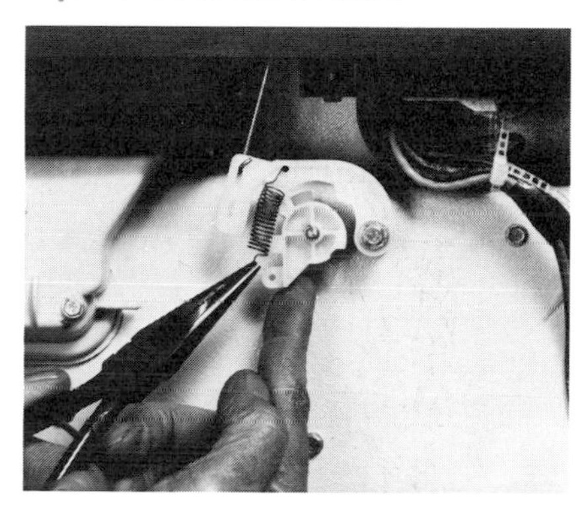

Step 9: Replace roll pin in shaft. Install cam. Replace screw or clip on end of shaft. Attach timer linkage, if any. Attach one end of spring to lever, and other end to cam. Reassemble dishwasher and reconnect power supply.

Procedure 18

Inspecting and replacing molded-cup type detergent dispenser

Skill Level Rating:	Easy	**Average**	Difficult	Very Difficult

Some dishwashers have detergent cups molded into the inner PermaTuf® door panel. A separate cover on one cup is opened mechanically by a lever. At the appropriate time in the cycle, the timer trips the lever and opens the cup.

A smaller cavity without a cover is also molded into the door panel. Extra detergent can be placed here, to be released when the dishwasher door is closed.

Note: There are two types of detergent dispensers used on GE and Hotpoint dishwashers. This procedure covers molded-type dispensers found on some models with Perma-Tuf® interiors. Standard single or dual-cup dispensers are covered in Procedure #17. This manual does not cover dispensers used on electronic models, as these should be repaired an authorized GE service technician.

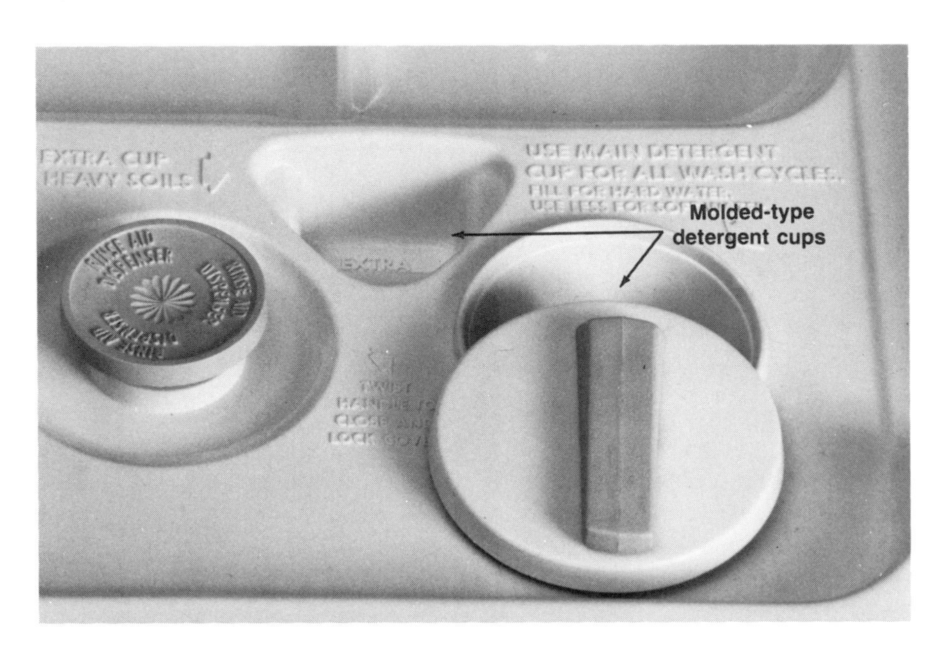

Step 1: Be sure all dishwasher controls are turned **OFF**. Disconnect power supply at distribution panel. Watch for sharp edges.

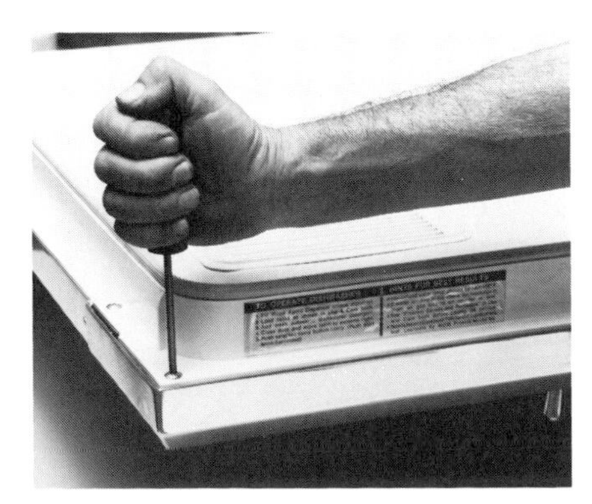

Step 2: This procedure requires removal of the inner door panel from your dishwasher. If you are unfamiliar with this process, please refer to Procedure #3: Removing Service Panels.

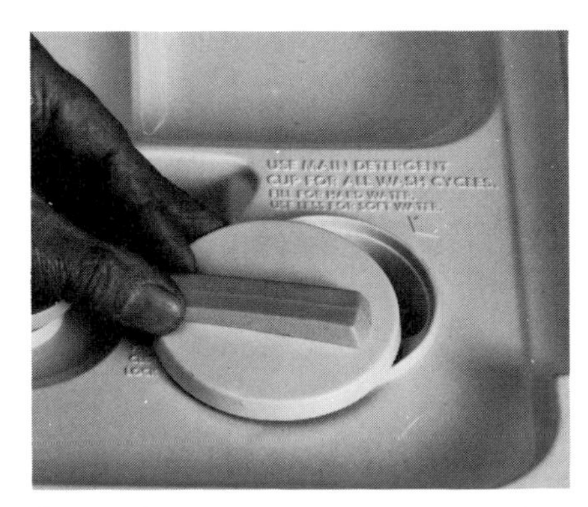

Step 3: Inspect cup for clogging due to caked detergent. Move cover by hand to see that it operates freely.

Molded-cup type detergent dispenser (continued)

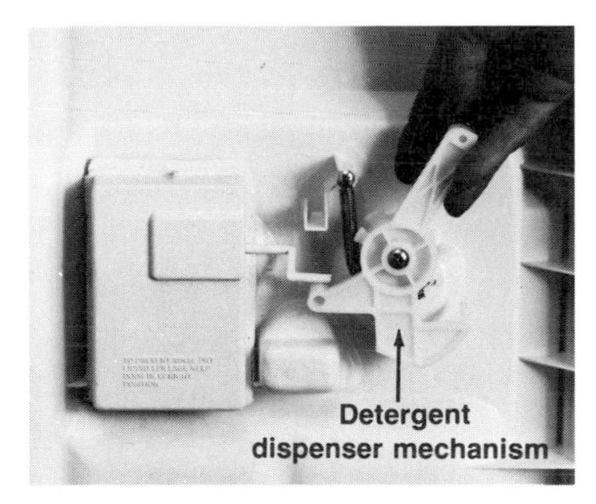

Step 4: Remove inner door panel. Visually inspect detergent dispenser mechanism for broken or binding parts. Move lever by hand to be sure it operates freely.

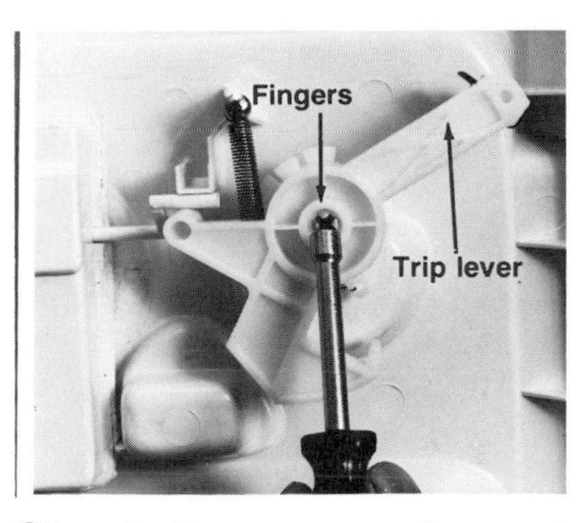

Step 5: Remove screw from end of shaft. Using a nutdriver, press the four fingers on the end of the shaft together. Pull cover and shaft off from inside dishwasher. Remove trip lever.

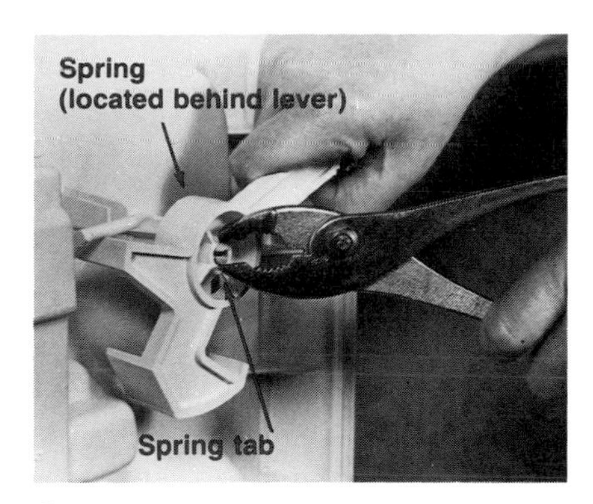

Step 6: On some models, the spring is wrapped behind the trip lever and does not show. To remove trip lever on these models, squeeze spring tabs together with pliers and lift trip lever off.

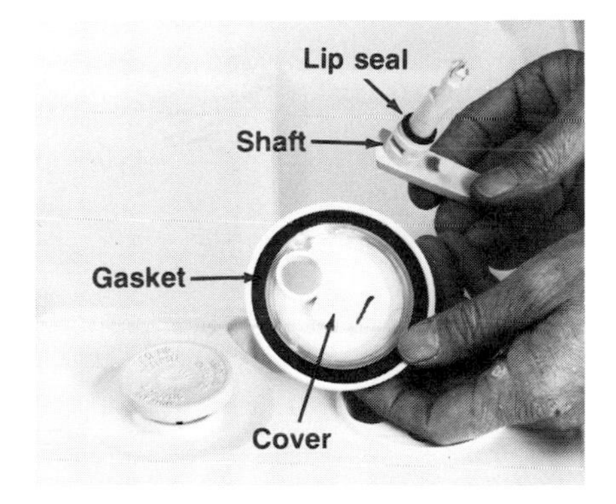

Step 7: If cup leaks, inspect cover gasket and lip seal for damage. (On some models, there is no lip seal). Replace any defective components.

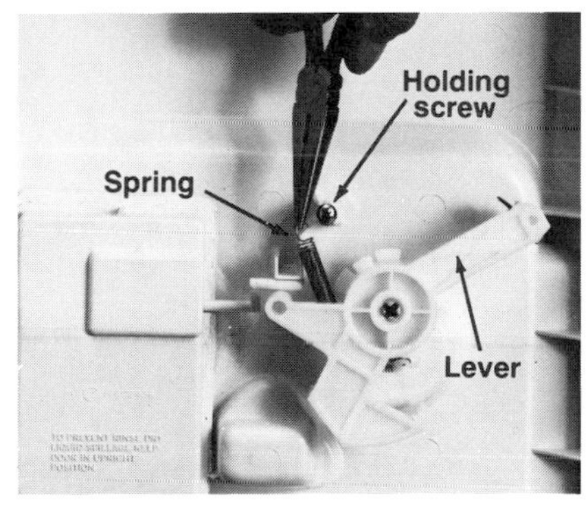

Step 8: Install shaft, lip seal, cover and gasket. Attach one end of spring to lever. Install lever on shaft. Wind spring clockwise and secure to holding screw. Replace mounting screw to end of shaft.

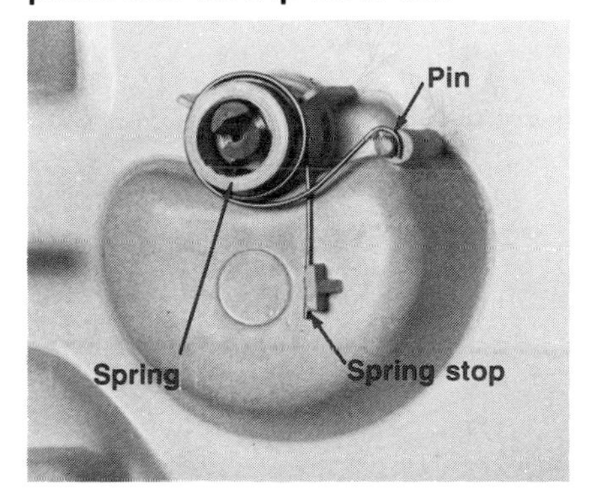

Step 9: For models where spring fits behind lever, place spring on shaft with hook on left and straight wire pointing down to left of stop. Wind the spring counterclockwise and hook end onto pin.

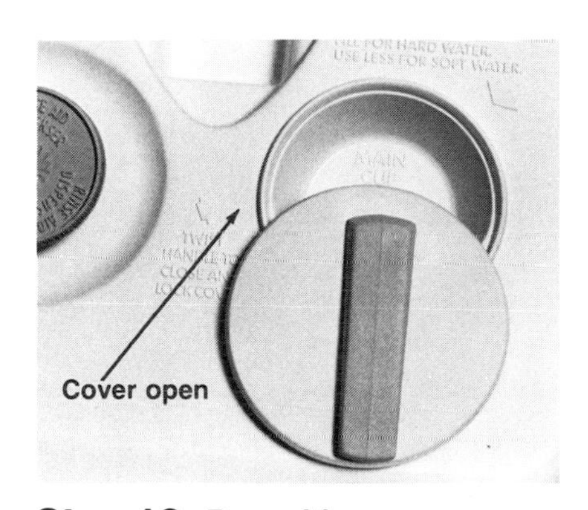

Step 10: Reposition cup on inside door with shaft handle pointing up (i.e., cover open).

Step 11: Reposition trip lever on shaft as shown. While holding cup and handle in place inside door, press lever onto shaft. Turn lever counterclockwise and check for tension. Reassemble dishwasher and reconnect power supply.

Procedure 19

Inspecting and replacing electrical rinse agent dispenser

Skill Level Rating:	Easy	Average	**Difficult**	Very Difficult

The rinse agent dispenser on some model dishwashers automatically injects a small amount of liquid rinse agent into the dishwasher during the final rinse period. This wetting solution acts to break down the surface tension of the water, minimizing formation of spots and streaks on dishes and glasses.

The tank of the rinse agent dispenser holds about a three-month supply of rinse agent. A measuring chamber in the dispenser holds a pre-measured amount of the solution. During the final rinse period, the timer activates a bimetal strip above the rinse agent tank. The bimetal strip heats and rises, pulling up a rubber-tipped valve pin. This allows the rinse agent to be released into the dishwasher, where it is distributed by the action of the water.

Note: There are two types of rinse agent dispensers used on GE and Hotpoint dishwashers. This procedure covers electrically-operated dispensers. Mechanically-operated dispensers, found on some models with PermaTuf® interiors, are covered in Procedure #20.

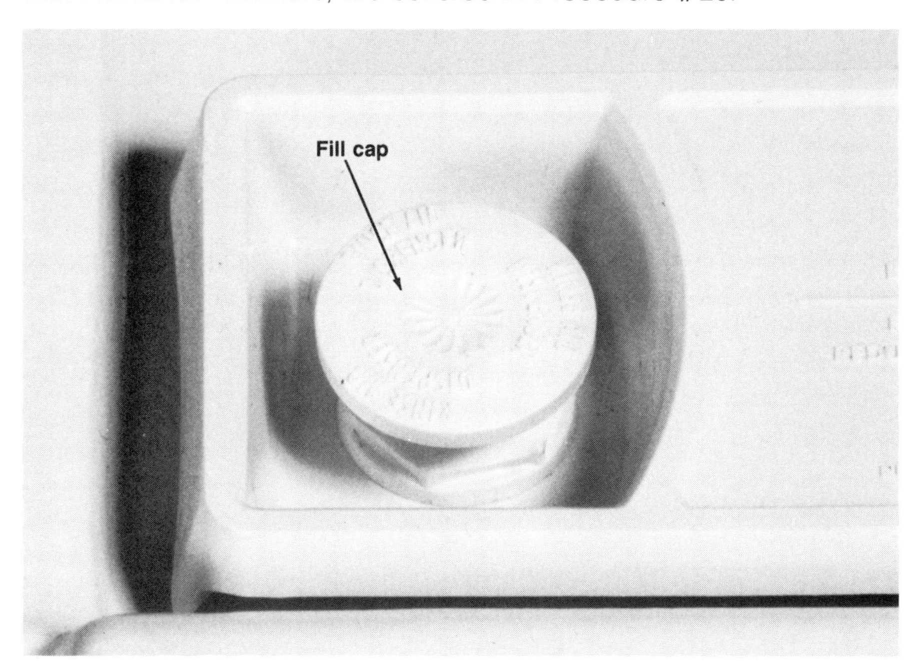

Rinse agent dispenser

Electrical rinse agent dispenser (continued)

Step 1: Be sure all dishwasher controls are turned **OFF**. Disconnect power supply at distribution panel. For convertible models, also unplug power cord from receptacle. Watch for sharp edges.

Step 2: This procedure requires the use of an ohmmeter. For instructions on how to use an ohmmeter, please refer to Tools and Testing Equipment, page 95.

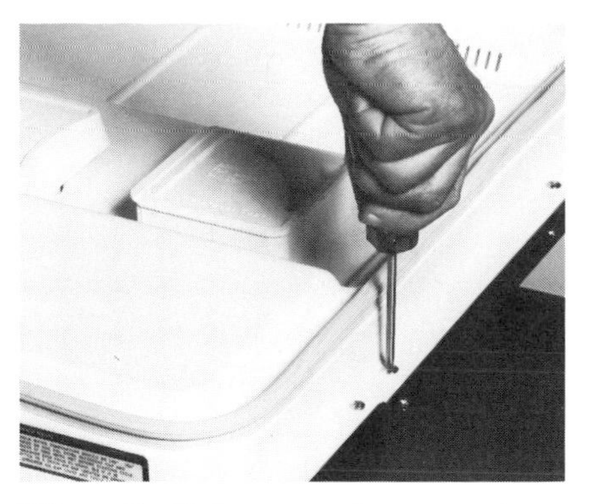

Step 3: This procedure requires removal of the outer door panel from your dishwasher. If you are unfamiliar with this process, please refer to Procedure #3: Removing Service Panels.

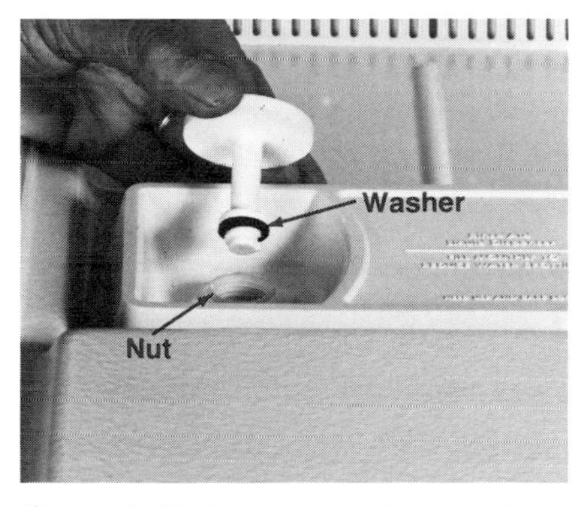

Step 4: If rinse agent leaks, check fill cap fit or replace washer. Open dishwasher door to reset dispenser. Close and wait 5 minutes. If seepage shows on door, check tank and valve pin.

Step 5: Remove outer door panel. Inspect rinse agent tank for signs of leakage. If tank is split or cracked, it must be replaced.

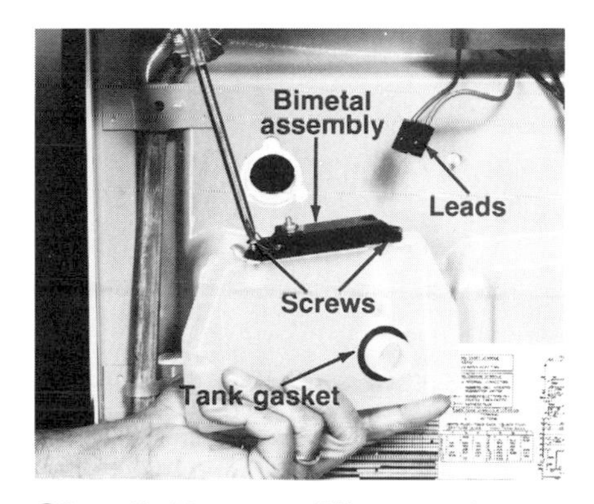

Step 6: Remove fill cap and screw off large nut under it. Detach wire leads and lift tank off. Check tank gasket for damage. Remove screws at each end and detach bimetal assembly.

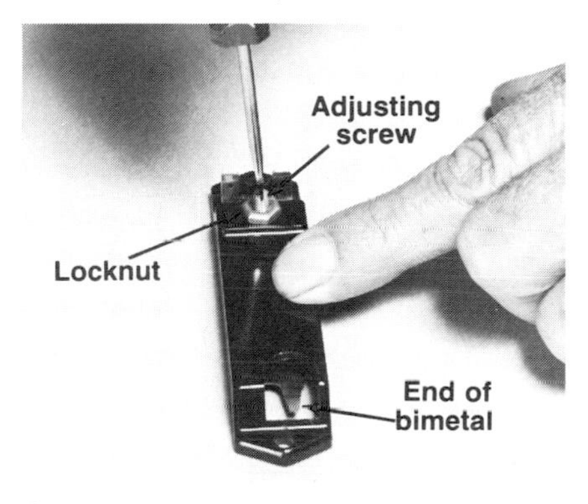

Step 7: Adjust bimetal to prevent leakage. Place on flat surface. Loosen locknut. Turn adjusting screw until end of bimetal touches surface. Tighten locknut and replace assembly on tank.

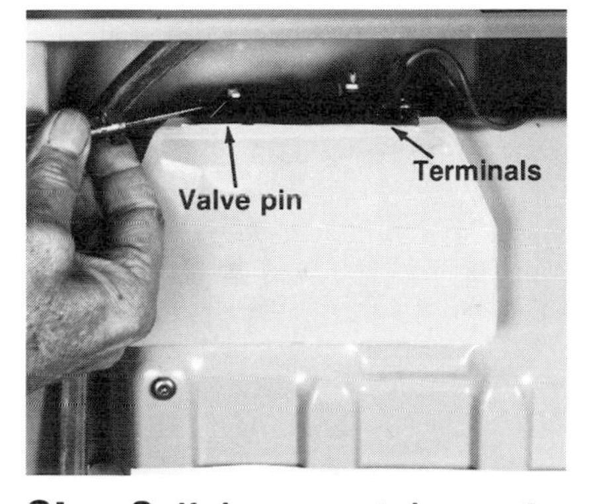

Step 8: If rinse agent does not dispense properly, pull up end of bimetal to check that valve pin moves freely. Replace if binding. Examine terminals for loose or damaged connections.

Step 9: Remove bimetal leads. Set ohmmeter to R x 1. Place probes on terminals. Needle should sweep upscale to indicate continuity. If no continuity, replace bimetal. Reassemble and reconnect power supply.

Procedure 20

Inspecting and replacing mechanical rinse agent dispenser

Skill Level Rating:	Easy	**Average**	Difficult	Very Difficult

Dishwashers with the removable PermaTuf® inner door panel have a mechanically operated rinse agent dispenser. The rinse agent tank is similar to that on other models, holding several ounces of liquid wetting solution. An internal measuring chamber fills automatically when the dishwasher door is opened, holding the precise amount of rinse agent needed for the final rinse.

This type of dispenser does not operate electrically. An arm on the dispenser tank is tripped by a lever on the detergent dispenser at the appropriate point in the cycle, allowing the rinse agent solution to be released into the dishwasher tub.

Note: For best results, rinse agent must be released at the proper time in the dishwasher cycle. If a malfunction causes the dispenser to trip late, the rinse agent will not be dispersed by the action of the water. If this occurs, rinse agent will be visible on the inner door liner or in the bottom of the tub at the end of the drying period.

Note: There are two types of rinse agent dispensers used on GE and Hotpoint dishwashers. This procedure covers mechanically-operated dispensers, found on some models with PermaTuf® interiors. Electrically-operated dispensers are covered in Procedure #19.

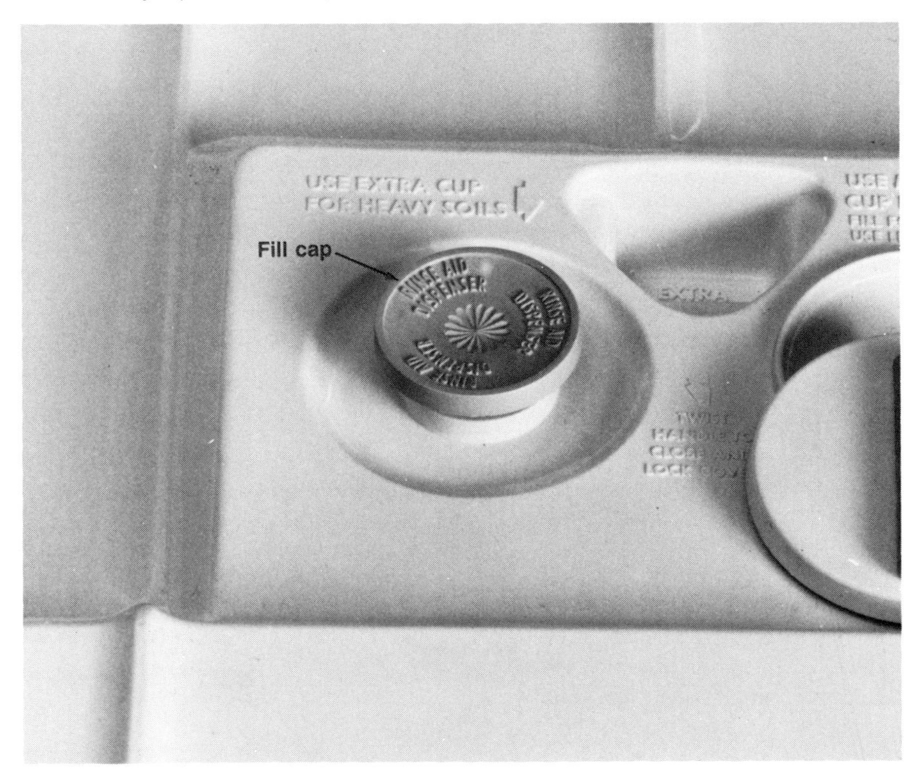

Rinse agent dispenser

Mechanical rinse agent dispenser (continued)

Step 1: Be sure all dishwasher controls are turned **OFF**. Disconnect power supply at distribution panel. Watch for sharp edges.

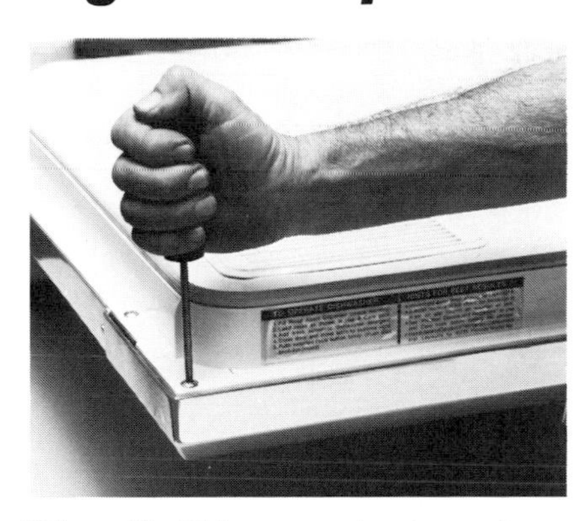

Step 2: This procedure requires removal of the inner door panel from your dishwasher. If you are unfamiliar with this process, please refer to Procedure #3: Removing Service Panels.

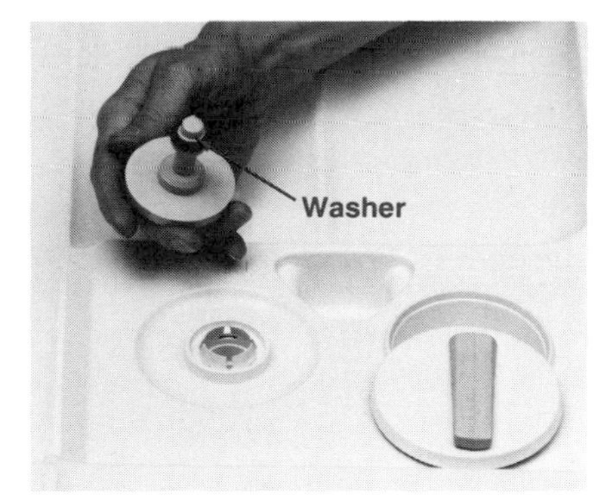

Step 3: If rinse agent leaks into dishwasher prematurely, check that fill cap is tightly fitted. Inspect cap washer for deterioration and replace if necessary.

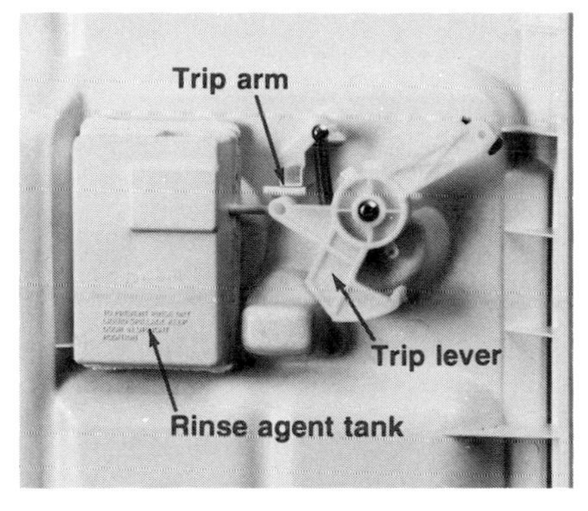

Step 4: Remove inner door panel and inspect for signs of leakage. Examine tank and replace if damaged. Check that trip arm and trip lever are intact and able to move freely.

Step 5: To replace tank, remove fill cap. Under cap are four plasic "fingers" which hold tank in place. Squeeze holding fingers together to release tank.

Step 6: Pull tank away from door panel. Replacement tank simply snaps into place. Trip arm is automatically positioned correctly.

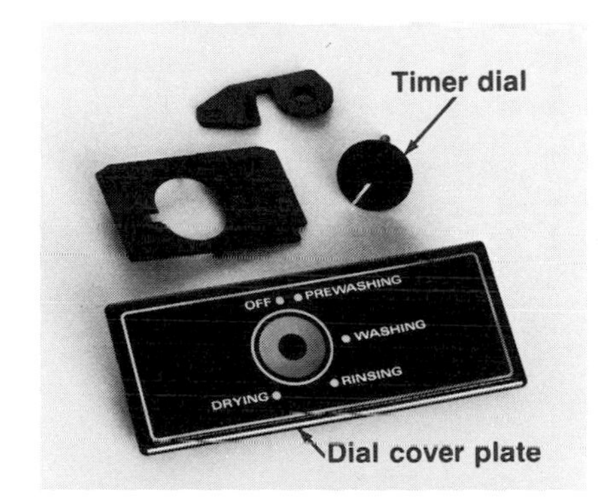

Step 7: If you have observed rinse agent on the inside of the door or in bottom of dishwasher at end of drying period, check timer trip lever. Remove timer dial knob, if any. On models with no dial knob, pry off dial cover plate on control panel. Remove timer dial and other parts, noting how they are installed.

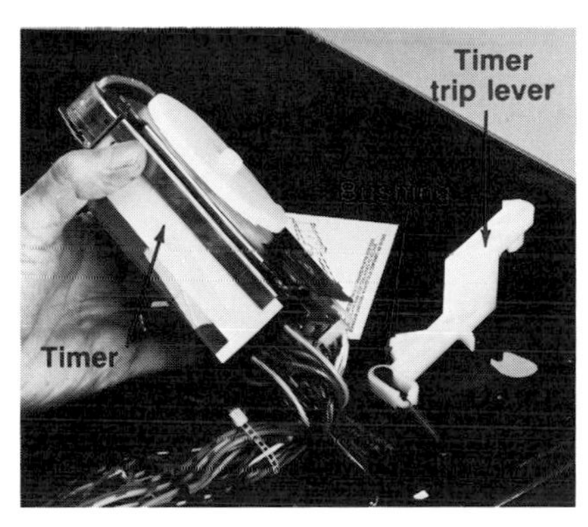

Step 8: Remove cover on outer door panel. Remove timer mounting screw, bending hold tab and pull timer up. Inspect rubber bushing on timer trip lever post. Replace if damaged or missing.

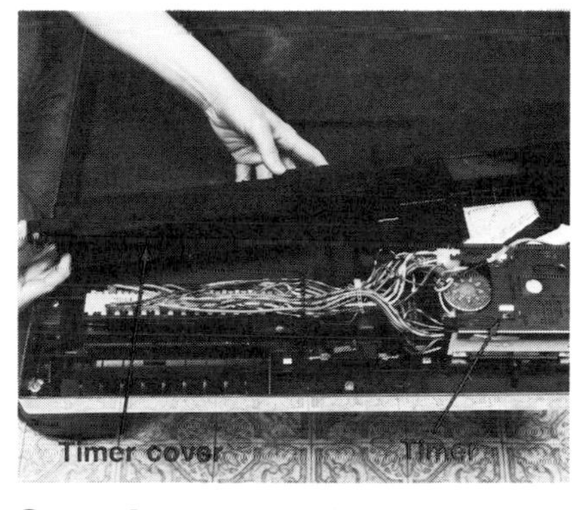

Step 9: Replace timer, mounting screw and cover. Close door and install timer dial knob or timer dial components in same position as original installation. Reassemble dishwasher and reconnect power supply.

Procedure 21

Inspecting and replacing Calrod® heating unit

Skill Level Rating: Easy | Average | **Difficult** | Very Difficult

The Calrod® heating unit is located at the bottom of the dishwasher tub, shaped either like a square or horseshoe. When the unit is energized during the drying cycle, it heats the air which is drawn in at the bottom of the tub. The warmed air rises through the dishwasher and is vented near the top of the door. This airflow provides rapid and efficient dish drying.

An inner resistance coil of nichrome wire, which does the actual heating, is completely surrounded by an electrical insulation material. This assembly is protected by a metal sheath to help reduce damage and oxidation. Since you can't see the internal coil which does the heating, you have to rely on the ohmmeter to tell you when the unit is not working, except in cases damage is visible on the metal sheath or terminals.

CAUTION: To prevent electrical shock, turn power off at distribution panel when inspecting heating unit. Terminals are not grounded and are "hot" when power is connected to dishwasher.

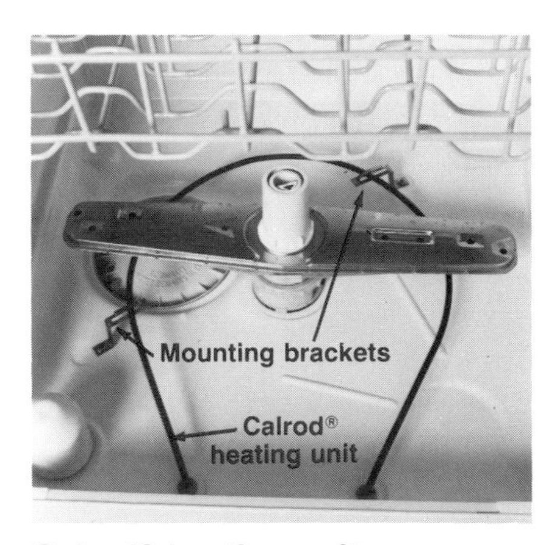

Calrod® heating unit

Step 1: Be sure all dishwasher controls are turned **OFF**. Disconnect power supply at distribution panel. For convertible models, also unplug power cord from receptacle. Watch for sharp edges.

Step 2: This procedure requires the use of an ohmmeter. For instructions on how to use an ohmmeter, please refer to Tools and Testing, page 95.

Step 3: This procedure requires removal of lower access panel from your dishwasher and may be easier to perform with dishwasher pulled out and tilted back. If you are unfamiliar with this process, refer to Procedure #3: Removing Service Panels.

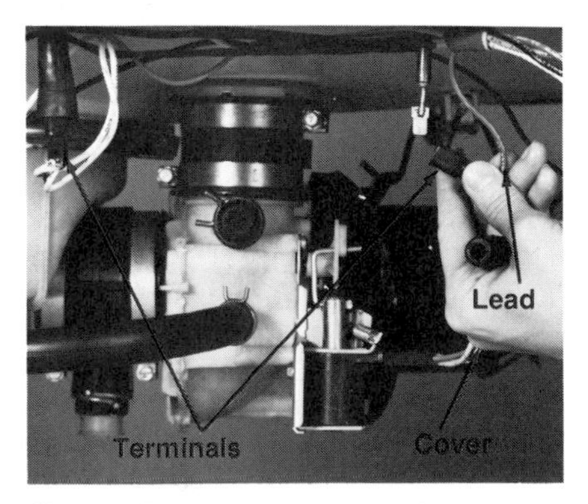

Step 4: Remove lower front access panel. Locate heating unit system under dishwasher tub.

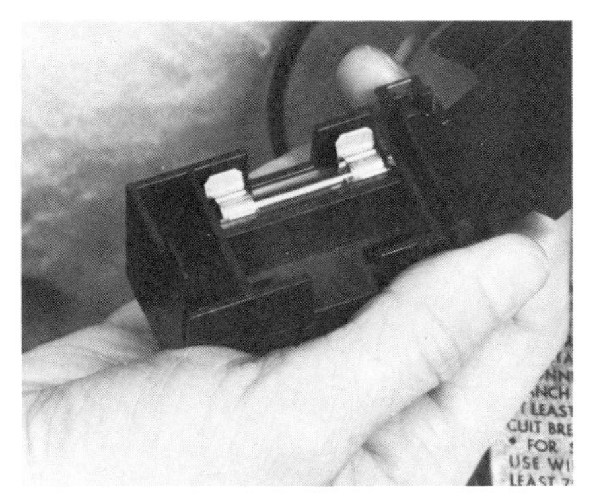

Step 5: Some dishwashers have 1 or 2 internal fuses to protect heater. The fuse box, if any, is on side of body under tub. Depress tabs on side of box and pull out. Replace a blown fuse with one of same size and amp rating.

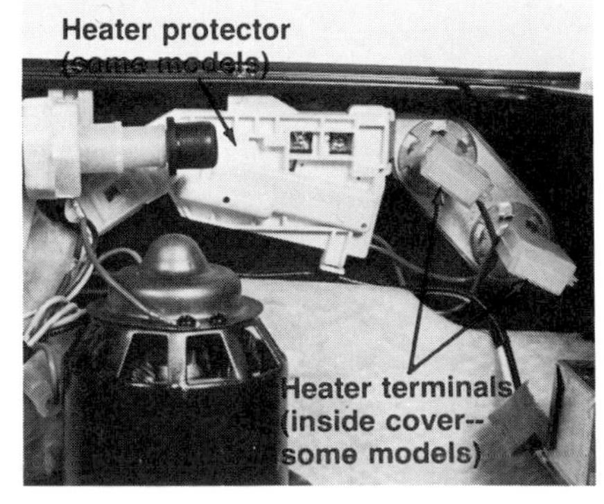

Step 6: Some other dishwashers have a heater protector to break the circuit if the heater overheats. (Dishwasher is tilted back for better view).

Calrod® heating unit (continued)

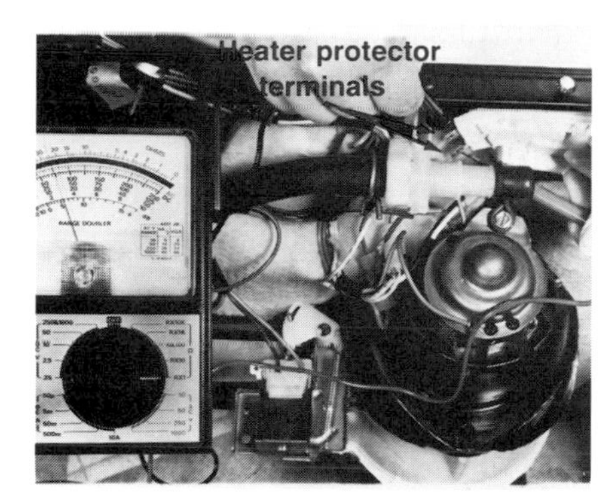

Step 7: If your dishwasher has a heater protector, check both it and heating unit by testing protector terminals with ohmmeter. Ohmmeter should read about 25 ohms when set on R x 1 scale. If it does not, check heating unit terminals.

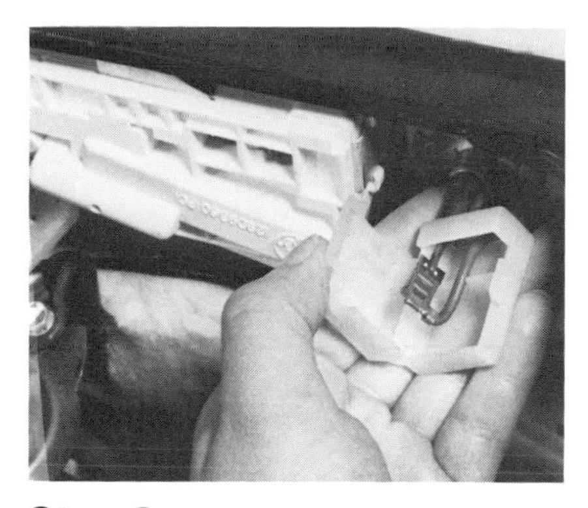

Step 8: Your heating unit terminals may be covered with insulating covers. Be sure power to dishwasher is OFF, then depress tab on side to open.

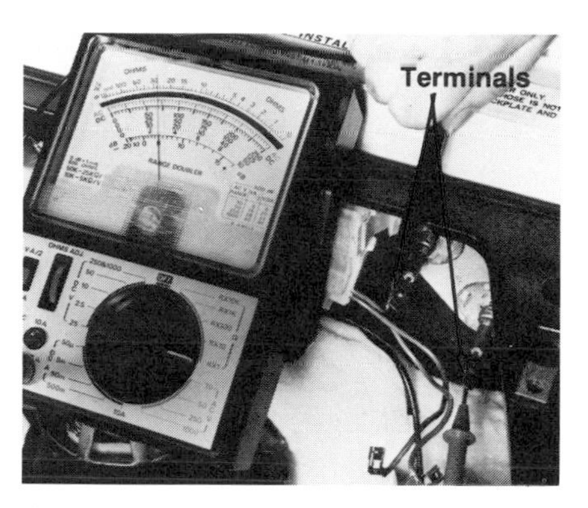

Step 9: Remove leads from terminals. Set ohmmeter to R x 1 and place one test probe on each Calrod® heating unit terminal. Needle should sweep partially upscale to indicate continuity. If no continuity, replace unit.

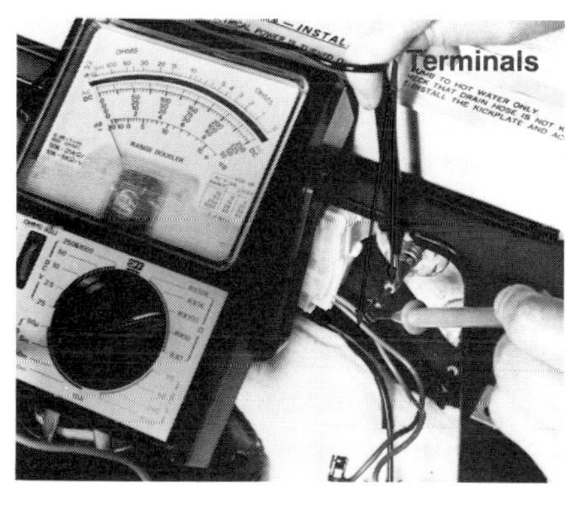

Step 10: Test for ground with ohmmeter at R x 100. Place one test probe on one terminal and other probe on metal sheath of the Calrod® unit. If needle moves upscale, unit is grounded and should be replaced.

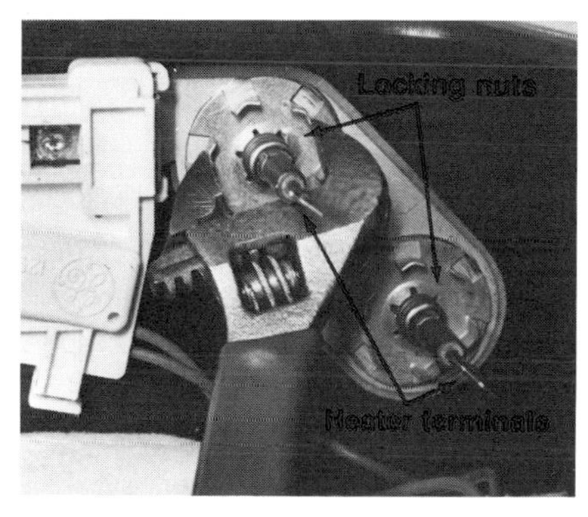

Step 11: To replace Calrod® heating unit, detach wire leads from unit. (For installation reference, make note of how wires are connected.) Remove locking nuts which secure unit to dishwasher tub.

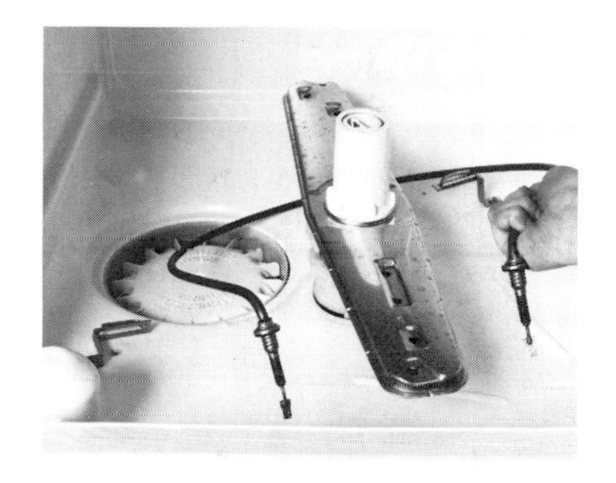

Step 12: Heating unit is secured inside tub with brackets. Remove brackets and lift unit straight up. Insert new unit into brackets. Replace locking nuts and wire leads.

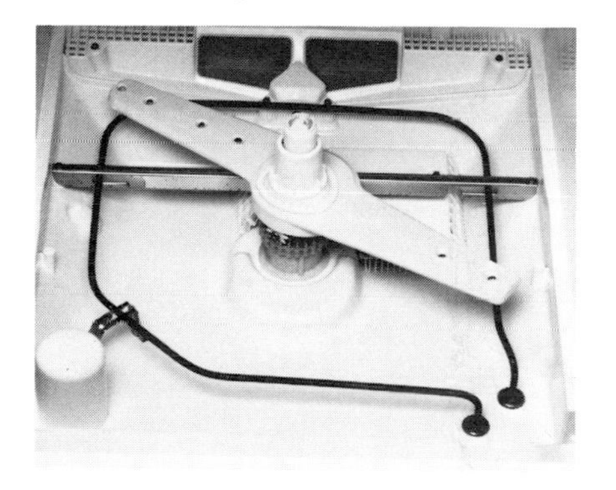

Step 13: Some Calrod® units are square-shaped. They are checked and replaced the same way.

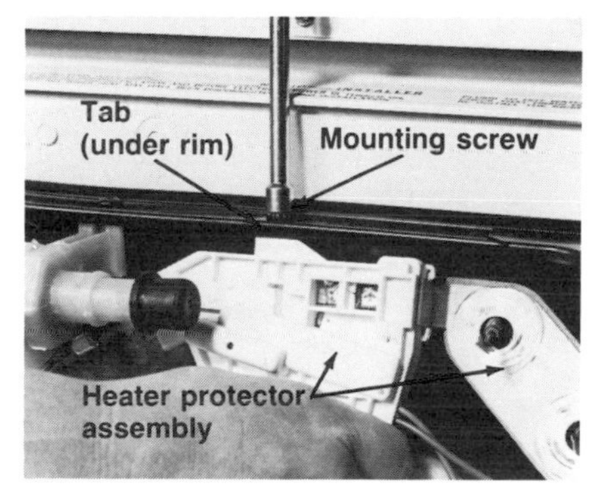

Step 14: If heater checked good, but you did not get a 25 ohm reading in Step 7, replace heater protector. Remove lock nuts as described in Step 11 and mounting screw that holds heater protector to rim.

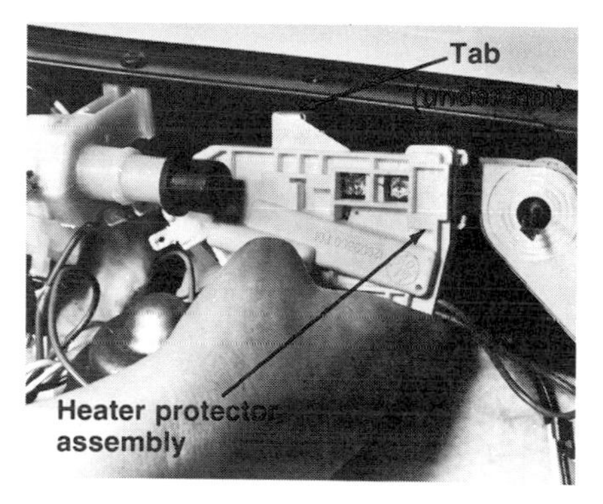

Step 15: Slide new heater protector assembly onto heater terminals with mounting tab underneath rim. Attach mounting screw and lock nuts. Reassemble dishwasher and reconnect power supply.

Procedure 22

Inspecting and replacing thermostats

Skill Level Rating: | Easy | Average | **Difficult** | Very Difficult |

On some dishwasher models with the water heat feature, a control thermostat is used along with the cycle extender switch to control the temperature of the wash and final rinse water. When the water reaches a suitable temperature for good dishwashing results, the contacts of the control thermostat open and re-energize the timer to continue the wash cycle. (Note: On a very few models, the control thermostat is normally open and closes when the desired water temperature is reached). This extra water heating period is desirable for households where lower water heater temperatures are used to save energy.

A second type of thermostat, if used, acts as a temperature limit switch. This thermostat is a safety device which opens a switch if a malfunction allows the temperature inside the dishwasher tub to rise beyond a specific limit. The opening of the switch interrupts power to the Calrod® heating unit and prevents damage to the dishwasher tub.

High temperature wash cycles

Thermostat

Thermostats (continued)

Step 1: Be sure all dishwasher controls are turned **OFF**. Disconnect power supply at distribution panel. For convertible models, also unplug power cord from receptacle. Watch for sharp edges.

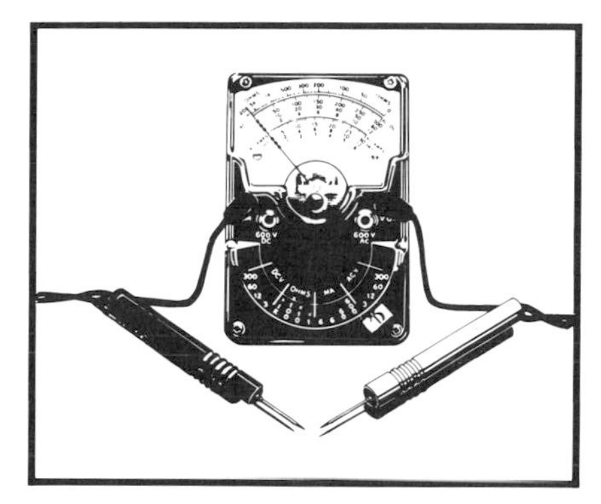

Step 2: This procedure requires the use of an ohmmeter. For instructions on how to use an ohmmeter, please refer to Tools and Testing Equipment, page 95.

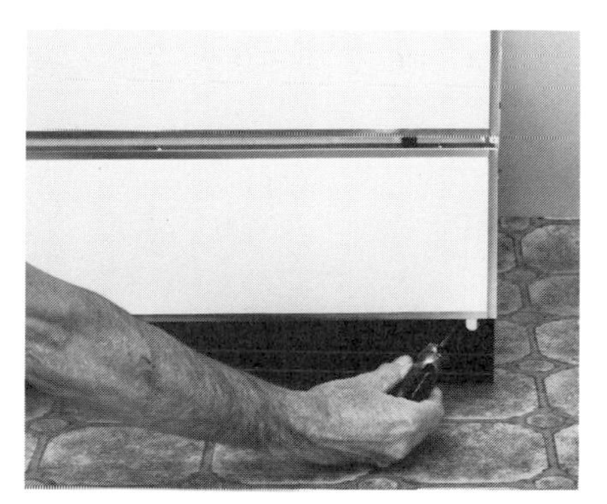

Step 3: This procedure requires removal of service panels from your dishwasher. If you are unfamiliar with this process, please refer to Procedure #3: Removing Service Panels.

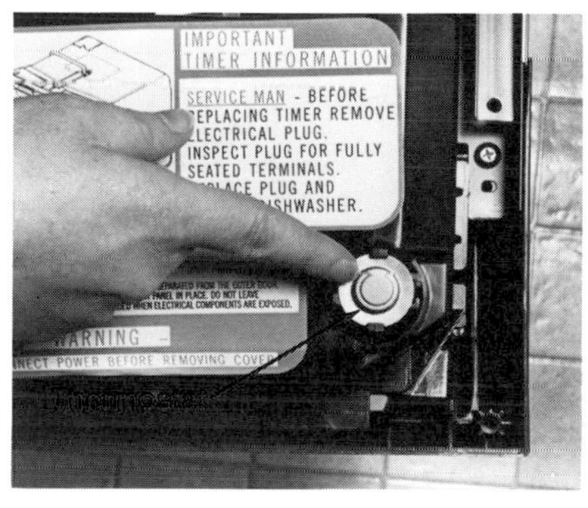

Step 4: GE control thermostat. On some models, the thermostat is located inside the outer door panel on the control housing. Do not attempt to test or repair this thermostat if your dishwasher has electronic touch controls.

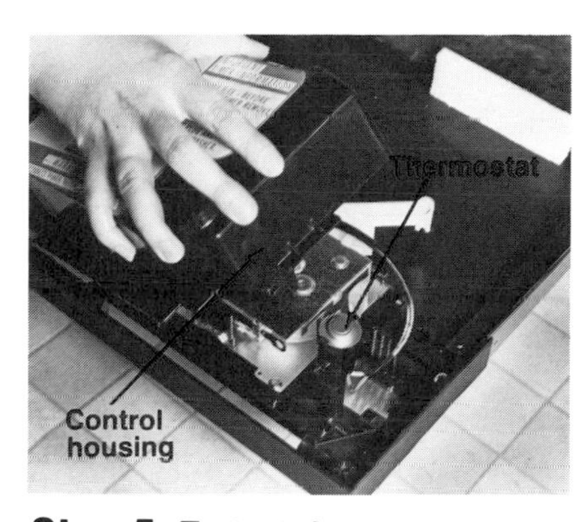

Step 5: To test thermostat on electromechanical control models, lift off control housing by pressing in on side tab.

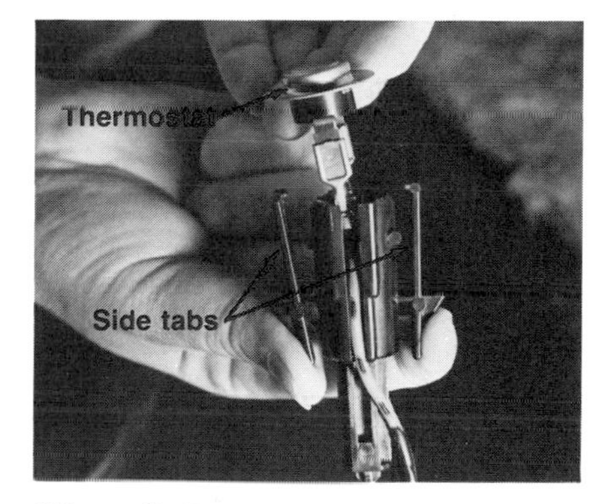

Step 6: To access thermostat terminals, squeeze side tabs together on thermostat housing and gently pull out thermostat from the top.

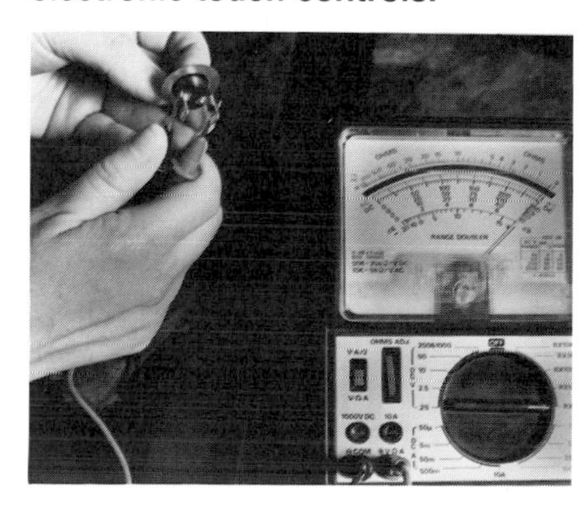

Step 7: To test thermostat, set ohmmeter to R x 1. Remove leads, making note of how wires are connected. Place one test probe on each thermostat terminal. Needle should sweep upscale to indicate continuity. If no continuity, replace thermostat.

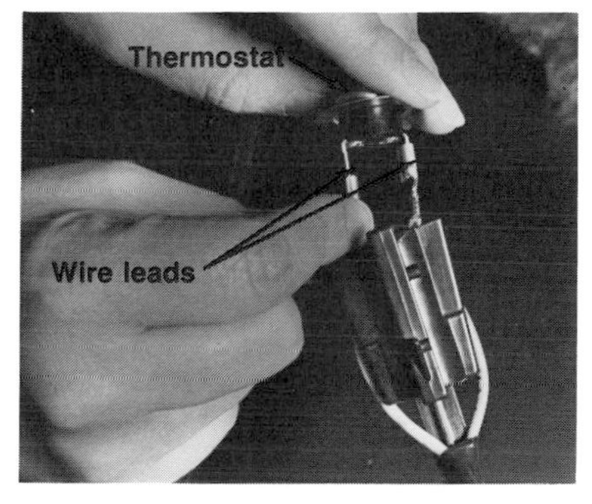

Step 8: When replacing thermostat, make sure wire leads are secured. Reposition thermostat inside housing and on stand inside control housing.

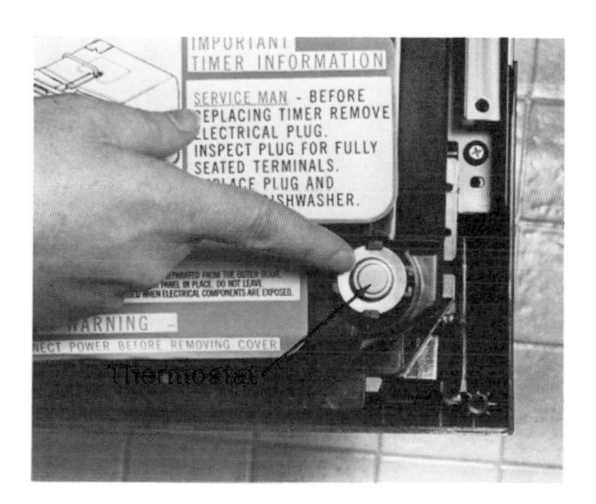

Step 9: When control housing is secured, press on thermostat; it should spring up and down. If it does not, remove housing and readjust thermostat position.

Thermostats (continued)

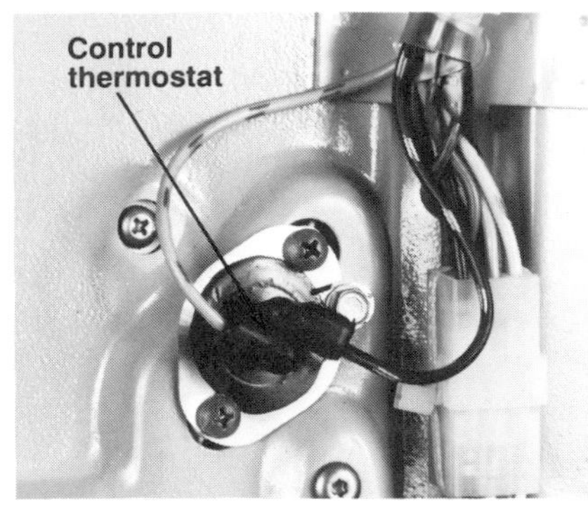

Step 10: On a few models, control thermostat is mounted on inner door panel. Remove the outer door panel and locate the thermostat. Visually inspect for loose connections or broken wires.

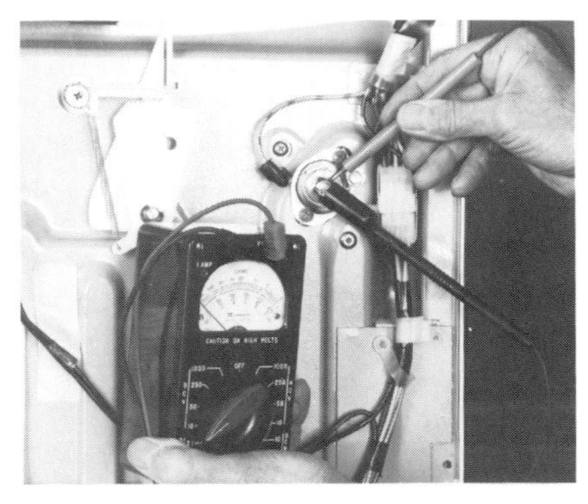

Step 11: To test thermostat, remove leads. Set ohmmeter to R x 1 and place one test probe on each thermostat terminal. Needle should not move. If test shows continuity, replace thermostat.

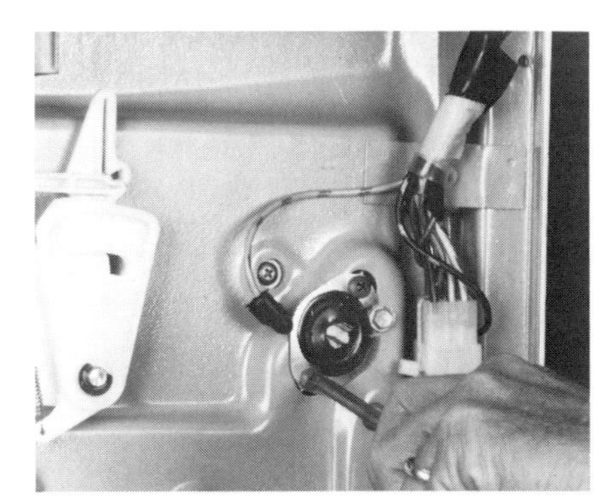

Step 12: To replace thermostat, remove leads. (For installation reference, make note of how wires are connected.) Remove mounting screws and pull thermostat off. Install new thermostat and reconnect leads.

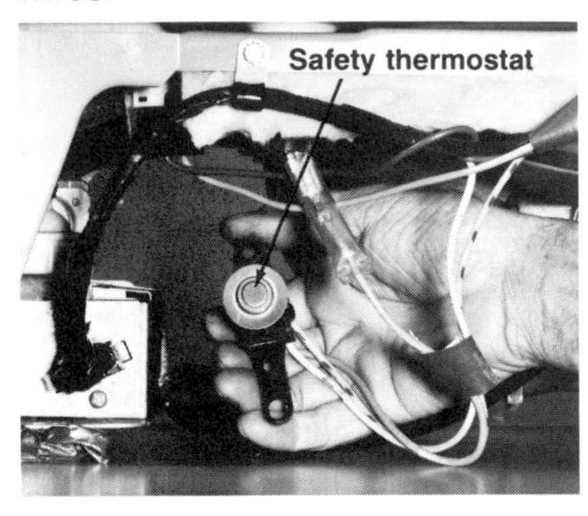

Step 13: GE safety thermostat. Remove the lower access panel and locate thermostat under tub. Remove mounting screws and pull thermostat assembly out.

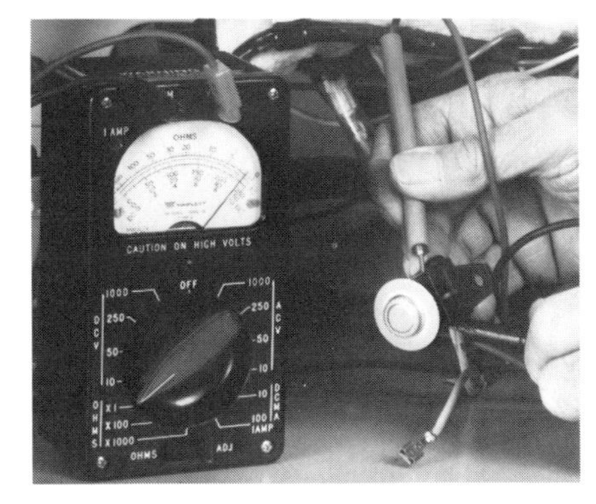

Step 14: To test thermostat, set ohmmeter to R x 1. Lift side tab and pull out lead. Place one test probe on each thermostat terminal. Needle should sweep upscale to indicate continuity. If no continuity, replace thermostat.

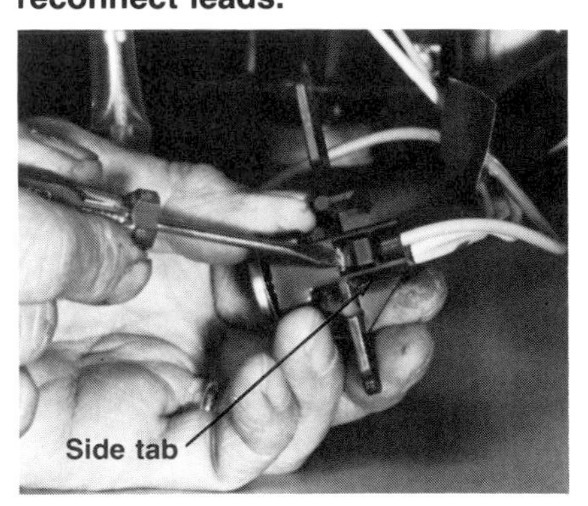

Step 15: To replace thermostat, lift side tabs and pull connectors out to disconnect leads. (For installation reference, make note of how wires are connected.) Snap leads into new thermostat and reinstall under tub bottom.

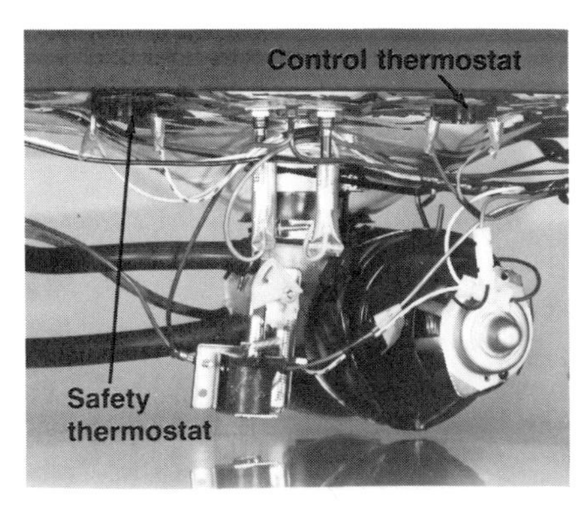

Step 16: Hotpoint thermostats. Remove lower access panel. Control thermostat is on right under tub, and safety thermostat is on left, as you face dishwasher. Safety thermostat is marked in red.

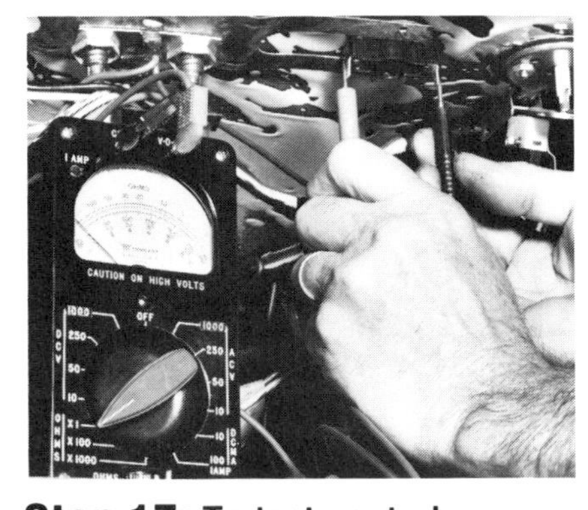

Step 17: To test control thermostat, remove one lead. With ohmmeter at R x 1, place one test probe on each thermostat terminal. Needle should not move. If test shows continuity, replace thermostat.

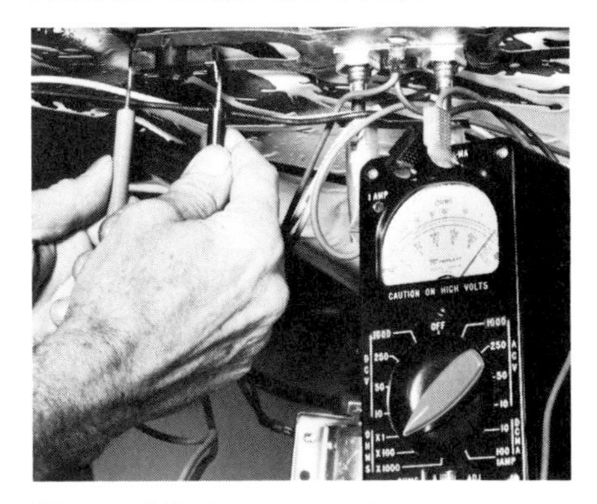

Step 18: To test safety thermostat, remove one lead. With ohmmeter at R x 1, place one test probe on each terminal. Needle should sweep upscale to indicate continuity. If no continuity, replace thermostat.

Thermostats (continued)

Step 19: To replace either thermostat, disconnect leads. For installation reference, make note of how wires are connected. Squeeze spring clips and push up. Pull bracket down and remove thermostat.

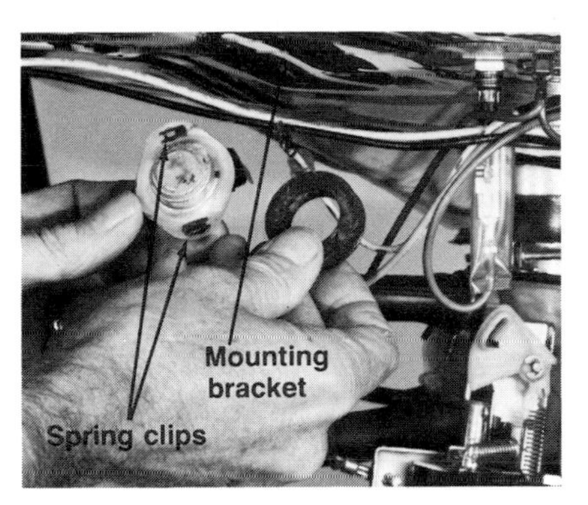

Step 20: Replace rubber ring on new thermostat. Position spring clips and slide assembly under bracket. Reconnect leads. CAUTION: Do not interchange thermostats. Control thermostat must be on right as you face dishwasher.

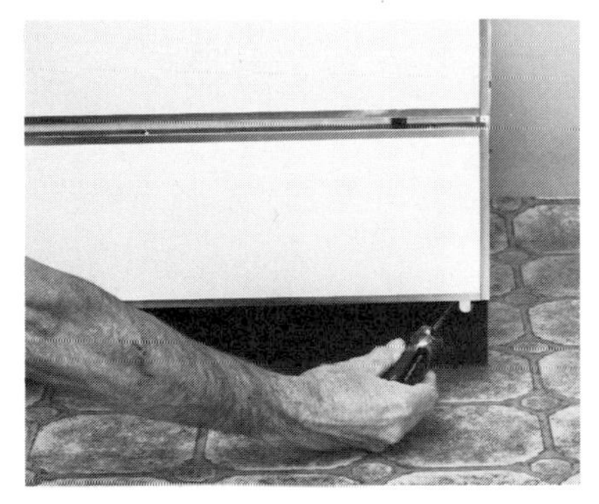

Step 21: Reassemble dishwasher and reconnect power supply.

Procedure 23

Inspecting and replacing racks

Skill Level Rating:	Easy	**Average**	Difficult	Very Difficult

The racks in your dishwasher are constructed of heavy gauge steel, coated with a protective layer of vinyl. Each rack moves in and out on rollers to make loading convenient. The lower rack rollers ride on ledges formed into the sides of the dishwasher tub. The rollers of the upper rack ride in metal slides which provide support when the rack is fully extended and loaded. Each slide runs in and out between two sets of large rollers. On some dishwasher models, the upper rack can be adjusted up and down to allow loading of different sized items.

Note: This procedure covers repairs for two types of adjustable racks as well as standard upper and lower racks. Most dishwashers use standard racks, covered in Steps 1 through 9. Subsequent steps cover adjustable racks, found only in some dishwasher models.

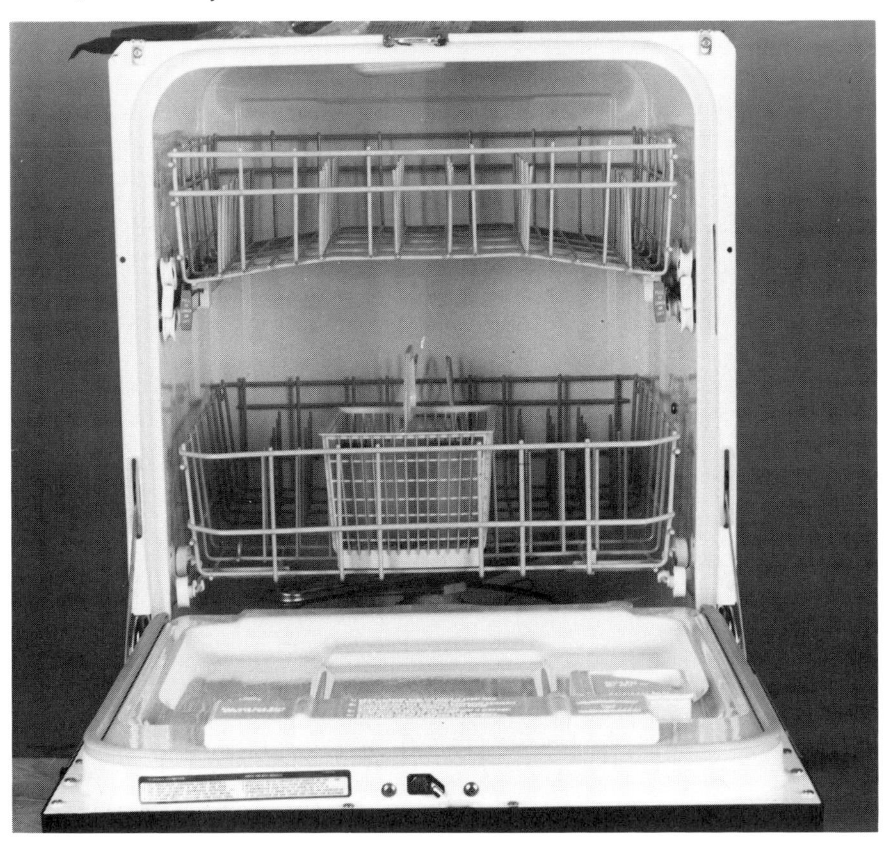

Vinyl coated racks

Racks (continued)

Step 1: Be sure all dishwasher controls are turned **OFF**. For your personal safety, exercise caution when working with any electrical appliance. Watch for sharp edges.

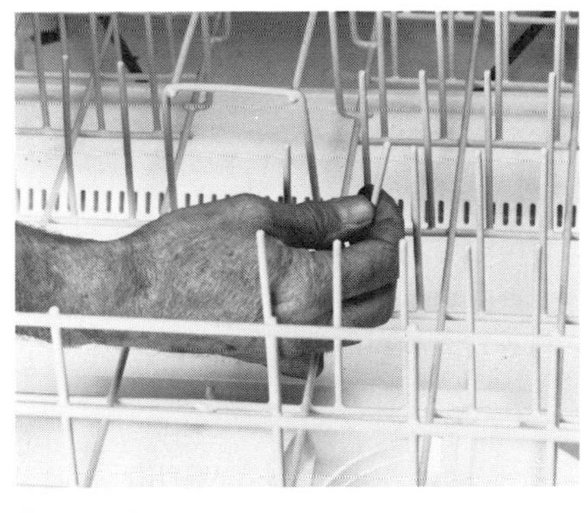

Step 2: Repair small nicks or cuts in vinyl rack coating with GE specified epoxy repair kit. Follow kit instructions carefully. If rack fingers are bent, straighten them gently.

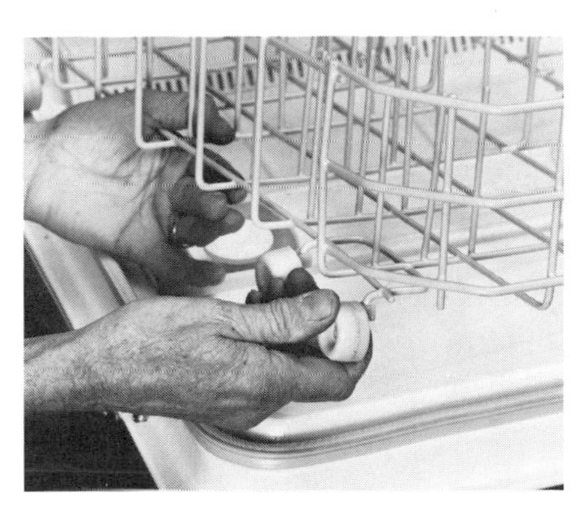

Step 3: Check rollers on top and bottom racks. Rollers should be straight and able to turn freely. Replace any missing or damaged rollers. Straighten lower rack roller axles if bent.

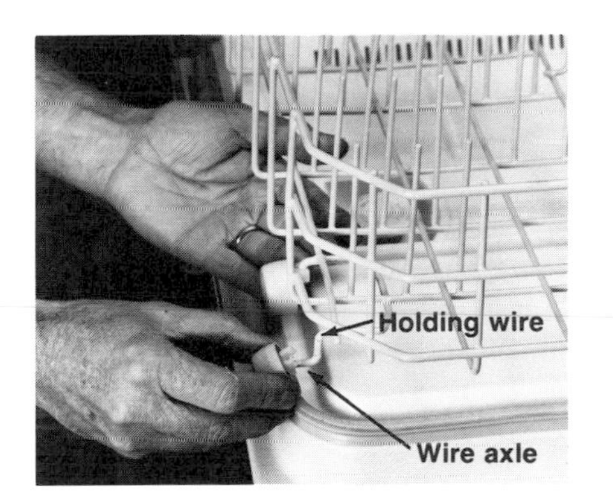

Step 4: Lower rack. To replace lower rack rollers on most models, snap off old roller. Soak new roller in hot water to soften and prevent breakage. Slip new roller over wire axle and snap onto holding wire.

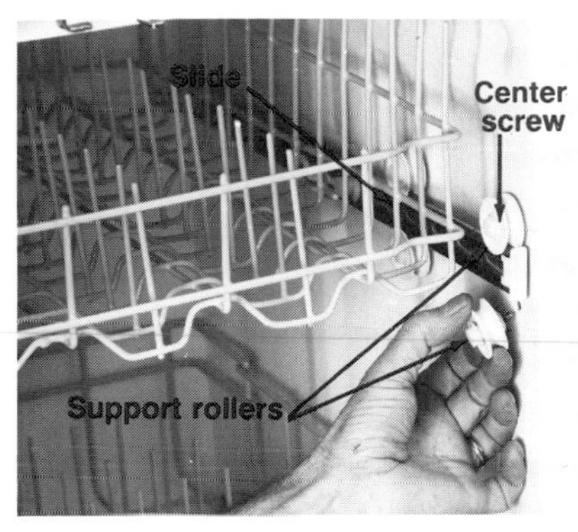

Step 5: Upper rack. To detach support rollers, remove center screws. Do not remove both top and bottom support rollers at the same time, to prevent nut strip outside tub from dropping off.

Step 6: To remove upper rack, remove bottom support rollers only, at front and rear on each side. Pull rack and metal slide assembly down and forward. Snap rollers off rack.

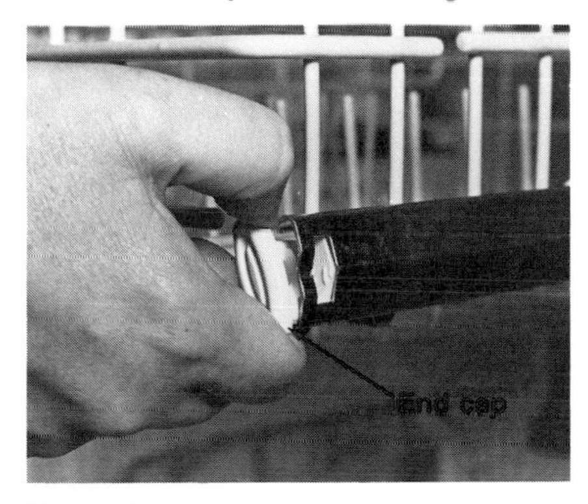

Step 7: On some models, the end cap can be easily removed by prying back on the tab then pivoting the end cap inward. If the tab is held tightly inside the flange, use a blade screwdriver to release it.

Step 8: On other models you will have to remove end cap from slide by releasing locking tab as shown. Remove rollers from slide. Replace missing or damaged rollers, reinstall end cap and bend tab to hold.

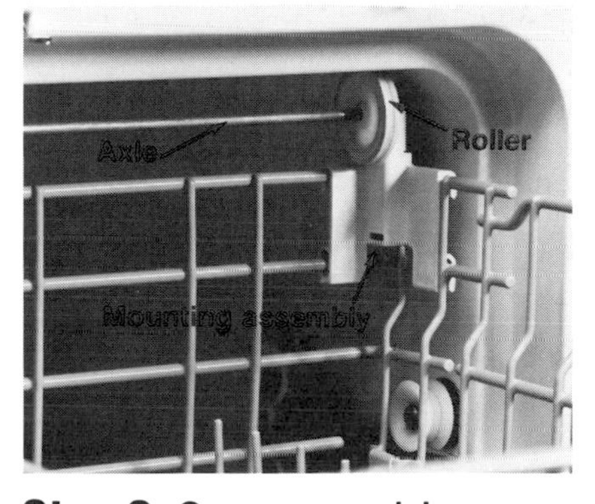

Step 9: On some models, a rear roller assembly helps stabilize upper rack. Detach bottom support rollers and remove rack from dishwasher. To replace, lift out axle with roller. Snap mounting assembly off rack.

Racks (continued)

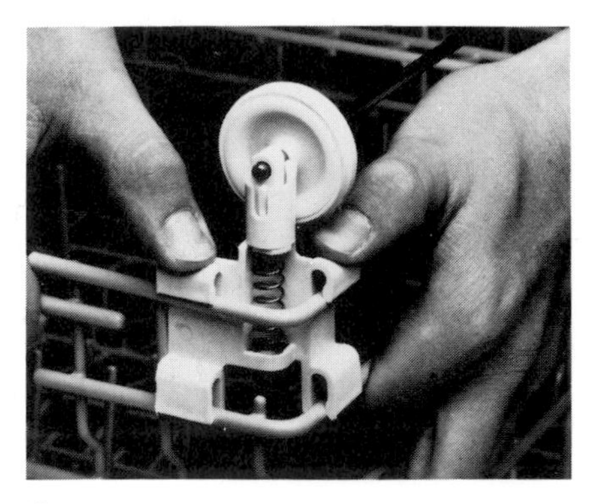

Step 10: Mounting assembly on rear roller assembly snaps onto top rack at back corners. Snap mounting assembly off rack.

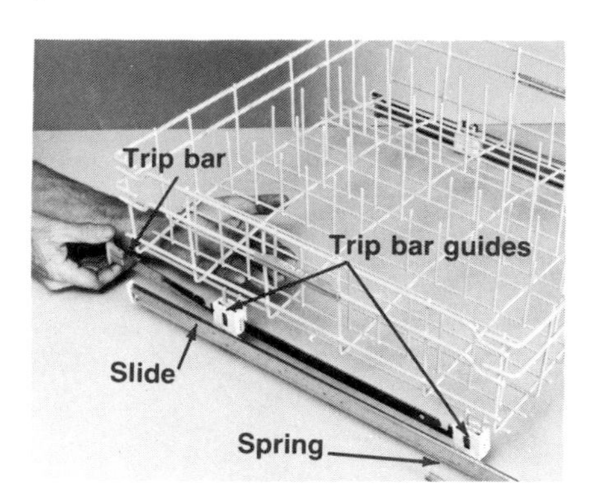

Step 11: Select-A-Level upper rack. Detach bottom support rollers and remove rack from dishwasher. Remove spring from back of trip bar. Pull trip bar forward and free roller/slide assembly.

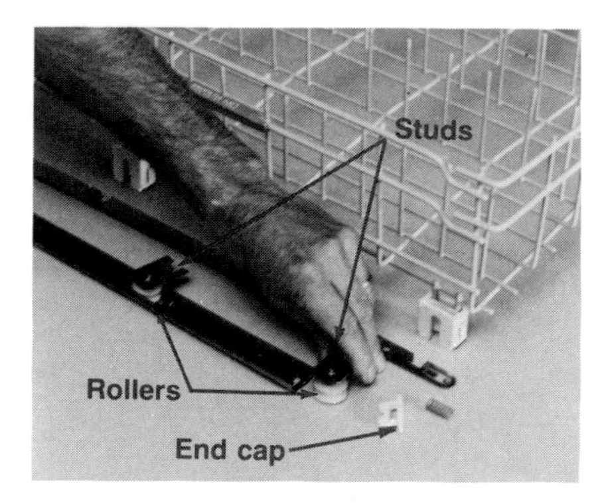

Step 12: To replace a roller, bend locking tab and remove end cap from slide. Insert new roller/stud assembly. (Roller and stud form single replacement unit.) Replace end cap.

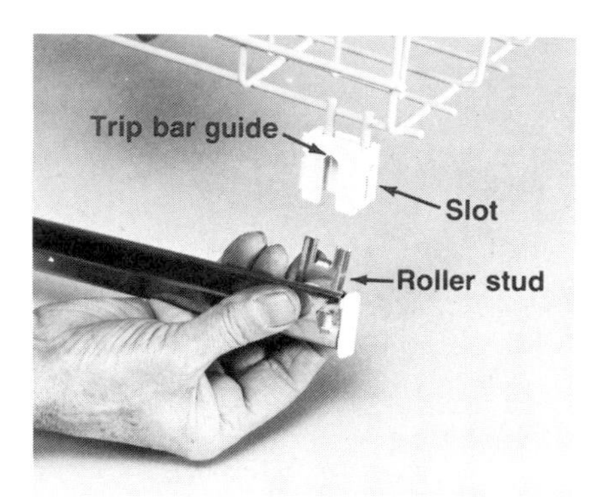

Step 13: To replace damaged trip bar guide, pull off rack. Snap new trip bar guide into place. Insert roller studs into guides. Slide trip bar through slots in guides. Replace spring over rear tabs of trip bar.

Notes

Procedure 24

Inspecting and replacing gaskets

Skill Level Rating:	Easy	**Average**	Difficult	Very Difficult

Several types of gaskets are used on dishwashers to prevent leakage. One long gasket runs around the sides and top of the dishwasher door, creating a water-tight seal between the door and tub body when the door is securely latched. Some dishwasher models also use corner gaskets in the tub for extra protection against leaks at these vulnerable points.

The tub flange gasket on some models seals the area between the lower edge of the dishwasher door and the lip of the tub opening. This gasket acts as a baffle, retaining water inside the tub while allowing air to enter during the drying portion of the cycle.

Note: Exercise caution when using spray paint or appliance polish near gaskets. Vinyl gaskets may react chemically with some paints and household chemicals, resulting in damage to gasket. Contact with paint may also cause paint to remain soft and sticky.

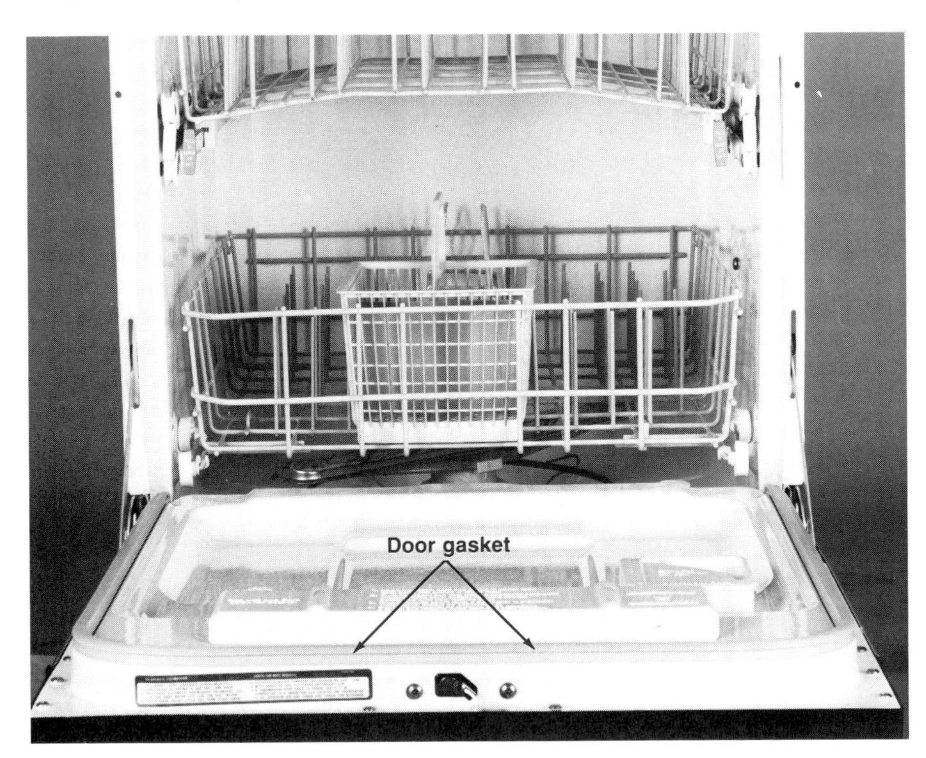

Dishwasher door gasket

Gaskets (continued)

Step 1: Be sure all dishwasher controls are turned **OFF.** Disconnect power supply at distribution panel. For convertible models, also unplug power cord from receptacle.

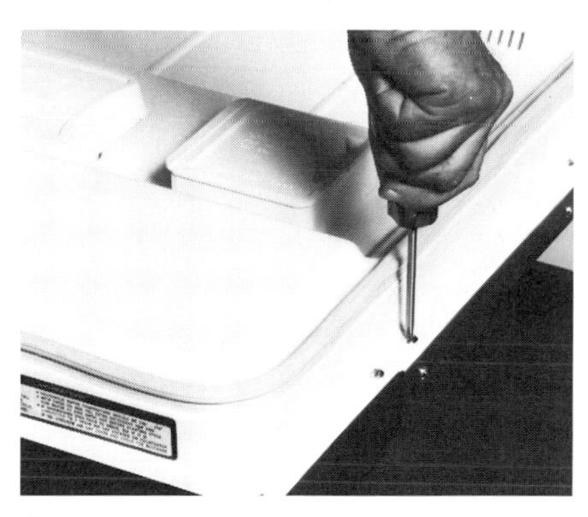

Step 2: This procedure may require removal of service panels from your dishwasher. If you are unfamiliar with this process, please refer to Procedure #3: Removing Service Panels.

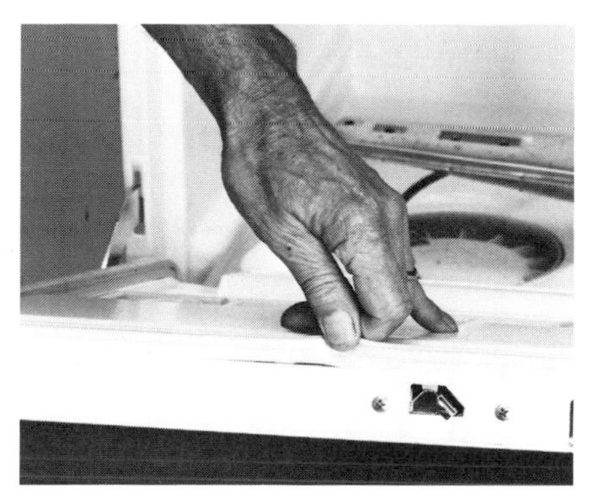

Step 3: Open dishwasher door and visually inspect all gaskets. Remove lower access panel to inspect tub flange gasket. Replace any gasket that is split, distorted, or damaged.

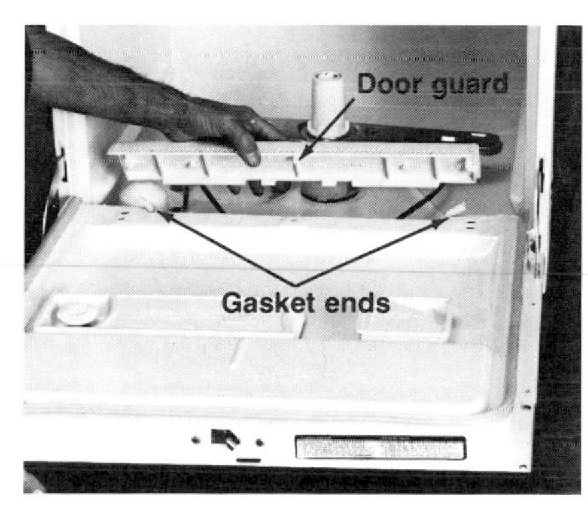

Step 4: Release ends of door gasket, noting how they are secured. Separate door panels or remove door guard at bottom inside door. Pull off old gasket. Replace with identical type.

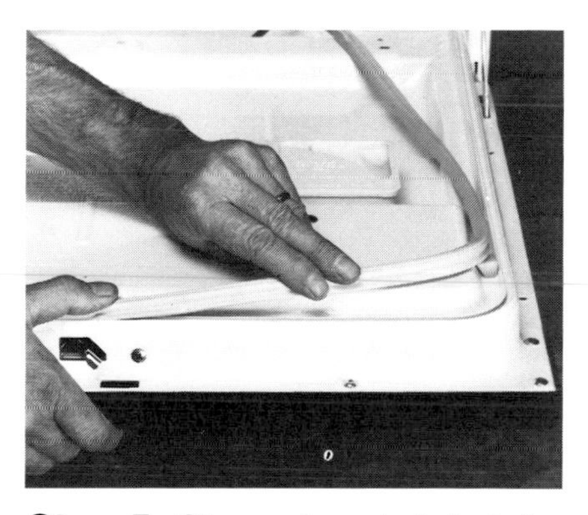

Step 5: Channel gasket. Lubricate gasket with soapy water or silicone for easy insertion. Do not use oil or grease. Insert center of gasket into channel at center top of door. Press into channel working around door.

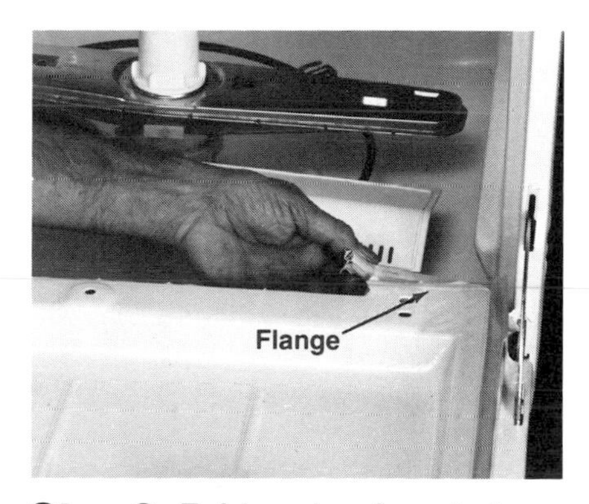

Step 6: Fold ends of gasket around flange at base of door. Secure model under door guard. On some models, pass ends under door and pull through holes in corner door brackets. Clean off lubricant.

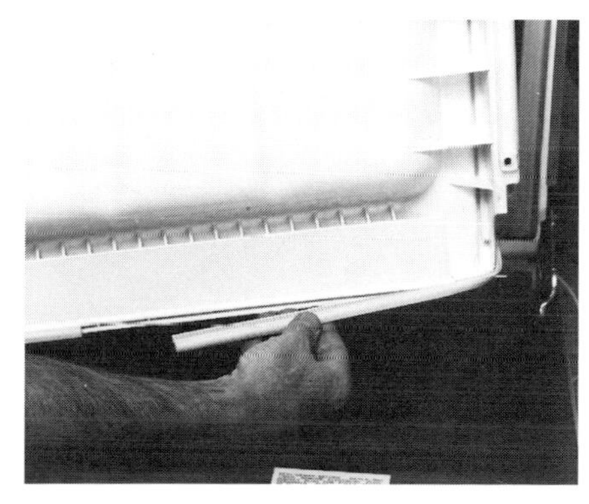

Step 7: On some models with removable PermaTuf® inner door panel, door gasket continues almost completely across bottom of door. Press gasket into channel around corner and along base of door.

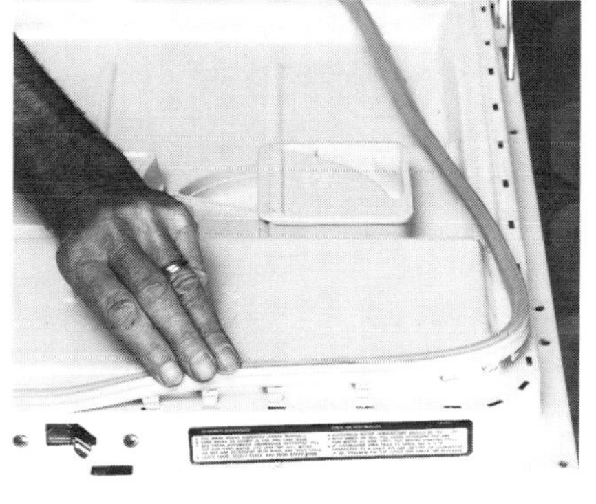

Step 8: Molded tab gasket. Remove control panel escutcheon. Soak gasket in hot water to make it pliable and prevent breaking tabs. Begin at top center, matching wider-spaced tabs with wider-spaced holes in door.

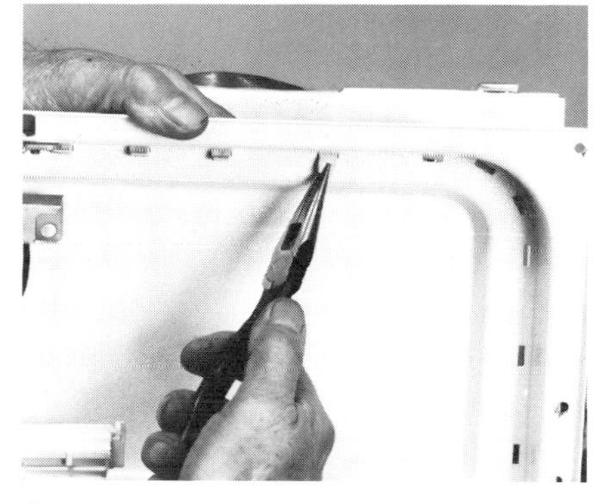

Step 9: Before inserting tabs into holes in door, lubricate the tabs with soapy water or silicone. Start from top center and work around door. Pull tabs through with needle-nose pilers. Push from side to side to lock. Handle gently to avoid damage. You may want to keep gasket warm with blow dryer.

Gaskets (continued)

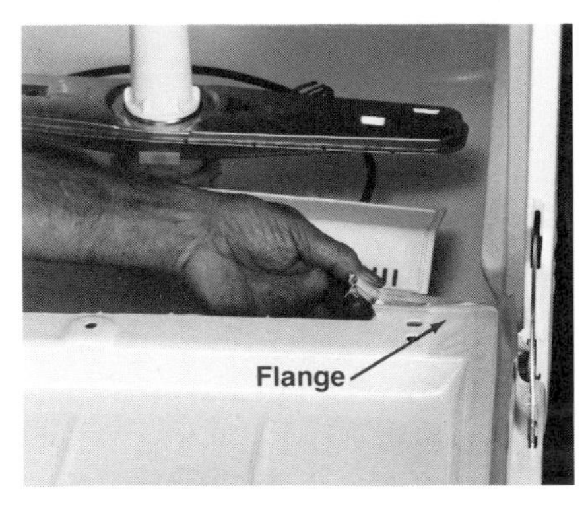

Step 10: To fasten ends, fold around flange at base of inner door panel. Replace door guard to secure ends.

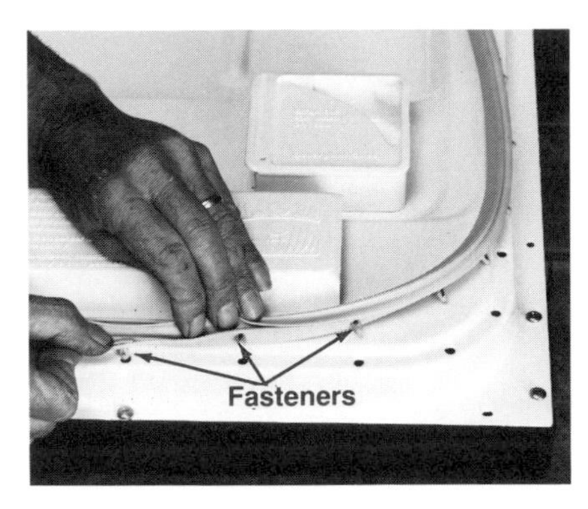

Step 11: Gaskets with separate fasteners. Insert fastener through center hole of gasket into center top hole of dishwasher door. Continue along top of door and down sides.

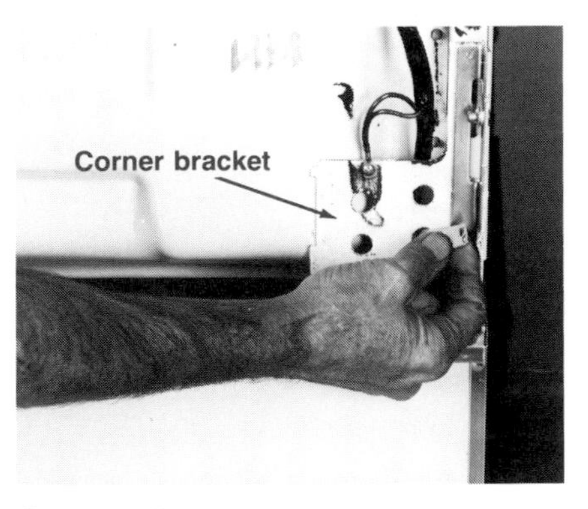

Step 12: To fasten ends, pass them under bottom of door and pull tight. Secure gasket ends through holes in corner door brackets.

Step 13: Corner gasket. Pull out old gasket. Replace, using hardware, if required, or waterproof rubber cement. Allow cement to dry before using dishwasher.

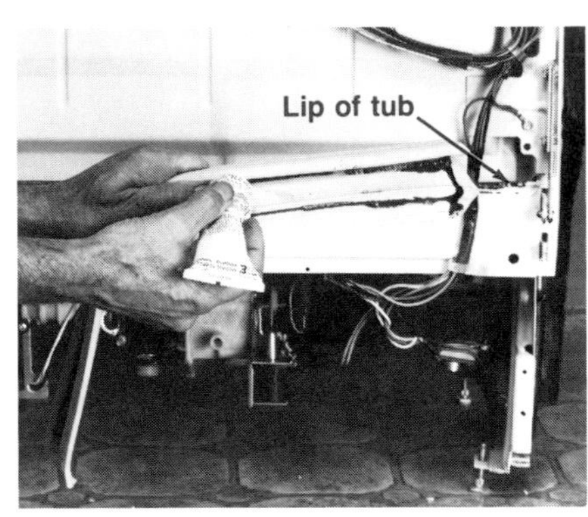

Step 14: Tub flange gasket. Remove outer door panel and lower access panel. Pull old gasket off lip of tub. Run bead of waterproof rubber cement down center fold of new gasket.

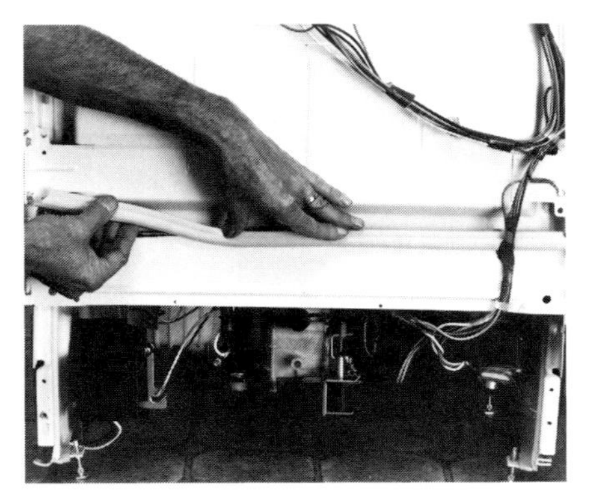

Step 15: Place new flange gasket over lip of tub at base and press tightly into place. Allow time for cement to dry before using dishwasher.

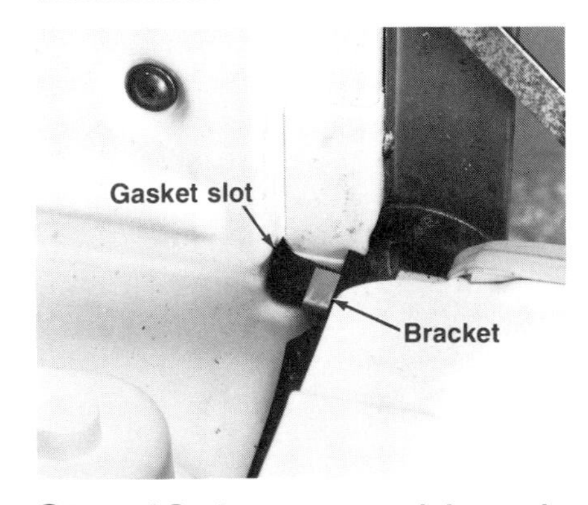

Step 16: On some models, ends of flange gasket are secured by a bracket at front corner of tub. Swivel bracket up. Insert bracket end into slot of gasket. Push bracket back down and smooth gasket into corner.

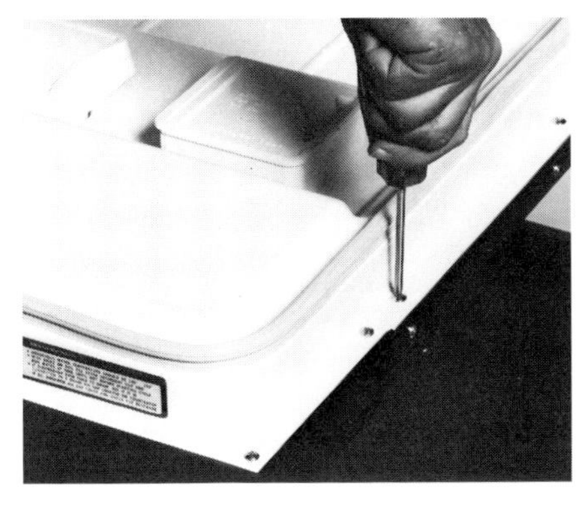

Step 17: Reassemble dishwasher and reconnect power supply.

Notes

Procedure 25

Cosmetic repairs

Skill Level Rating:	**Easy**	Average	Difficult	Very Difficult

At some point, you may encounter the need for cosmetic repairs to your dishwasher. Such repairs include replacing damaged panels or touching up a scratch. Most dishwasher exterior surfaces are covered with durable baked-on enamel. Minor scratches can be touched up with matching paint available in aerosol cans and/or touch-up kits. More serious damage may necessitate replacement or refinishing of an entire panel. Dishwasher parts for recent models can be ordered through your authorized local appliance parts dealer.

Repairing a minor nick or cut in the Tuff Tub® interior of your dishwasher may prevent more extensive damage from developing. Minor blemishes on racks or in the Tuff Tub® interior can be repaired with General Electric's specified epoxy repair kit. Be sure to use the correct model number when purchasing paint or epoxy repair kit. To repair a damaged PermaTuf® interior, call a qualified service technician.

CAUTION: Paint is flammable. Always paint in well-ventilated area away from open flame. Read all instructions on paint container carefully. Do not allow paint to contact gaskets or plastic surfaces. Vinyl gaskets react chemically with most paints, and paint will become soft and sticky.

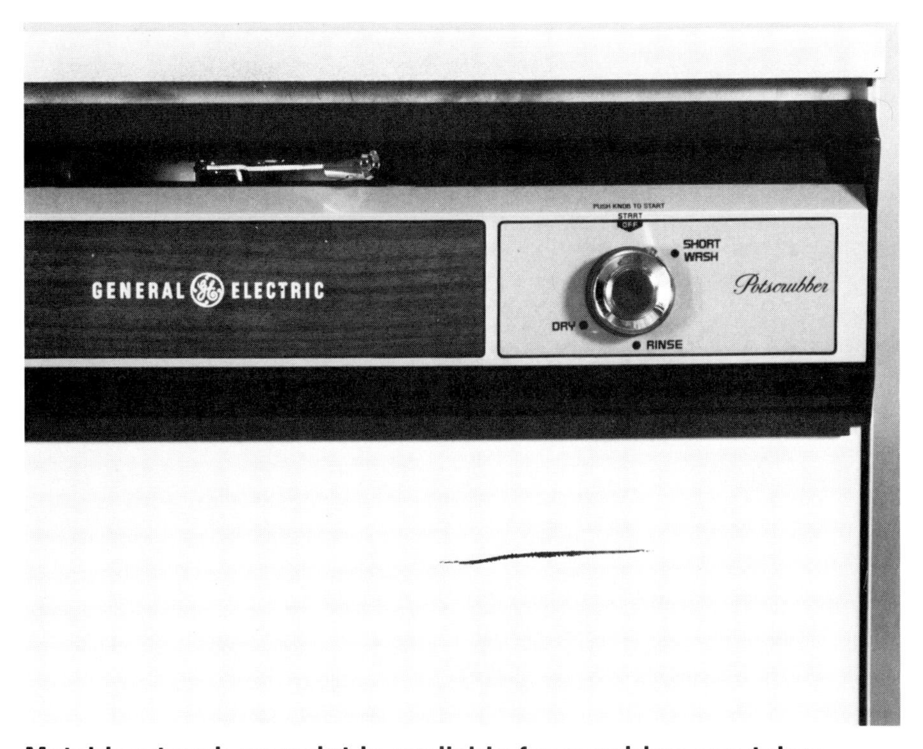

Matching touch-up paint is available for repairing scratches

Cosmetic repairs (continued)

Step 1: Be sure all dishwasher controls are turned **OFF.** Disconnect power supply at distribution panel. For convertible models, also unplug power cord from receptacle. Watch for sharp edges.

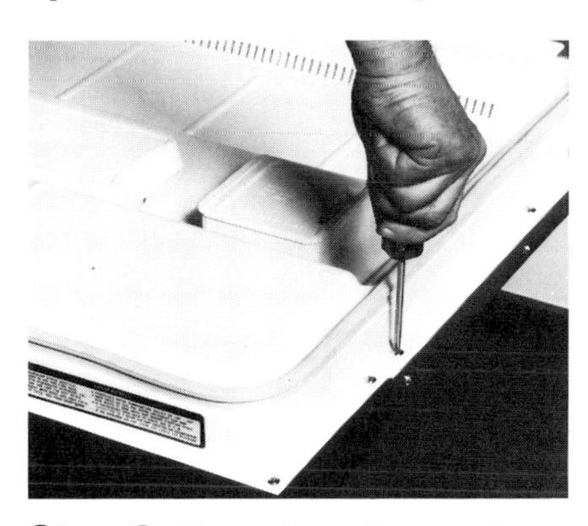

Step 2: To replace damaged panel, refer to Procedure #3: Removing Service Panels. Detach damaged panel and install new one. To avoid stripping screws or damaging finish, do not overtighten screws.

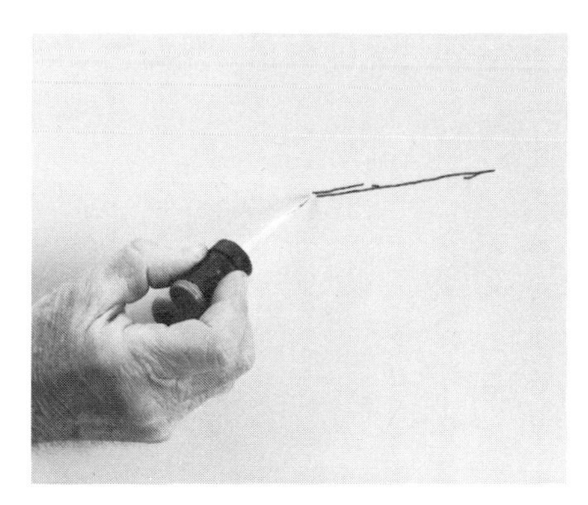

Step 3: To repair small scratches, use touch-up kit, or spray a small amount of paint into top of a can and dip torn end of paper match in paint. Fill scratch, using paint sparingly.

Step 4: Sand large scratches smooth with extra-fine sandpaper. Sand scratch until edge is "feathered" smoothly into exposed metal. Area to be painted must be clean, dry, and free of grease or rust.

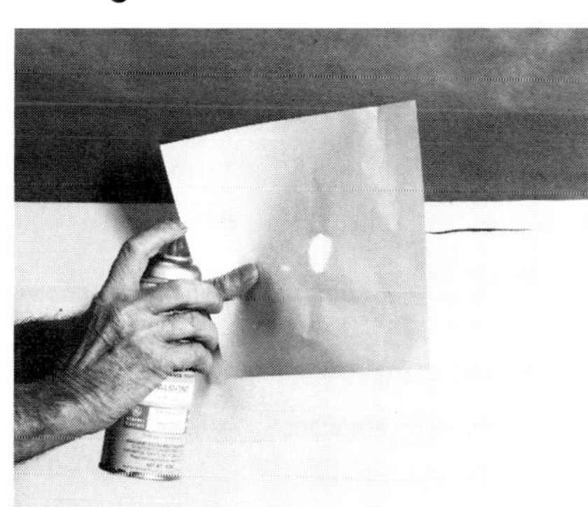

Step 5: Before spray painting, mask trim with paper. Follow instructions on paint can. Spray through an irregular hole torn in a sheet of paper to blend paint smoothly and avoid hard edges.

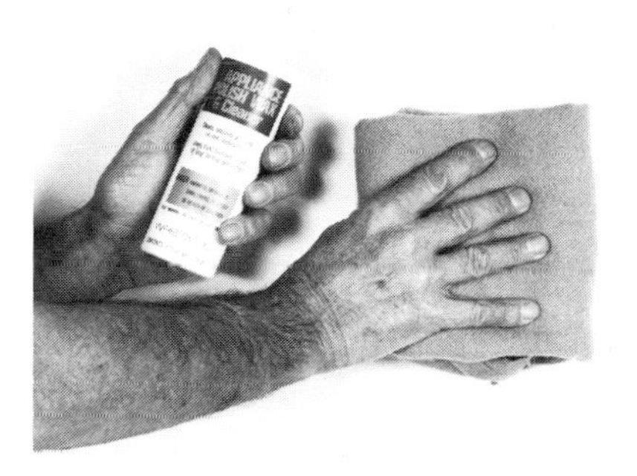

Step 6: Let paint dry thoroughly. To blend repair into panel, wax with appliance polish. Do not allow wax to come into contact with gaskets or plastic surfaces.

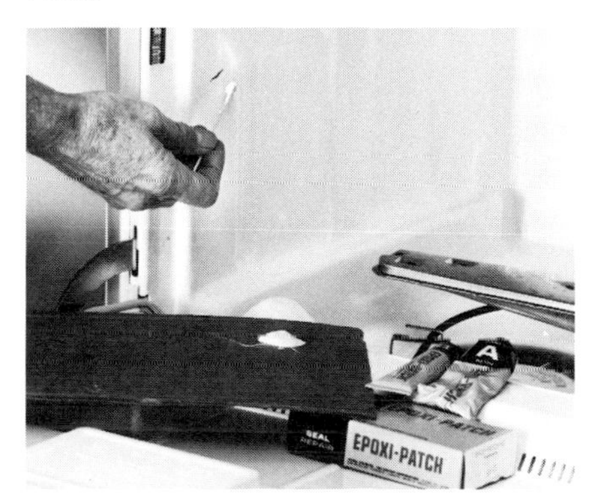

Step 7: Touch up small nicks on rack, or cuts on rack or Tuff Tub® interior with a GE-specified epoxy repair kit. Follow package instructions carefully. Let dry 24 hours before using dishwasher.

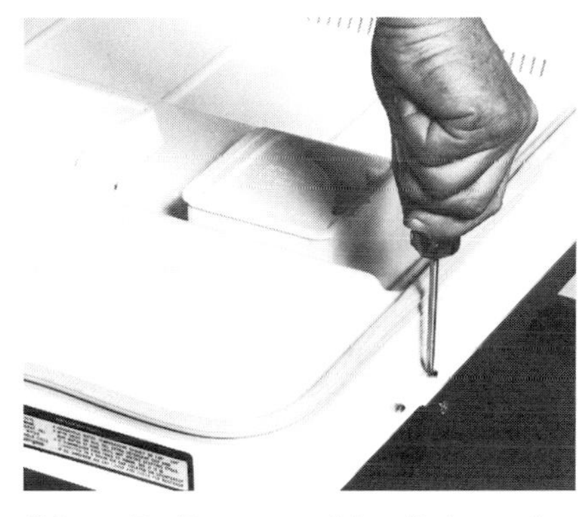

Step 8: Reassemble dishwasher and reconnect power supply.

Procedure 26

Inspecting and replacing anti-tip mechanism and door springs

Skill Level Rating:	Easy	**Average**	Difficult	Very Difficult

All convertible dishwashers have built-in anti-tip mechanisms to prevent the machine from falling forward when the door is opened and the racks are pulled out.

In most General Electric convertible dishwashers, two stabilizer channels move out and down when the door is opened. A cable connected to the door hinge pulls the stabilizers out as the hinge moves. A strong spring retracts the stabilizers as the door closes and the pull on the cable relaxes.

Hotpoint convertible dishwashers and some GE models use arm extensions welded to the door stops. When the door is opened, the door stop comes forward, lowering the arm extensions. As the door closes, the door stops retract on their heavy springs, pulling the arm extensions up and backward.

All dishwashers have two door springs to let the door open and close properly. These springs can stretch or break, especially if the door receives a great deal of wear or has excess weight placed on the door. If the spring breaks, the door would fall open heavily. There are two types of spring systems used on GE dishwashers. On most models, there is a spring on either side of the door that is attached to the side of the dishwasher. On some models with PermaTuf® interiors, the door counterbalance is located under the toe kick and is a double spring/pulley design.

Note: Springs should always be replaced in pairs, even if only one is broken. This practice assures adequate tension on either side of the door. Also, if one spring breaks, it is usually not long before the other one needs repair.

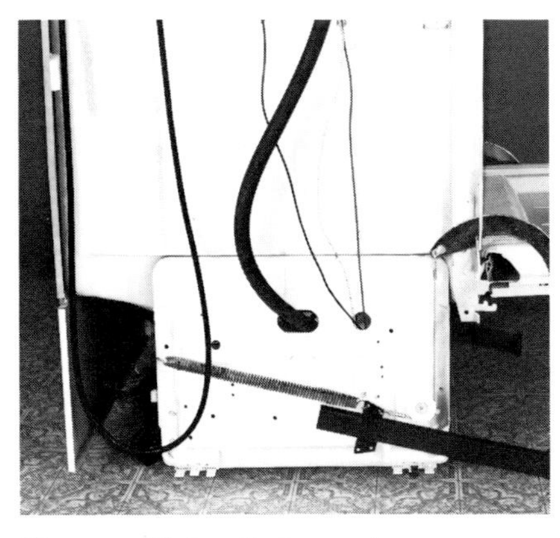

Convertible dishwasher stabilizer channel mechanism

Convertible dishwasher arm extension mechanism

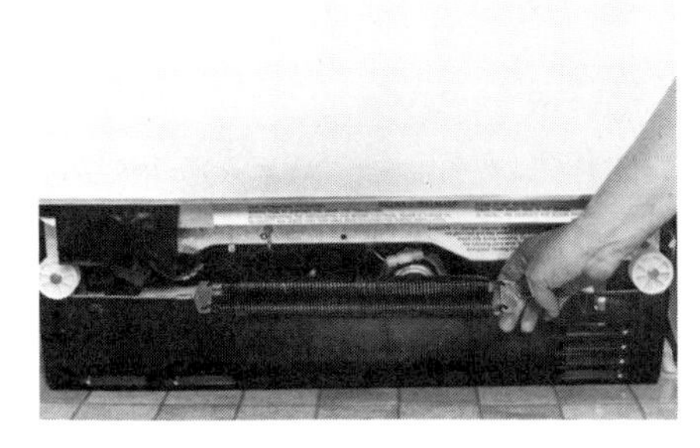

Bottom center counterbalance

Side door spring

Anti-tip mechanism and door springs (continued)

Step 1: Be sure all dishwasher controls are turned **OFF**. Disconnect power supply at distribution panel. Unplug power cord from receptacle. Watch for sharp edges.

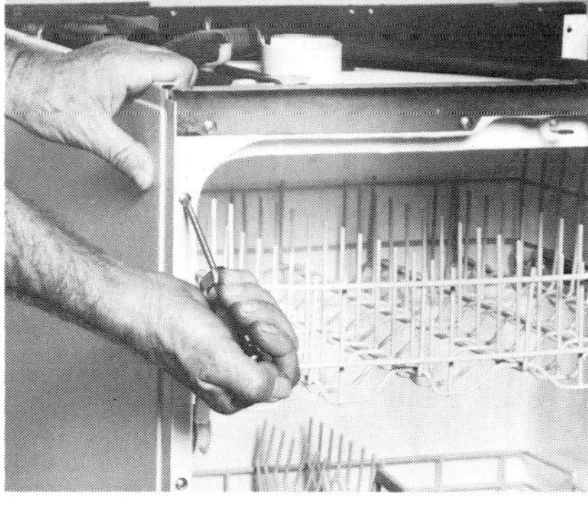

Step 2: This procedure requires removing the side panels from your dishwasher. If you are unfamiliar with this process, please refer to Procedure #3: Removing Service Panels.

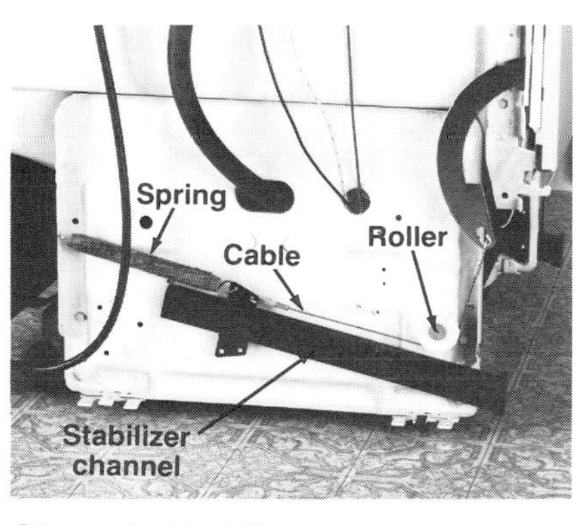

Step 3: Stabilizer channel mechanism. Remove side panel and visually check for broken, loose or damaged parts. Replace spring if broken or disconnected.

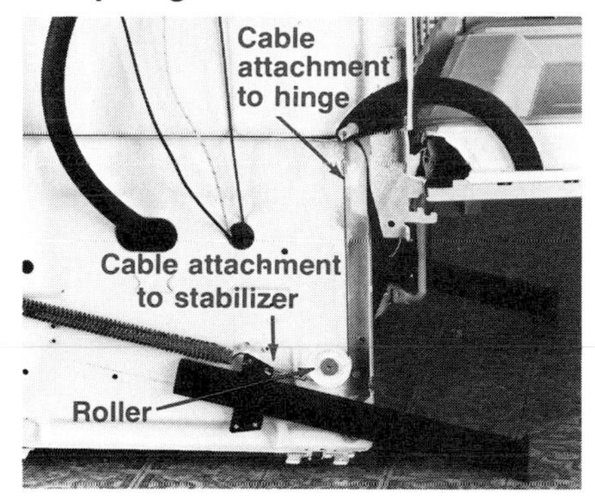

Step 4: Check cable for proper placement over the roller, as shown. Replace if it has slipped off. Replace roller if cable is noisy or binding. Be sure cable is securely attached to both door hinge and stabilizer channel.

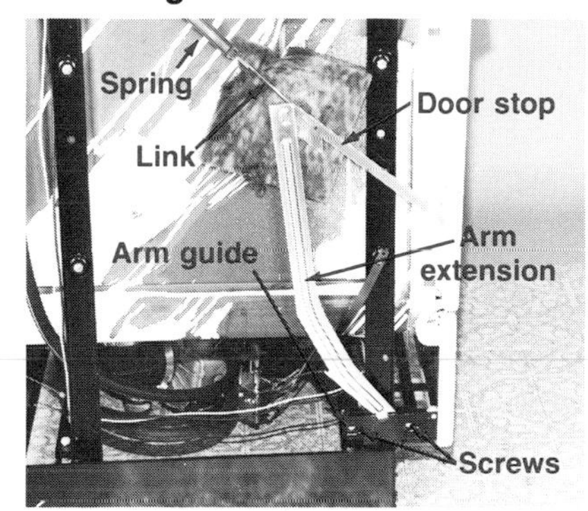

Step 5: Arm extension mechanism. Remove side panel and visually inspect for broken, loose or damaged parts. If arm is binding or noisy, check that neither arm, stop, nor link is bent.

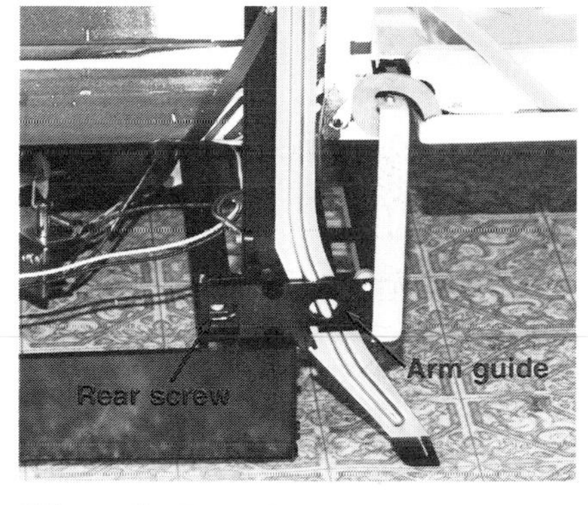

Step 6: To adjust stabilizer arm extension up or down slightly, loosen screws on arm guide. Open dishwasher door and adjust guide to contact arm. Tighten rear screw. Close door and tighten front screw.

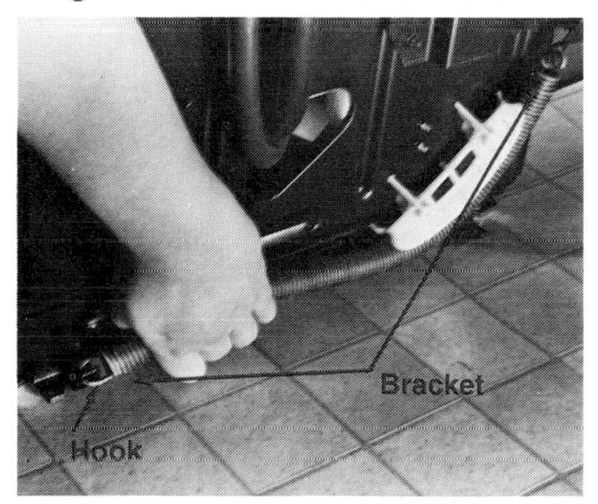

Step 7: If door does not open properly, check spring. Some models (shown above) have a spring on either side of the dishwasher. To remove, simply unhook from front and back support. Hook new spring into position.

Step 8: Other models have a counterbalance system under the toekick panel that has two springs in the center connected to a wire double eyelet. To replace, remove only one spring at a time, holding onto eyelet. Attach new spring to eyelets and guide wires around side pulleys.

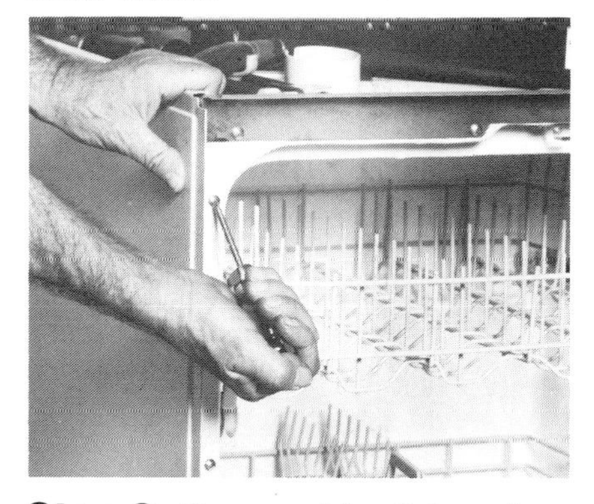

Step 9: Reassemble dishwasher and reconnect power supply.

Procedure 27

Inspecting and replacing unicouple

Skill Level Rating:	Easy	Average	**Difficult**	Very Difficult

The hose assembly for a convertible dishwasher is made up of a water inlet hose, drain hose and unicouple connector. The unicouple connects to the kitchen faucet with a special adapter and delivers hot water from the faucet to the dishwasher. On many models, the unicouple handle contains a pressure relief assembly that prevents water from spraying out when the unicouple is disconnected from the faucet. This assembly also acts as a bypass, allowing you to draw water from the faucet--even while the dishwasher is operating.

The drain hose from the dishwasher passes through the unicouple, allowing water to drain into the kitchen sink when the dishwasher is pumping out. It is designed to resist clogging from food particles, and to prevent excessive splashing in the sink.

The entire unicouple and hose assembly stores out of sight in a compartment under the top of the dishwasher. Unicouples vary somewhat, but the repair procedures are similar for all models.

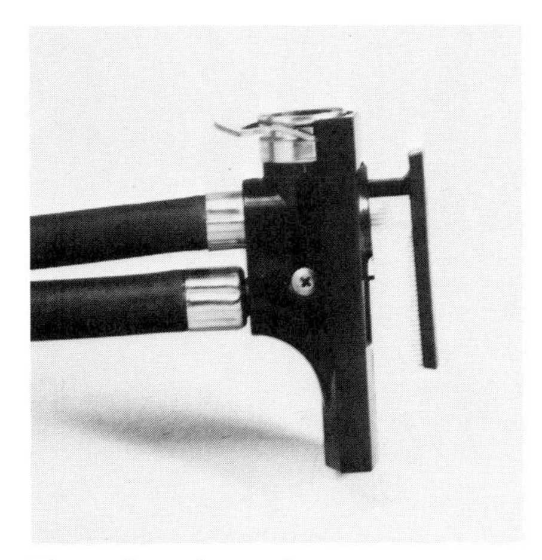

Type A unicouple

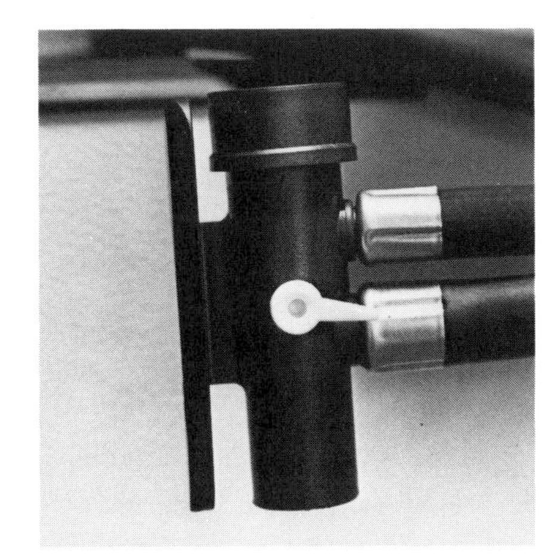

Type B unicouple

Unicouple (continued)

Step 1: Be sure all dishwasher controls are turned **OFF**. Disconnect power supply at the distribution panel. Unplug power cord from receptacle. Watch for sharp edges.

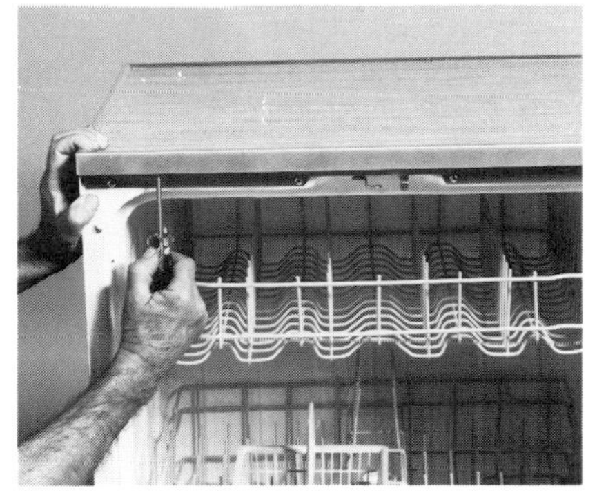

Step 2: This procedure may require removal of dishwasher top and right side panel. If you are unfamiliar with this process, please refer to Procedure #3: Removing Service Panels.

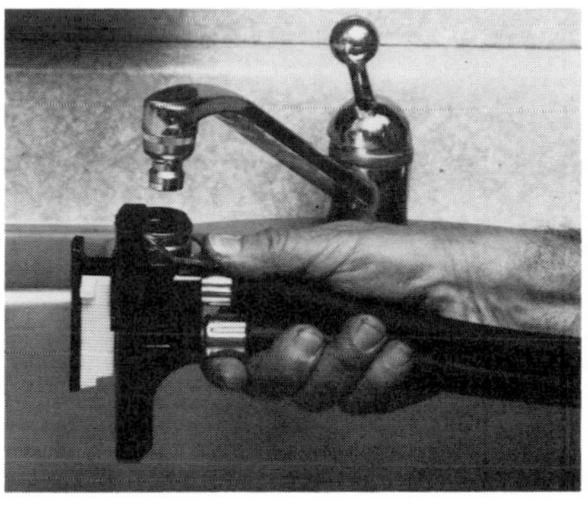

Step 3: Inspect unicouple connection at faucet. It should fit securely and not leak. If your model has a pressure relief mechanism to bleed off water into sink, test it by pressing in on slide bar or turning valve; slide or valve should not bind.

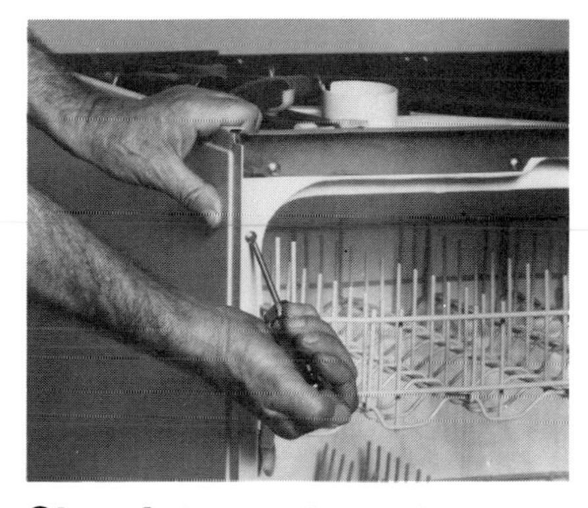

Step 4: Inspect hoses from unicouple to water inlet valve and pump drain outlet for leaks or deterioration. You may want to remove right side panel or tilt dishwasher back. If you are unfamiliar with this process, refer to Procedure #3: Removing Service Panels.

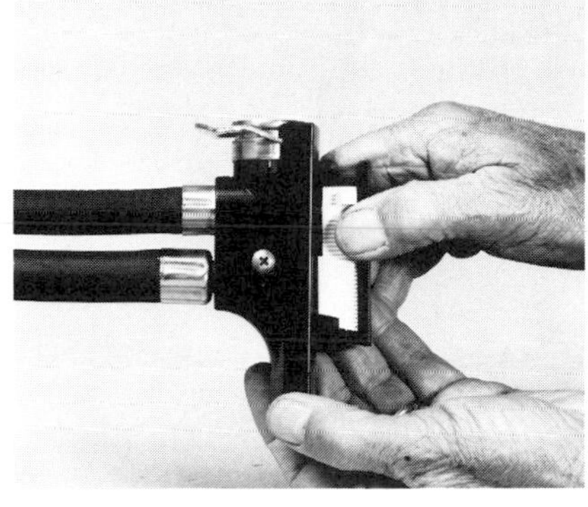

Step 5: Hose replacement and unicouple repair differ for each type of unicouple. Steps 6-18 refer to repair of Type A unicouple; Steps 19-24 refer to repair of Type B unicouple.

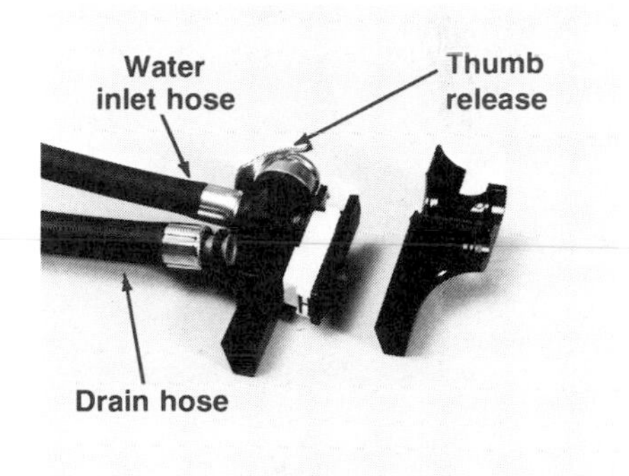

Step 6: Type A unicouple.
If you have problems at faucet connection, disassemble unicouple by removing shoulder screw. Separate handle, remove hoses and pressure relief slide, if any. (Make note of how thumb release is positioned.)

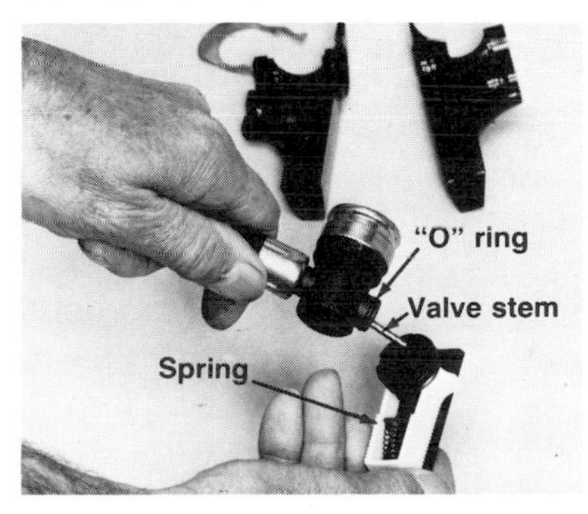

Step 7: If your model has a pressure relief slide, check it for damage or a missing or broken spring. For leaks at side, replace "O" ring at pressure relief valve stem.

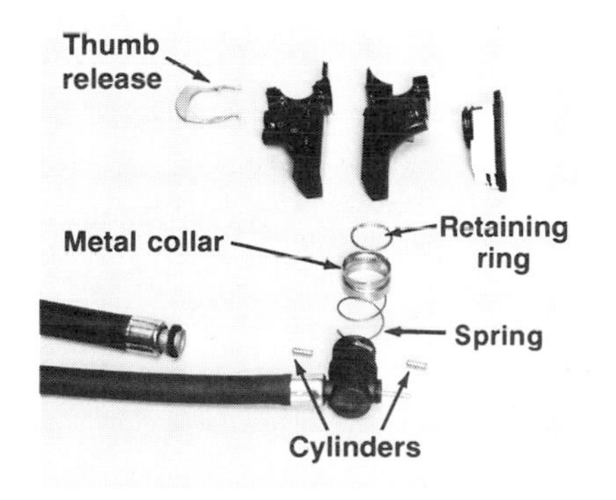

Step 8: If leaks occur at faucet, push down metal collar and pry off metal retaining ring. Separate other parts as shown, noting for reassembly how parts are connected.

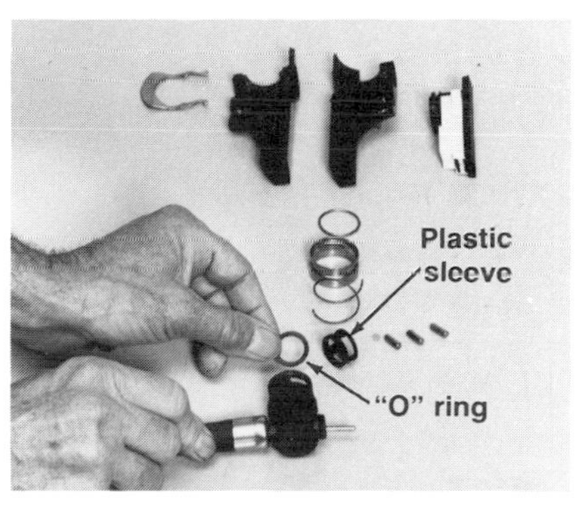

Step 9: Remove plastic sleeve from inside unicouple. Roll out "O" ring. Install new "O" ring with wider portion up so that slots line up.

Unicouple (continued)

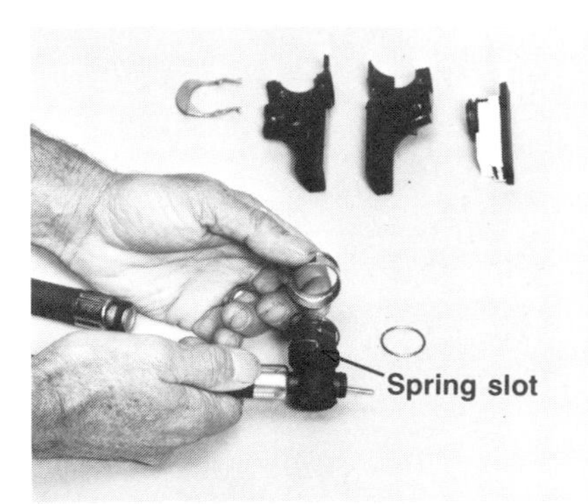

Step 10: To reassemble, replace spring, inserting end in spring slot on unicouple body. Insert cylinders in proper slots and hold in place. Install metal collar and replace metal retaining ring.

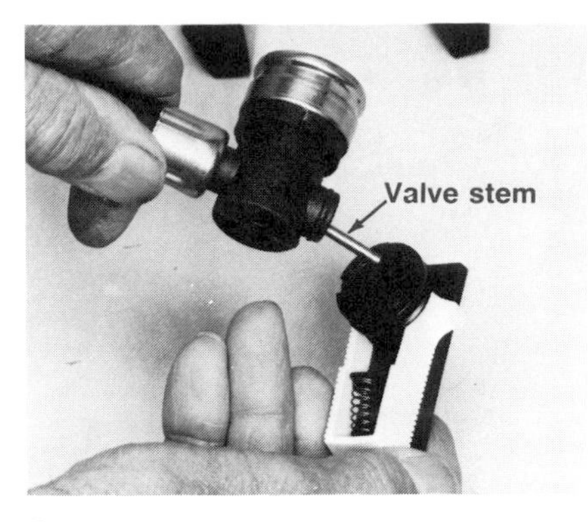

Step 11: If your model has a pressure relief assembly, slip valve stem into pressure relief slide. Position thumb release around unicouple assembly.

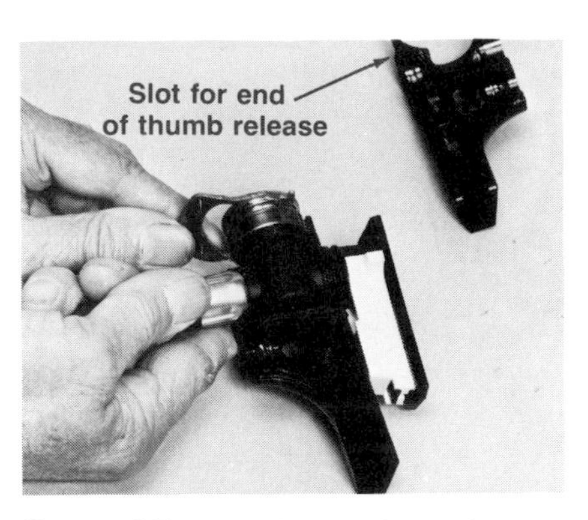

Step 12: Position unicouple assembly in handle, placing pressure relief slide, if any, into appropriate slot on side of handle. Make sure end of thumb release is inserted into slot at top of unicouple handle.

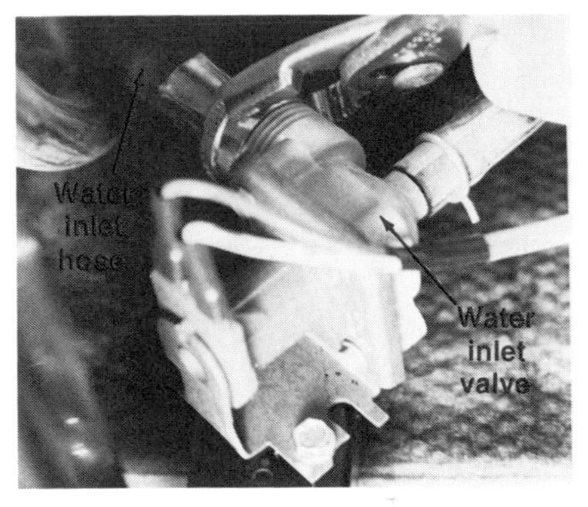

Step 13: If water inlet hose needs replacing, disconnect at water inlet valve. If you are unfamiliar with this valve, refer to Procedure #12: Inspecting and Replacing Water Inlet Valve. Prepare for some water drainage. Use pliers to loosen standard threaded ("garden hose") fitting.

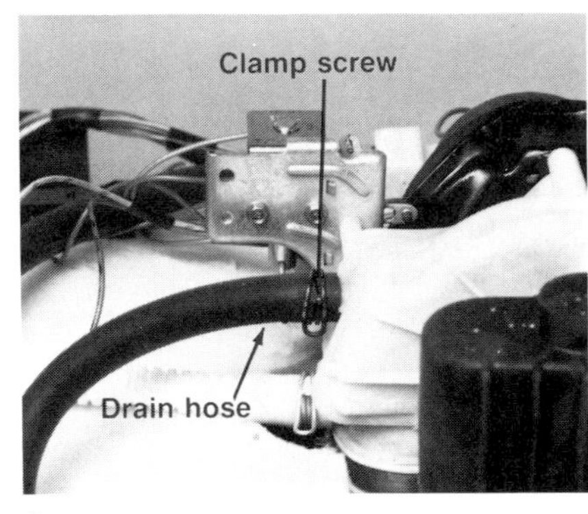

Step 14: If drain hose needs replacing, disconnect at pump drain outlet. If you are unfamiliar with this outlet, refer to Procedure #15: Inspecting and Replacing Motor/Pump Assembly. Prepare for some water leakage.

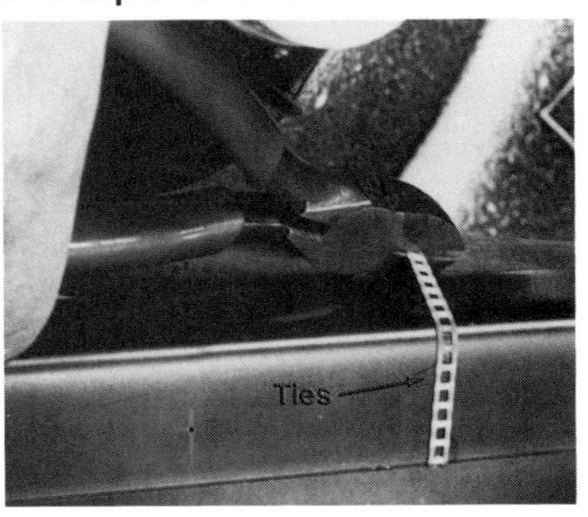

Step 15: Remove any plastic ties holding hoses to cabinet before removing hose(s). When installing new hose(s), use new plastic ties to secure them in place.

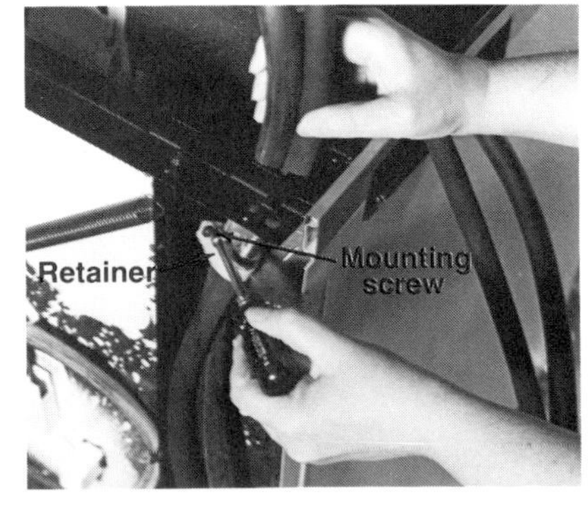

Step 16: Hoses are also secured through a retainer on the upper right side. You may want to remove side panel to release this retainer. New hoses should be properly positioned through this retainer and not kinked.

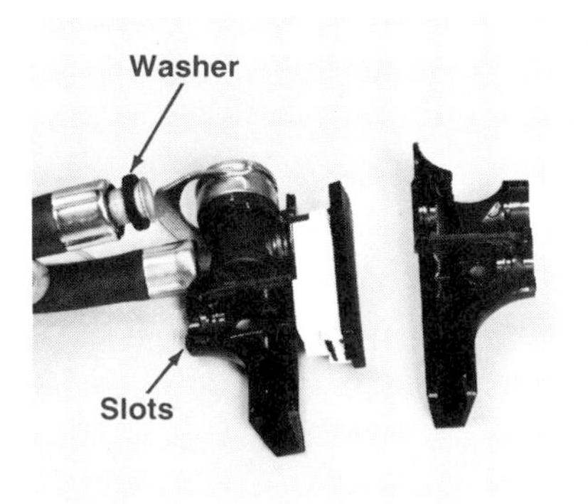

Step 17: Check drain hose washer for damage and replace if necessary. Install drain hose, fitting flared metal head and washer into proper slots on unicouple handle.

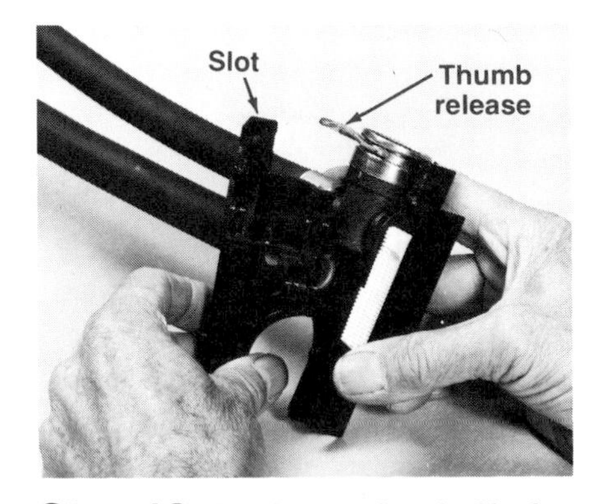

Step 18: Replace other half of unicouple handle, making sure end of thumb release fits into slot. Insert shoulder screw and tighten.

Unicouple (continued)

Step 19: Type B unicouple. Hoses cannot be detached from this type of unicouple. You can replace either entire unicouple assembly or top or bottom portion. Top and bottom pieces of this unicouple are separated by prying up under top hose stem with screwdriver. See Steps 13-16 for connecting hoses.

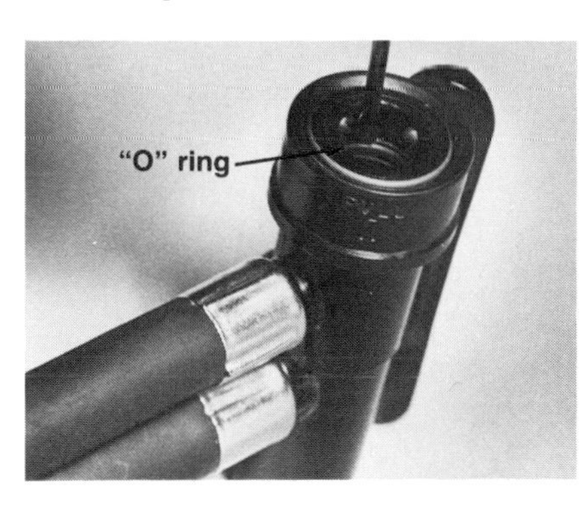

Step 20: If water leaks from unicouple, replace "O" ring inside groove in top half. Use small screwdriver to remove and refit.

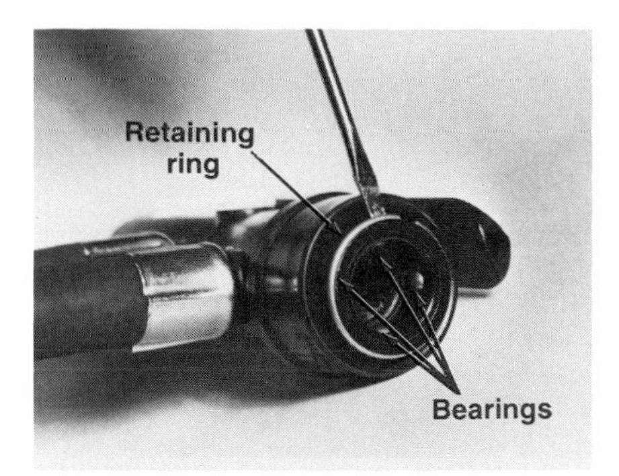

Step 21: If unicouple does not hold to faucet, replace ball bearings inside top half. Pry off outer retaining ring to loosen bearings. Reposition new bearings and reattach retainer.

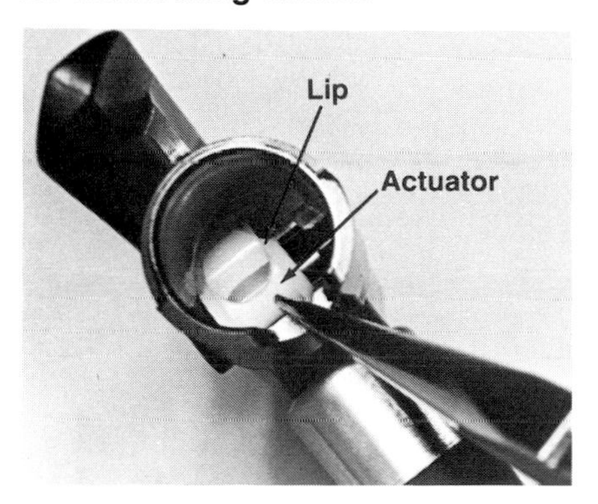

Step 22: If pressure relief valve does not work properly, replace lever arm and actuator in bottom half of unicouple. Use needle-nose pliers to fit lip of actuator down over edge inside, as shown. Reinsert lever.

Step 23: Snap two sections of unicouple body together. Reassemble dishwasher and reconnect power supply.

Technical assistance/Service record

This page is provided as a convenient reference for important dishwasher repair information. There are spaces for you to record your dishwasher model number, parts needed, repair notes (such as where wire leads reattach), and when repairs were made. There are also spaces for you to write down the phone numbers of your nearest GE/Hotpoint parts dealer and Factory Service Center.

Another important phone number for repair information belongs to the GE Answer Center® consumer information service. If you have difficulty in making any repair described in this book you can contact the GE Answer Center® consumer information service by calling 800-626-2000 toll free. The trained service professionals will try to talk you through the problem step. It helps to write down your model number, what you have done, and what is causing you difficulty before calling.

Model number: ______________________________

Parts components needed:

____

____

Repair notes:

____

____

Service record:

____

____

Water shut-off valve location: ______________________________

Fuse or circuit breaker location: ______________________________

Size fuse required: (15 amp) ______________________________

Phone number of GE/Hotpoint parts dealer: ______________________________

Phone number of GE/Hotpoint Factory Service Center: ______________________________

Preventive maintenance

At the GE, we're commited to your satisfaction--the basic do's and don'ts included in this section are our way of helping you obtain the best results from your GE or Hotpoint dishwasher. Preventive maintenance is a vital key to long life for your dishwasher. The few minutes you invest in caring for your dishwasher properly can save you a great deal of time and trouble.

This section outlines basic precautions and simple maintenance routines that will help prevent the small problems that can lead to big repair jobs. Please take a little time to read this part of the manual and follow the advice given.

Performance

- Be certain that your built-in dishwasher is correctly installed. The cabinet opening must be square and sized so that the dishwasher door cannot drag on the cabinets or hit the countertop mounting screws.
- Check that the dishwasher is properly leveled. The front leveling legs are easily adjustable up or down for this purpose.
- Be sure that voltage and wiring are adequate.
- Water pressure in your home must be adequate for best dishwashing results. 15 lbs. per square inch is the minimum pressure required.
- When using a convertible dishwasher, make sure sink drain is open and that faucet hook-up is correctly attached, with hot water turned on.
- If built-in dishwasher drains into a disposer, be sure plug is removed from disposer drain line connection.
- Make sure all dishes and utensils are dishwasher safe. Consult your ***Use and Care Book*** or check with the product manufacturer.
- Load the dishwasher correctly, using instructions in this manual or in your ***Use and Care Book***.
- There are no filters to clean in your dishwasher. The soft food disposer eliminates the need for screens that require manual cleaning. The filter provided in a few models is self-cleaning.
- A rinse agent aids in drying as well as helping to prevent spotting. It is especially important in hard water areas where minerals in the water contribute to the formation of spots.
- Wipe up spilled rinse agent immediately. Do not allow it to remain on floor. Also do not allow it to remain in dishwasher tub, where it will cause foaming and interfere with proper dishwashing.
- It is normal for a small amount of water to remain in the tub bottom after use. This helps keep the water seal from becoming brittle.

Safe operation

- Use your dishwasher only for its intended purpose, as described in the ***Use and Care Book***.
- Be sure your dishwasher is installed and grounded properly according to installation instructions and local codes.
- Use a separate 15-amp circuit for the dishwasher, with no other appliances on that circuit.
- If your dishwasher uses a power cord be certain that it is plugged into a grounded 3-prong outlet. Do not use a plug adapter. Under no circumstances should you attempt to remove the third (grounding) plug from the plug.
- Do not use an extension cord to plug in your dishwasher.
- Do not load light plastic items in the dishwasher where they might become dislodged and drop onto the Calrod® heating unit.
- Keep detergents and rinse agents away from children; many of them are toxic if taken internally.
- Hydrogen gas can be produced and can build up in a water heater if you have not used hot water for a period of two weeks or more. HYDROGEN GAS CAN BE EXPLOSIVE UNDER THESE CIRCUMSTANCES. To prevent possible damage or injury, run hot water from the kitchen faucet for several minutes before using your dishwasher or any other appliance connected to a hot water system that has not been in use. This will allow any hydrogen to escape. If the gas is present, you may hear a slight hissing or sputtering noise from the faucet as the water begins to flow. Do not smoke or allow any open flame near the faucet at this time.

Care and cleaning

- The exterior cabinet of your dishwasher is finished with durable baked-on enamel. Use a high-grade wax cleaner when necessary. Avoid harsh cleansers or abrasive scouring pads that may scratch the surface.
- The interior of the dishwasher is essentially self-cleaning. Use a mild cleansing powder if needed; do not use scouring pads or harsh cleansers.
- To prevent staining the dishwasher interior, do not clean furnace or electrostatic air filters in your dishwasher.
- If you have a convertible dishwasher with a wood top, wipe with a soft cloth to remove dust, and polish with mineral oil. Rub with more mineral oil the next day and allow to stand 4 to 6 hours before wiping off the excess oil.
- Do not allow water to stand on the wood top.
- Do not place frozen foods on the wood top for thawing.
- If a wood top becomes too stained or dirty, sand gently with 000 or 0000 sandpaper and treat with mineral oil as described above.
- If it becomes necessary to store your dishwasher in an unheated location for any length of time, check your ***Use and Care Book*** for proper preparation procedures.

Tools and testing equipment

Tools

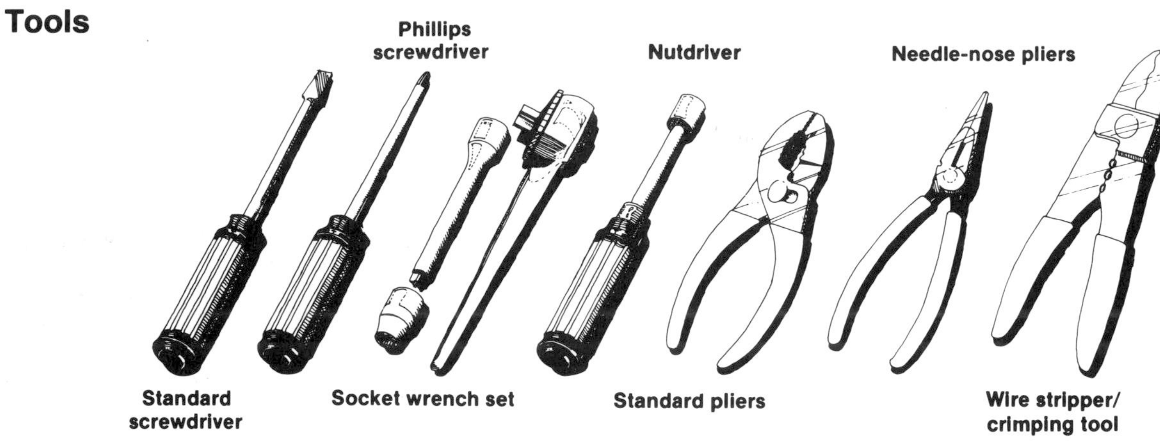

Chances are you already have some of the above tools in your home. For safety and efficiency reasons, it is important to use the proper tools when making dishwasher repairs. The tool you will use the most is the screwdriver. Various sizes of standard and Phillips screwdrivers will be necessary to remove the many screws on your dishwasher.

Some screws and nuts have hexagonal heads with no slots. To remove these, you will need either a nutdriver or socket wrench. The nutdriver is made like a screwdriver but has a small socket on one end. This socket fits over the hex head on the screw or nut. It's used just like a screwdriver.

The socket wrench usually has a handle with a ratchet that can be set to tighten or loosen a nut, an extension, and various sockets. Sockets usually come in a set containing several sizes, but the quarter-inch size is the most commonly used on the dishwasher.

To use a socket wrench, place the socket on the nut and turn the handle counterclockwise to loosen. If it makes a clicking sound and does not turn, flip the ratchet lever to the opposite direction and loosen the nut.

Testing equipment

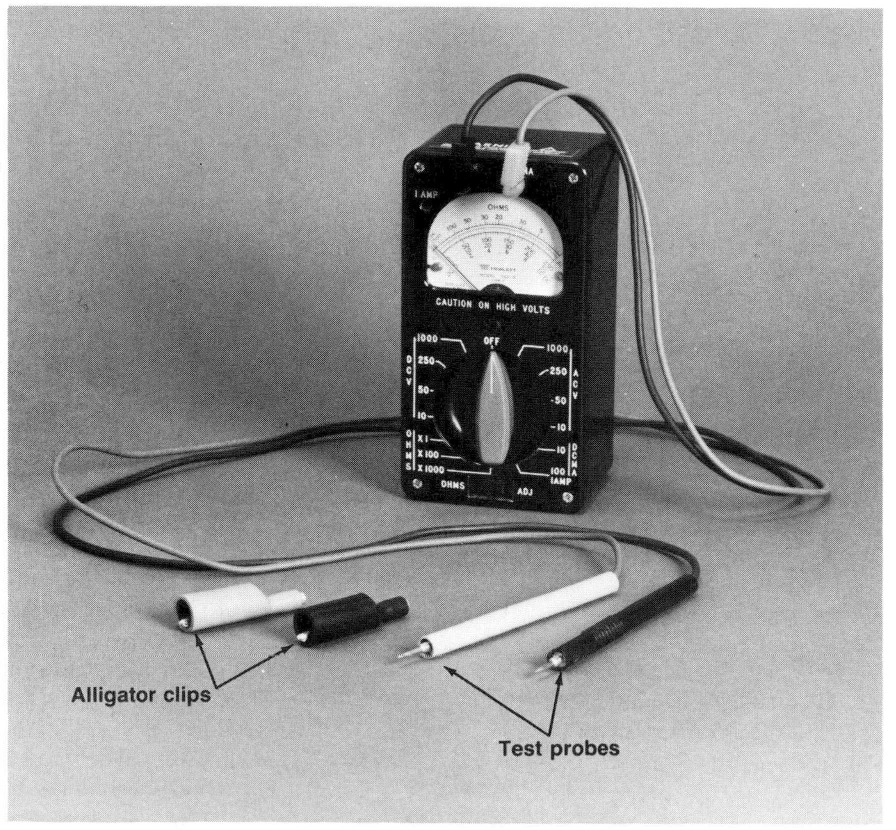

Ohmmeter

An ohmmeter is required to diagnose the electrical components of your dishwasher. The ohmmeter is a simple device that measures the amount of resistance in an electrical circuit. Ohmmeters are usually combined with a voltmeter into an instrument called a multimeter, multitester, or volt-ohmmeter (VOM). Volt-ohmmeters can measure the amount of both resistance and voltage in an electrical circuit. A simple, inexpensive ohmmeter will be sufficient for any dishwasher repairs presented in this manual.

Most problems that occur in an electrical circuit are invisible. For example, it is difficult to see contacts that are not closing inside a switch, or to find a break in the resistance wire inside a heating unit. For the most part, you'll be using the ohmmeter only as a continuity tester to determine whether or not current can pass through the circuit. By passing a small electrical current from a battery contained inside the ohmmeter through the circuit, you can tell if the circuit is complete.

To understand the basic flow of electricity, think of it in terms of a water pumping station. In order for water to flow through the pipes, it must have a complete "closed loop" from the pump, through the valves, then back to the pump again. If the line is broken or opened at any point, water would eventually cease to flow.

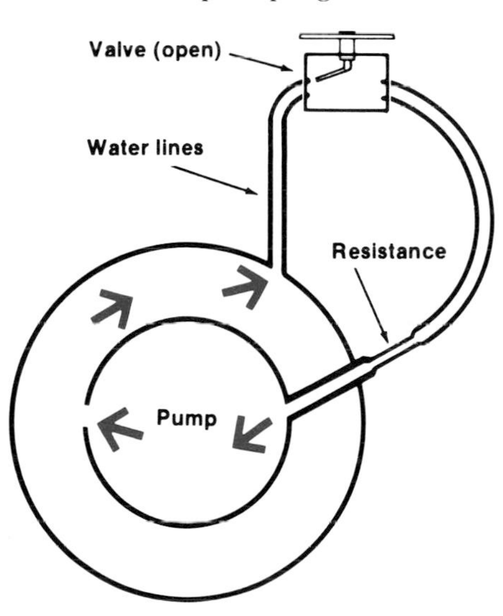

The flow of electricity through your dishwasher is similar to the pumping of water, except electrons rather than water are flowing through the circuitry. The pump is the plug-in or permanent electrical connection that provides the force to circulate current through the dishwasher circuits. The electrical circuit uses wires rather than pipes as the conductors of electricity and switches rather than valves to control the flow. Voltage is comparable to the pressure that exists in a water circuit, whereas electrical current could be compared to the flow rate of water that flows through the pipe.

Some tests with an ohmmeter will be needed for repair procedures presented in this manual. An ohmmeter will have either a switch or pair of jacks (plugs) that allow you to select the function of the meter. Resistance is measured in units called ohms and will be designated by the symbol Ω or the letter R. Your meter may have more than one range scale. When set at R × 1, the reading should be taken directly from the meter. When set at a higher scale, such as R × 100, the reading on the scale should be multiplied by 100 to obtain the correct resistance. Most measurements for testing components or circuits are made on the lowest scale, usually R × 1. Some newer digital ohmmeters do not use a multiplier and have only high, medium, and low ranges.

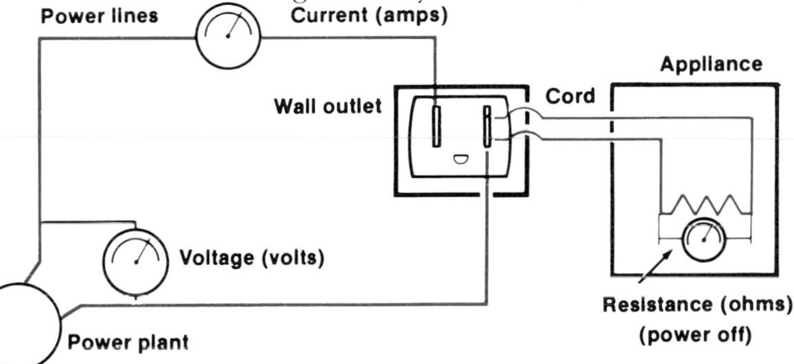

Plug the test leads in the jacks marked "ohms". The red lead goes in the positive (+) jack and the black one to negative (−). If your meter gives you a choice of functions, select the range first, then "zero" the meter by touching the two test probes together. With the probes tightly in contact with each other, the needle of the meter should sweep towards "0" (zero) resistance. Now, while holding the probes together, adjust the knob marked "zero adjust" or "ohms adjust" until the needle rests directly over "0".

At this point, you can see exactly how the meter works. If instead of touching the probes together you touch them to each end of a wire, or to a fuse, the needle should sweep toward "0". This indicates that the wire or fuse will conduct electricity. But if the wire or fuse is broken inside, the needle would not move. When this condition exists in a component or circuit, it is said to be "open", and it cannot conduct electricity. But if the needle moves to indicate that it does conduct electricity, then the component or circuit is said to have "continuity".

All wires in the electrical circuit should indicate "0" resistance when tested in this manner. Switches should indicate "0" resistance when they're turned on, and should be open when turned off. Components that do work, such as the Calrod® heating unit, will offer some electrical resistance, but will not be open. The meter reading for these instances should be somewhere between full scale and no reading.

Tools and testing equipment (continued)

Many repair procedures in this manual advise you to test for grounds when checking a component. When doing this, you should select the highest resistance scale on the ohmmeter. You will be directed to place one test probe on a terminal of the component and the other test probe on a metallic portion of the component housing. No current should flow through those paths; if the meter indicates that continuity exists under those conditions, the component is grounded and should be replaced.

The repair procedures in this manual will show you the test points (where to place the test probes) for various tests. You'll find the ohmmeter to be a valuable addition to your home tool collection. For further information on the function and operation of an ohmmeter, see pages 93 and 94.

Using the ohmmeter

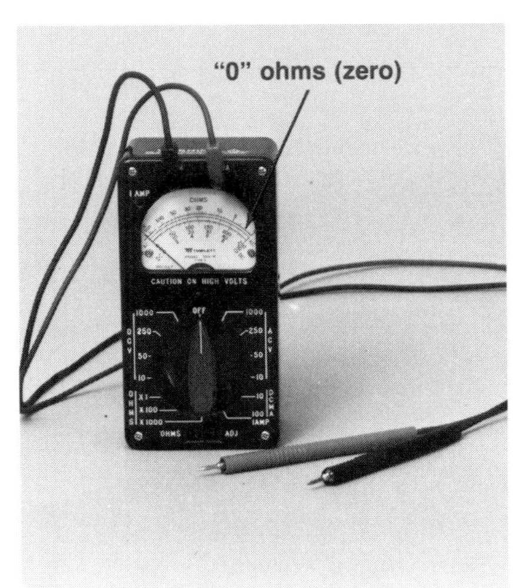

Full-featured ohmmeters like the one shown has numerous switch-selected ranges. Note that ohms scale at top is reversed – zero resistance is at full sweep upscale.

Inexpensive ohmmeters use jacks rather than switches to select function, but still provide zero ohms adjustment. Note that red lead plugs into positive (+) jack, black into negative (–) or common.

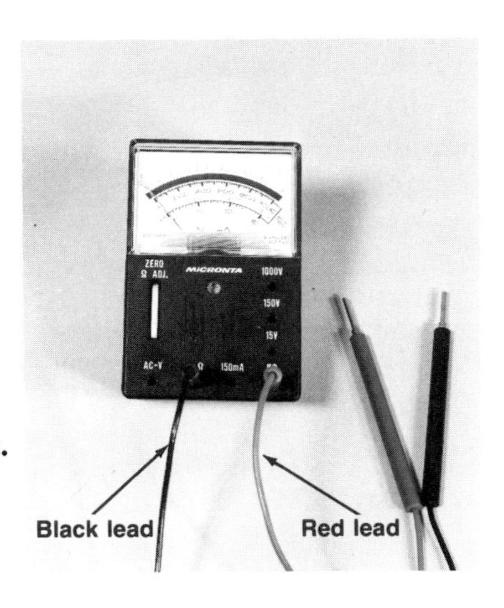

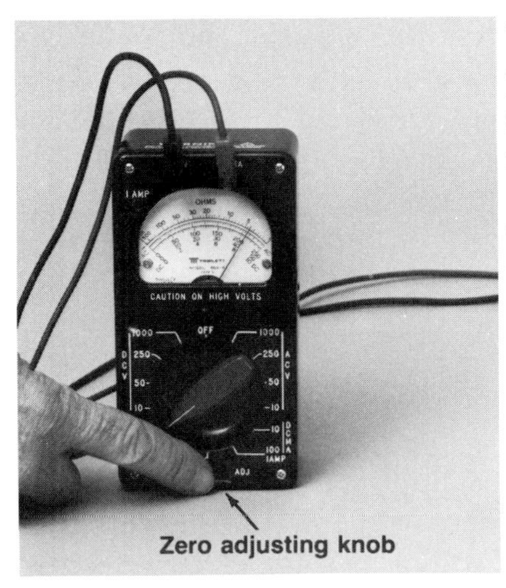

To zero ohmmeter, touch probes tightly together, turn zero adjustment knob until needle is centered over "O" (ZERO) at full sweep of scale. This adjusts readout to the battery condition and to the resistance selected.

Sometimes you can't identify a blown fuse, even when it has a glass shell. Saving a single service call for a simple problem like this can pay for the price of a meter.

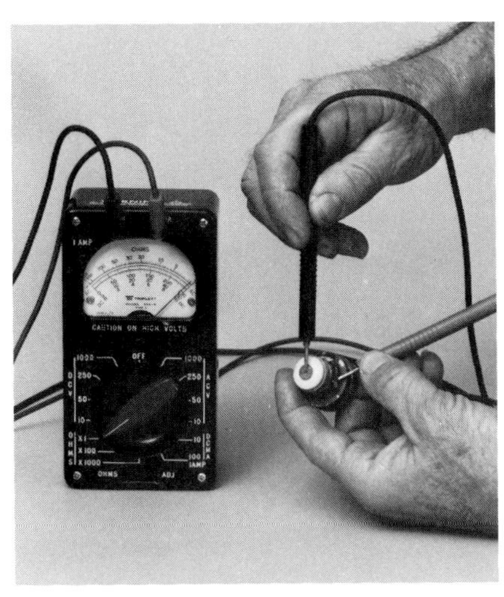

CAUTION: Do not attempt to test resistance of any circuit with the power turned on. Checking a live voltage circuit will result in damage to your testing meter.

How to interpret circuit diagrams

The circuit diagram that accompanies your dishwasher shows how wiring is connected between components and how the internal circuitry of the components is arranged. The circuit diagram for many dishwashers will be found glued inside the outer door panel. On more recent models, the circuit diagram is contained in an envelope attached to the dishwasher inside the lower front access panel.

Circuit diagrams may be drawn in several different ways. (Relevant symbols and abbreviations are listed at the end of this section.) Some component symbols may be different, but all show the path of current flow from the power lines through the switches and components. This flow of current shows the continuous loop required to complete an electrical circuit. Your dishwasher's circuit diagram will also show the color coding of the internal wiring.

The secret to using a circuit diagram as a diagnostic tool is to simplify the diagram. When reading a circuit diagram, focus your attention only on that part of the diagram that involves the area you are testing.

For explanatory purposes, let's study closely the circuit diagram shown. This is a diagram for a dishwasher with a dial control and two pushbuttons.

The diagram shows the 120-volt power supply at the top. Reading from right to left, we see a red or black (hot) wire running to a door switch. This switch closes when the dishwasher's door latch is engaged. Current flows through this switch to the timer

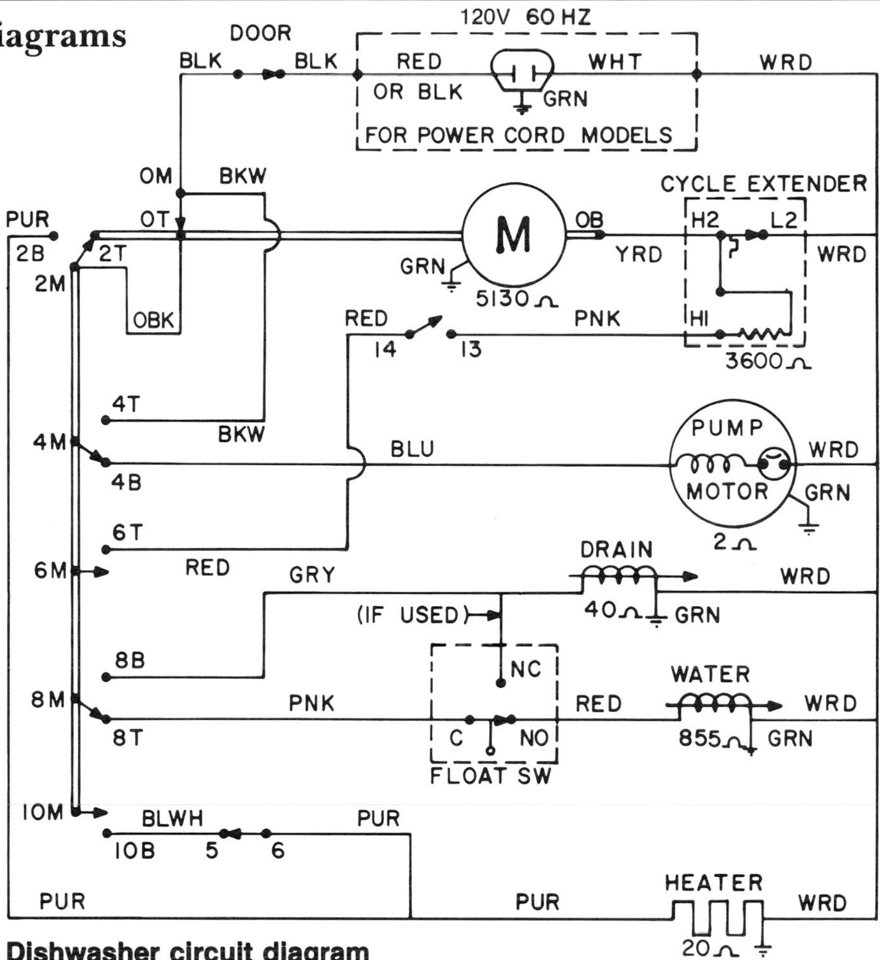

Dishwasher circuit diagram

terminal marked OM. The switch between this terminal and terminal OT is closed when the timer dial is turned or pushed in to start the dishwasher. A wire from this switch carries power to the timer motor, marked with a large M.

As the timer moves through the selected cycle, it closes different sets of contacts to energize the various components of the dishwasher. Timer contacts are indicated with both letters and numbers. On this diagram, terminals 8M and 8T are closed to supply power to the water inlet valve solenoid and allow the dishwasher to fill.

This circuit can be interrupted by a float switch. If the water level raises too high, this switch opens and shuts off power to the water inlet valve solenoid which controls water intake. Note the terminal marked NC above the float switch. On some models, the float switch opens and swings to make contact between terminals C and NC. This energizes the drain valve solenoid to remove excess water.

During ordinary operation terminals 8M and 8B close to provide power to the drain valve solenoid and allow water to pump out.

Contacts 4M and 4B will be closed during the entire wash and rinse portions of the cycle to provide power to the pump motor. During the dry portion of the cycle, these contacts open, shutting off the motor. Contacts 10M and 10B then close to energize the Calrod® heating unit.

Tools and testing equipment (continued)

Bar chart

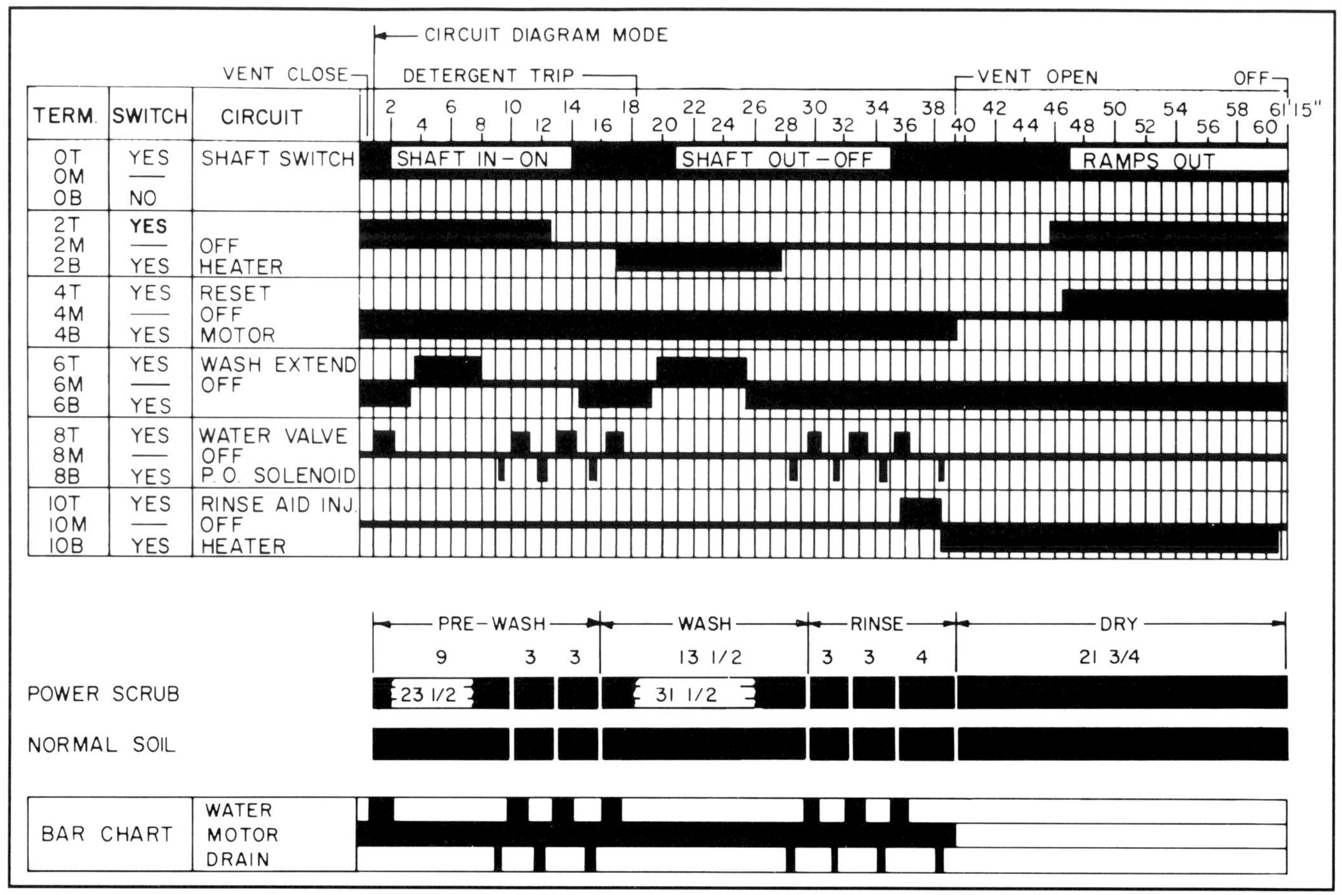

Pushbutton switches will be represented in the circuit diagram by letters of the alphabet, or by numbers, but not both. This particular diagram features two pushbuttons, indicated on the diagram by contacts 5-6 and contacts 13-14.

Contacts 5 and 6 are closed during normal dry. When the Energy Saver Dry option is selected, the pushbutton opens these contacts. With contacts 5 and 6 open, the circuit from timer to heating element is not complete; the timer will advance to the end of the cycle without energizing the heater.

Pushbutton contacts 13 and 14 are open during the normal wash portion of the cycle. When the Power Scrub cycle is selected, that pushbutton closes these contacts to energize the cycle extender switch.

The cycle extender switch lengthens the wash time by "pulsing" the timer motor on and off. When contacts 13 and 14 are closed, they provide power to the 3600-ohm resistor, causing it to heat. As the resistor heats, it expands and opens contacts H2 and L2, cutting off power to the timer motor. When the resistor cools, the contacts reclose and energize the timer motor once again.

You can use your dishwasher's circuit diagram to trace current flow through the circuits at any given time in the cycle. The circuit diagram on the preceding page, for example, shows the dishwasher approximately one minute into a normal wash cycle. The door interlock switch at top left of the diagram is closed; the manual start control (contacts OM and OT) is also closed.

You can follow the circuit from there through the timer to see which components of the dishwasher have been energized. The switch between contacts 4M and 4B is closed, supplying power to the pump motor. Contacts 8M and 8T are closed, energizing the water valve solenoid. With all these switches properly closed, the dishwasher is in the initial fill portion of the cycle.

A bar chart, such as that shown above, is supplied with the circuit diagram for your dishwasher. This chart shows which timer switch contacts are closed at specific times in the dishwasher cycle. The black bars on the chart show the length of time, in minutes, that each switch remains closed.

The top line of this chart shows that when the shaft switch is closed (timer dial is pushed in or turned), contacts OM and OT are closed. This switch powers the timer motor, and is closed during the entire cycle. The second line of the chart shows contacts 2M and 2B closing during the main wash portion of the cycle. This energizes the heating element to maintain proper water temperature, even though pushbutton switch 5-6 may be open to select Energy Saver Dry.

The third bar of the chart illustrates contacts 4M and 4B closing during the wash and rinse portions of the cycle to energize the pump motor. Next, we see contacts 6M and 6T closing during both the prewash and wash portions of the cycle. This allows power to be supplied to the cycle extender switch if Power Scrub cycle pushbutton contacts 13 and 14 are closed. If these contacts are open, power will not reach the cycle extender switch, and the timer will simply advance to the next portion of the cycle.

The fifth chart line indicates that contacts 8T and 8M are closed first for approximately 1-¼ minutes, allowing the water valve to open and the tub to fill. After a 9-minute prewash, contacts 8M and 8B close to activate the pump-out solenoid and drain the tub. Additional bars on these two lines of the chart show how these two components are cycled on and off to drain and refill the dishwasher.

The sixth line of the chart shows that contacts 10T and 10M close approximately 35 minutes into the cycle to operate the rinse aid dispenser, if the dishwasher has this feature. As the rinse time ends, contacts 10M and 10B close to energize the heating element and dry the dishes, provided that the Energy Saver Dry switch has not been pushed.

By learning to interpret circuit diagrams properly, you will have an insight into your dishwasher's electrical functions. This should allow you to use your ohmmeter to pinpoint a problem quickly and accurately.

Symbols

The following Legend of Symbols and Abbreviations will assist you in reading the circuit diagrams.

- GROUND
- HARNESS PLUG
- HEATING UNIT
- INTERNAL CONNECTION
- LAMP--INCANDESCENT
- LAMP--NEON
- MOTOR
- OVERLOAD
- RELAY
- RESISTOR
- RINSE AID OR DETERGENT DISPENSER BIMETAL
- SOLENOID OR MOTOR WINDING
- SWITCH OR CONTACT
- SWITCH--PUSHBUTTON (INDICATED BY LETTERS ONLY OR NUMBERS ONLY) — 5 6
- SWITCH--TIMER (INDICATED BY LETTERS AND NUMBERS) — 2M 2T
- THERMOSTAT
- WIRES CONNECTED
- WIRES CROSSING

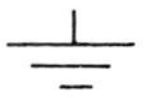

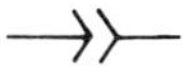

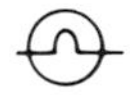

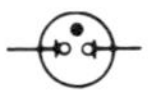

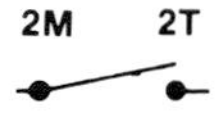

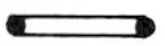

Abbreviations

- D.S. OR DOOR - DOOR SWITCH
- DET. INJ. - DETERGENT DISPENSER
- F.S. - FLOAT SWITCH
- HTR - HEATER
- Hz - HERTZ (CYCLES PER SECOND)
- JCT BOX - JUNCTION BOX
- P.L. - PILOT LIGHT
- P.O. SOL - PUMP OUT SOLENOID
- PWR - POWER
- RINSE INJ. - RINSE AGENT DISPENSER
- RLY - RELAY
- SW - SWITCH
- V - VOLT
- WDG - WINDING

Dishwasher accessories

In addition to supplying quality original replacement parts for your dishwasher, GE also provides a variety of useful dishwasher accessories to keep your dishwasher looking and working like new. The most popular and widely available dishwasher accessories are featured below.

Appliance paint

High quality paints in spray cans and touch-up applicators are available in five colors to match GE/Hotpoint appliances. Camouflaging most nicks and scratches, GE appliance paint is an easy-to-use and long-lasting way to improve your dishwasher's appearance.

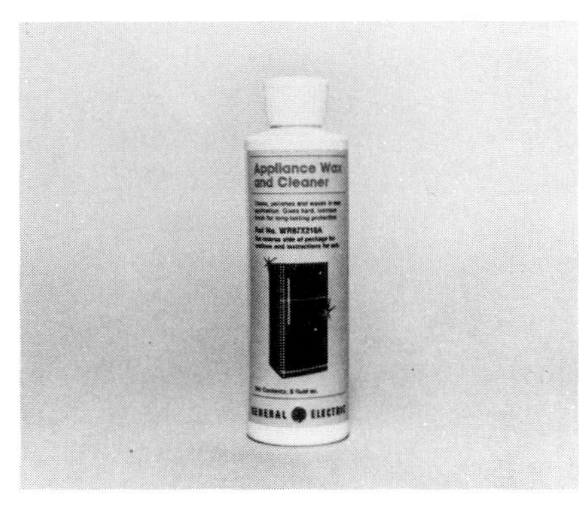

Appliance wax and cleaner

Protective liquid wax contains silicone sealant to clean, polish and wax in one easy step. The 8-oz. squeeze bottle contains enough liquid wax for several applications to keep your dishwasher finish in like-new condition.

WR97X216

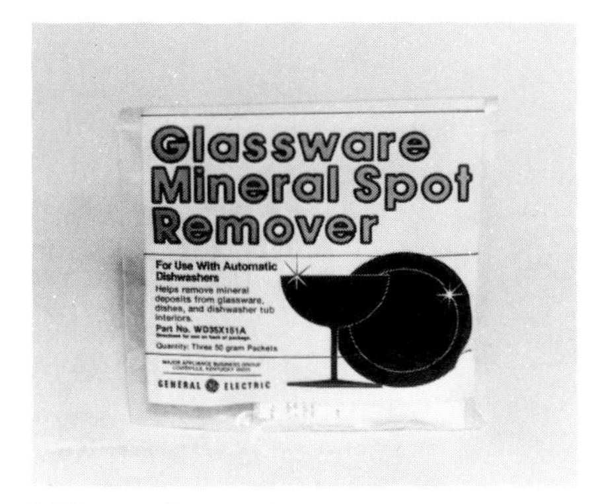

Mineral spot remover

Spot remover is formulated to help remove mineral deposits from glassware, dishes, and dishwasher tub interior during the ordinary wash cycle. Easy to use in premeasured packets, simply open and place in soap dispenser. Spot remover is ideal for combating hard water build-up.

WD35X151A

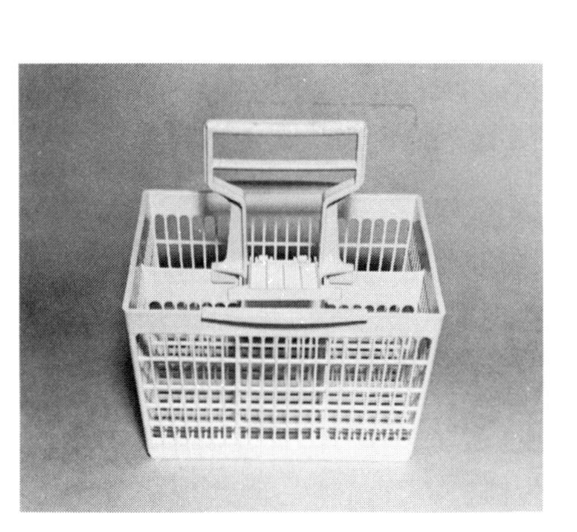

Silverware basket

Durable styrene silverware basket features convenient carrying handle, six individual compartments, and flip down cover over center compartment to protect lightweight items. Ideal for upgrading or replacing your present silverware basket, it will fit all GE/Hotpoint dishwashers.

WD28X245A

Dishwasher racks

Heavy gauge steel replacement racks have a protective vinyl coating that is both stain and rust resistant. Soft cushioned coating also helps to prevent accidental chipping or scratching of dishes and glassware. Replacement racks are available for either top or bottom installation to help renew your GE/Hotpoint dishwasher's appearance and performance.

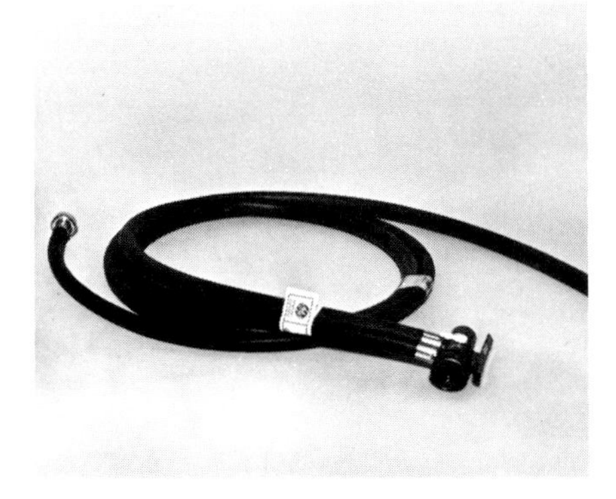

Fill hose

Replacement fill hose is supplied according to specifications for GE or Hotpoint dishwashers. Heavy duty hose has precise fittings for easy, leakproof installation of your appliance.

Glossary of terms

Allen wrench
"L"-shaped tool, made of hexagonal rod of steel bent at right angles.

Bar chart
Chart showing which switches are opened and closed in timer at various points in the dishwasher cycle.

Bell connector
Solderless connector for splicing wiring. Insulating cover crimps onto twisted ends of wires to assure solid connection.

Bimetal
Metal strip consisting of two sides of different metals bonded together. Each metal expands at a different rate when heated, causing strip to bend.

Circuit
Path of electrical current from power supply through wiring to point of use and back to source.

Circuit breaker
Device to protect circuit from current overload. "Tripped" circuit breaker interrupts circuit when current exceeds specified amount. See also FUSE.

Circuit diagram
Drawing using standard symbols to represent path of current from power supply through switches and components back to source. Shows how wiring is connected between components and how internal wiring of components is arranged.

Closed (circuit)
Complete circuit which can conduct electricity.

Component
An individual electrical or mechanical part of a dishwasher system.

Connector
Any device on the end of a wire to facilitate either connection or disconnection.

Contact
Switch component which opens and closes to complete or break an electrical circuit.

Continuity
Ability of completed circuit to conduct electricity.

Defective
In this manual, used to mean a component which does not function properly and which must be replaced.

Distribution panel
Fuse or circuit breaker box that distributes incoming power from outside line into a number of household circuits.

Glossary of terms (continued)

Energize
To supply electrical current for operation of a component.

Feedback
In testing for continuity, current returning to meter through a part of circuit other than component being tested, giving false reading.

Fuse
Device to protect circuit from current overload. "Blown" fuse automatically interrupts circuit when current exceeds specified amount. See also CIRCUIT BREAKER.

Gasket
Flexible material designed to provide water-tight seal between components or parts of dishwasher body.

Ground
Connection to earth or to another conducting body which transmits current to earth. Metal components in a circuit must be grounded to prevent their accidentally becoming electrically charged, causing injury.

Heating unit
Nickel-chrome alloy resistance coil encased in electrical insulation material and steel sheath; generates heat when current is passed through it.

Impeller
Rotating blade inside pump chamber which moves water.

Inoperative
In this manual, used to mean a component which does not function, but which can be checked and possibly repaired.

Insulation
Material which does not conduct electricity. Used to separate current-carrying wires or components from other metal parts of the dishwasher.

Lead
Portion of electrical wiring attached to a component.

Nutdriver
Tool used to remove and reinstall hexagonal-head screws or nuts. Resembles a screwdriver with a small socket at the end instead of a blade.

Ohm
Measurement unit for electrical resistance.

Ohmmeter
Battery-operated test instrument for determining the continuity of a circuit and measuring its resistance.

Open (circuit)
Incomplete circuit which cannot conduct electricity.

Receptacle
Wall socket into which prongs of power cord plug can be inserted to connect with house wiring terminal.

Resistance
Restriction of current in an electrical circuit.

Seal
Gasket-type flexible material used to form water-tight connection between parts.

Short (circuit)
Accidentally created circuit between hot wire and any ground, allowing excessive current with little or no resistance.

Solenoid
Cylindrical coil of insulated wire that establishes a magnetic field in the presence of current.

Switch
Device to turn current on and off in an electrical circuit.

Terminal
Connection point between wiring and electrical components. Commonly used terminals in dishwashers are push-on terminals, which are held in place by snug fit.

Terminal block
Internal terminals that connect several wires to several points on the component or to several wires in another terminal block.

Test probes
Metal components of ohmmeter which are attached to either end of a circuit during testing for continuity or resistance. See also OHMMETER.

Thermostat
Heat-sensing component that controls temperature levels by turning heat source on and off.

Upscale
Reading from ohmmeter that indicates continuity in a circuit.

Valve
Mechanical device to regulate water flow by opening, closing or partially obstructing passageway.

Volt
Measurement unit for electrical pressure.

Watt
Measurement unit for electrical power.

Index

A

Access Panels (see also Service Panels)
  removing 23-25
Accessories 99
Aerator
  description 67
  inspecting and replacing 67-68
Air Gap
  inspecting and cleaning 33-34
Answer Center 4, 91
Anti-Tip Mechanism (Convertible Dishwashers)
  inspecting and replacing 85-86
Appliance paint 99
Appliance wax 99

B

Bar Chart (see also Circuit Diagram)
  definition 100
  usage 97-98
Bearings
  wash system 56, 57
Bell Connector (see also Connector--Wiring)
  definition 100
Bimetal
  definition 100
  rinse agent dispenser 63-64
Body Repair (see Cosmetic Repairs)
Built-in Dishwasher 6

C

Calrod® Heating Unit (see also Heating Unit)
  definition 101
  inspecting and replacing 69-70
China/Crystal Cycle (see Aerator)
Circuit(See also Circuit Breaker, Circuit Diagram)
  closed 100
  definition 100
  open 101
  short 102
  testing 93-98
Circuit Breaker
  definition 100
  inspecting 19-20
Circuit Diagram
  abbreviations 98
  definition 100
  interpreting 96-98
  typical timer 38
  typical pushbuttons 42
  symbols 98
Cleaning (see also Preventive Maintenance)
  exterior 92
  interior 92
  top 92
Closed Circuit
  definition 100
  testing 94-98
Component
  definition 100
Connections (see Power Supply)
Connector--Faucet (see Unicouple)
Connector--Pump (see Motor/Pump Assembly)
Connector--Wiring
  definition 100
  inspecting and replacing 27-28
Contact
  definition 100
Continuity
  definition 100
  testing 94-98
Control Panel (see Service Panels)
Convertible Dishwasher 6
Cosmetic Repairs
  replacing panels 23-25, 83-84
  scratches 83-84
Cycle Extender Switch
  description 43
  inspecting and replacing 43-44

D

Detergent (see also Detergent Dispenser)
  usage 31-32
Detergent Dispenser
  single or dual cup type 61-62
  molded-cup type 63-64
Dial-A-Level® Rack (see Racks)
Dishwasher
  accessories 99
  built-in 6
  convertible 6
  operation 5
  parts 3-4
  racks 15, 75-77, 99
Dishwasher Problems
Introduction 7
  All dishwasher models:
  1. Motor and timer do not run (no water fill) 8
  2. Motor does not run or hum (initial water fill OK and timer advances) 8
  3. Motor hums, but does not run 8
  4. Too little or no water fill 9
  5. Water does not shut off 9
  6. Timer does not shut dishwasher off 9
  7. Timer does not advance 10

8. Water does not pump out 10
9. Dishwasher leaks 11
10. Detergent remains in detergent cup 11-12
11. Rinse agent dispenser does not release rinse agent (electrical dispenser) 12
12. Rinse agent dispenser does not release rinse agent (mechanical dispenser) 12
13. Rinse agent dispenser leaks (electrical dispenser) 12
14. Rinse agent dispenser leaks (mechanical dispenser) 12
15. Poor dishwashing results 13-14
16. Poor drying 14-15
17. Condensation on dishwasher door 15
18. Dishwasher door is difficult to open or close 15
19. Dishwasher door falls open 15
20. Racks binding or out of place 15
21. Rack finish defects 15
22. Tub and inner door liner finish defects 15
23. Cabinet exterior defects 16
24. Noise during operation 16
Convertible dishwasher models
25. Top defective 17
26. Anti-tip mechanism noisy or inoperative 17
27. Unicouple leaks 17
28. Unicouple hoses won't store 17
29. Power cord won't store 17

Dishwasher Repair Procedures
Introduction 18
All dishwasher models:
1. Circuit breakers and fuses 19
2. Power connections 21
3. Service panels 23
4. Wiring and connections 27
5. Loading 29
6. Water and detergent 31
7. Air gap and drain lines 33
8. Door latch mechanism 35
9. Timer 37
10. Pushbutton switches 41
11. Cycle extender switch 43
12. Water inlet valve 45
13. Float switch 47
14. Drain valve solenoid 49
15. Motor/pump assembly 51
16. Wash system parts 55
17. Single or dual cup detergent dispenser 61
18. Molded-cup type detergent dispenser 63
19 Mechanical rinse agent dispenser 67
20. Electrical rinse agent dispenser
21. Calrod® heating unit 69
22. Thermostats 71
23. Racks 75
24. Gaskets 79
25. Dishwasher body cosmetics 83
26. Door springs 85
Convertible dishwasher models
26. Anti-tip mechanism 85
27. Unicouple 87

Distribution Panel
definition 100
inspecting 19-20
Door Latch
inspecting and replacing 35-36
Door Panels (see also Service Panels)
removing 23-25
repairing 83-84
Door Springs 85
Drain Valve Solenoid
inspecting and replacing 49-50
Drainage (see also Drain Valve Solenoid)
inspecting air gap and drain lines 33-34
inspecting unicouple 87-90
Drying
Calrod® heating unit 69-70
problems 14-15

E

Electrical Outlets (see Receptacles)
Energize
definition 101
Epoxy (see also Cosmetic Repairs)
interior repair 83-84
rack repair 76, 83-84
Extended Wash (see Cycle Extender Switch)

F

Feedback
definition 101
Float Switch
description 47
inspecting and replacing 47-48

Index (continued)

Fuse
definition 101
dishwasher 69
distribution panel 19-20
replacing 20
testing 20

G

Gasket
definition 101
inspecting and replacing 79-81
General Electric Answer Center 4, 91
General Electric replacement parts 4, 99
Glossary of Terms 100-102
Grader/cutter (soft food cutter, see also Motor/Pump Assembly)
inspecting and replacing 51-54
usage 5, 51
Ground
definition 101
testing for 95
Ground wire
safety 2, 27
Grounding (see also Installation)
grounding plug 21-22

H

Heating Unit
Calrod® heating unit 69-70
definition 101
protector devices 70
High temperature wash cycles 71
Hose
drain 33-34
fill 99
unicouple 87-90

I

Impeller (see also Motor/Pump Assembly)
definition 101
inspecting and replacing 51-54
Installation of dishwasher 6, 92
Insulation
definition 101

L

Latch (see Door Latch)
Lead
definition 101
Leak--Detergent Cup (see Detergent Dispenser)
Leak--Rinse Agent (see Rinse Agent Dispenser)
Leak--Water
problem diagnosis 11
Loading Dishwasher 29-30

M

Maintenance (see Preventive Maintenance)
Mineral Spot Remover 99
Model Identification Plate
location 3
Model Number
location 3
usage 3
Models Covered 6
Motor
main (see Motor/Pump Assembly)
Motor/Pump Assembly
how assembly operates 51
inspecting and replacing 51-54
Multi-Orbit™ Wash Arm (see Wash System)

N

Noise
problem diagnosis 16
Nutdriver
definition 101
usage 93

O

Ohm
definition 101
Ohmmeter (see also Testing Equipment)
definition 101
usage 93-95
Open Circuit
definition 101
testing 94

P

Paint (see Cosmetic Repairs)
Parts Information 3-4
Performance Checks
loading dishwasher 29-30
water and detergent 31-32
air gap and drain lines 33-34
Performance, poor
problem diagnosis 13-14
PermaTuf® Interior
cleaning 92
description 6
Polish (see also Cleaning)
appliance polish 84, 92, 99
Porcelain Interior
cleaning 92
description 6
POTSCRUBBER Cycle (see Cycle Extender Switch)

Power Connections
inspecting 21-22
Power Cord (see also Power Connections)
inspecting 21-22
safety 92
Power Scrub Cycle (see Cycle Extender Switch)
Power Shower® spray arm (see Wash System)
Power Supply
main distribution panel 19-20
dishwasher power connections 21-22
Power Tower™ sprayer (see Wash System)
Preventive Maintenance 92
Problem Diagnostic Charts 7-17
Pump (see Motor/Pump Assembly)
Pushbuttons
inspecting and replacing 41-42

R

Racks
epoxy repair 76, 83-84
inspecting and replacing 75-77
replacement part 99
Receptacle
definition 102
grounded 22
Repair Procedures
introduction 18
all dishwasher models 19-86
convertible dishwasher models 85-90
Resistance
definition 102
measuring 93-95
Rinse Agent (see also Rinse Agent Dispenser)
usage 32, 92
spills 92
Rinse Agent Dispenser
electrical 65-66
mechanical 67-68
Rollers (see Racks)

S

Safety Information 2, 92
Scratches (see Cosmetic Repairs)
Seal
definition 102
motor seal (see Motor/Pump Assembly)
Select-A-Level Racks (see Racks)
Service Panels
control panel escutcheon 24
inner door panel 25
lower access panel 24
outer door panel 24
removing 23-25
side panel (convertible dishwashers) 25
top (convertible dishwashers) 25
Short Circuit
definition 102
Side Panels (see Service Panels)
Silverware Basket 99
Soft Food Disposer (see also Grader/Cutter)
description 5
Solenoid
definition 102
drain valve 49-50
water inlet valve 45-46
Spot Remover 99
Stabilizer Mechanism (see Anti-Tip Mechanism)
Sump (see Motor/Pump Assembly)
Switch
cycle extender 43-44
definition 102
door latch 35-36
float 47-48
pushbutton 41-42
timer 37-40, 94-98

T

Technical Assistance 91
Terminal
definition 102
replacing 27-28
Terminal Block
definition 102
inspecting and replacing 27-28
Test Probes (see also Ohmmeter)
definition 102
Testing Equipment 93-95
Thermostats 71-74
control 71-74
definition 102
safety 71-74
Timer
description 37
inspecting and replacing 37-40
Tools 93
safety 2

Index (continued)

Top (Convertible Dishwashers)
maintenance 92
refinishing 92
removing 25
Tuff-Tub® Interior
cleaning 92
damaged 83-84
description 6

U

Unicouple (Convertible Dishwashers)
description 87
inspecting and replacing 87-90
Upscale(see also Ohmmeter)
definition 102

Valve
definition 102
drain 49-50
water inlet 45-46
Volt
definition 102
Volt-Ohmmeter (see Ohmmeter)

Wash Arm (see Wash System)
Wash System
function 5
inspecting and replacing 55-60
Washing, Poor
problem diagnosis 13-14
Water 31-32 (see also Drainage, Leaks)
Water Inlet Valve (see also Float Switch)
inspecting and replacing 45-46
Watt
definition 102
Wiring 27-28 (see also Power Supply)